THE ECONOMICS OF MIDDLE EASTERN OIL

THE ECONOMICS OF MIDDLE EASTERN OIL

Charles Issawi
and
Mohammed Yeganeh

FREDERICK A. PRAEGER, *Publisher*
New York

BOOKS THAT MATTER

Published in the United States of America in 1962
by Frederick A. Praeger, Inc., Publisher
64 University Place, New York 3, N.Y.

Library of Congress Catalog Card Number: 62–21694

Printed in the United States of America

ERRATA

P. 96, l. 25	should read "55 per cent."
P. 134, l. 3 (*from bottom*)	should read "crude oil produced and marketed, or delivered to refineries, by oil companies."
P. 139, l. 8 (*from bottom*)	should read "That with Lebanon in 1962 provides for similar transit fees, plus terminal fees of 2¢ per barrel, ..."
P. 147, l. 26	should read ". . . LL 295 million, and the ratio is now somewhat higher."
P. 173, l. 2	for "the rate" read "the rates."
P. 205, l. 14 (*from bottom*)	for "h.c." read "C."
P. 208, l. 13 (*from bottom*)	should read: "The Nelson Index of Refining Operating Cost rose from 58.5 in 1946 to 108.8 in 1960 (1956 = 100)."
P. 209, l. 15 (*from bottom*)	"pp. 167, 427, and 438, royalty may be regarded . . ."
P. 221, l. 14	should be deleted.

Preface*

The publication of yet another book on the Middle Eastern oil industry calls for a word of explanation. Ours can only be that this book deals with an aspect of the industry that has, so far, received very little attention. Excellent studies have been made on the history and development of the petroleum industry in the Middle East, its political and social implications, its labor relations, and its place in the world oil industry. But so far little analysis has been done on its receipts and outlays, its investments and returns; it is hoped that this study may help to fill some of these gaps.

This book is chiefly concerned with the oil-producing countries of the Persian Gulf: Bahrein, Iran, Iraq, Kuwait, Qatar, Saudi Arabia, and the Neutral Zone lying between Kuwait and Saudi Arabia. Oil operations in other Middle Eastern countries, whether in the field of crude production, as in Israel, Turkey, and the United Arab Republic (Egypt); of refining, as in these and other countries; or of exploration and marketing, as in practically every country in the region, have not been specifically dealt with in this study. They are, however, included in some of the estimates covering the region, for example, in some of the total figures on investment and production and consumption. In all doubtful cases, the exact coverage of the figures given is indicated. Moreover, attention has been paid to the arrangements made for transporting Persian Gulf oil to the Mediterranean by pipelines crossing Syria, Jordan, Lebanon, and Israel; certain aspects of oil transit through the Suez Canal have also been touched upon. The operations of the Aden Refinery have been included, since in many ways it can be regarded as an extension of the Persian Gulf oil industry. The activities of local oil companies are not covered; this study deals only with the operations of the foreign oil companies in the region.

Attention should be drawn to the fact that the operations of foreign oil companies in the Middle East form only a part of the world-wide activities carried on by them or their parent companies. The present

* After this manuscript had been completed, an interesting book on Middle East petroleum was published: Wayne Leeman, *The Price of Middle East Oil* (Ithaca: Cornell University Press, 1962). The reader is referred to that study for a more extensive treatment of some of the questions discussed in Chapters III and VIII of this book.

study deals exclusively with the operations taking place within the limits of the Middle East—production, refining, and transport carried on within the region, but not the transport, refining, or marketing of Persian Gulf oil in other parts of the world. It covers, therefore, only one part of a very large and complex whole. The object of the book has not been to provide an account of the activities of the petroleum companies that operate in the Middle East and elsewhere, but to give an analysis of a very important sector of Middle Eastern economic activity, a sector that plays a vital role in the economic development of the producing countries and a leading one in the whole region. The authors would strongly urge the reader to keep this fact in mind when interpreting the data and conclusions and to pay particular attention to the qualifications by which they are accompanied. A complete picture of the operations of the oil companies in the Middle East can be obtained only if they are viewed in their world-wide context, a task that lies beyond the scope of this study.

This book deals primarily with the period 1948–60, which witnessed an unprecedented growth in the Middle Eastern oil industry. The earlier history of the industry has, however, been sketched in outline and more recent developments have been discussed in greater detail, with a view to determining the trends at present prevailing and the new patterns emerging in the region. The reader is again urged to bear in mind the fact that the period covered was one of exceptional profitability for the industry, and that the position of the latter became somewhat less favorable after 1959. No attempts have been made to suggest any recommendations for future policy. The authors, however, believe that their study shows the great degree of interdependence existing between producers, transit countries, and consumers, and it should not prove impossible to carry out whatever adjustments are necessary by methods acceptable to all parties concerned.

The authors have received much help, in the form of both information and critical comment, from many sources. They wish to thank, in particular, Professor Donald Dewey, Messrs. George Hakim, Harold Lubell, and Samuel Lurié and especially Professor J. C. Hurewitz for their valuable assistance. They also wish to thank their much-enduring wives, who showed great patience and understanding and who helped in numerous ways, and Miss Julia Sobol and Miss Isabel Ludeman for typing the manuscript. In conclusion, there is one disclaimer that must be made. One of the authors is a member of the Department of Economic and Social Affairs of the United Nations, but the views expressed in this book do not in any way reflect those of any body or organization.

Contents

List of Tables

CHAPTER V

CHAPTER VI

CHAPTER VII

CHAPTER VIII

Appendix Tables

Symbols and Rates of Conversion

Three dots (. . .) indicate that data are not available.

A dash (—) indicates that the amount is nil or negligible.

Use of a slash (/) between dates indicates a fiscal or financial year, e.g., 1956/57.

Use of a hyphen (-) between dates signifies the full period involved, including the beginning and end years, e.g., 1954-1956.

A long ton (2,240 lbs) equals 1.016 metric tons.

A metric ton of petroleum equals 6.5–8.2 barrels, depending on the specific gravity.

Figures expressed in barrels per day may be converted, approximately, into tons per annum by multiplying by 50.

THE ECONOMICS OF MIDDLE EASTERN OIL

I. Growth of the Petroleum Industry in the Middle East

A. Growth of the World Petroleum Industry

The petroleum industry is a latecomer in the field of energy resources; it reached its present position by a succession of quick strides as new horizons opened before it. Petroleum gained importance as a source of power only after the turn of this century. The Industrial Revolution was based mainly on the utilization of coal as a source of heat to produce the steam needed for driving engines; but the operation of these new machines required lubricants, the demand for which steadily increased with the development of mechanized industries and transport. The lubricants used until the mid-nineteenth century were of animal or vegetable origin, such as tallow, lard, and castor oil, but the deficiencies inherent in these products stimulated the search for a superior and more flexible lubricant; petroleum, which was widely known at the time, was employed for this purpose.[1] The growing use of petroleum lubricants, combined with the rising demand for lamp oil (kerosene), brought about the birth of the modern oil industry. In the mid-1850's, shafts were sunk into the ground in Roumania; this led to the discovery and production of oil. In 1859, Colonel Edwin L. Drake struck oil in Pennsylvania. These discoveries were followed by an increasing search for oil in the United States and other countries, a process that has continued at an accelerated rate.

During the early years of modern petroleum development, from the wide range of derivatives of crude petroleum only kerosene and lubricants were extracted and utilized in large quantities, while the other constituents (including gas products, gasoline, and light and heavy fuel oils) were disposed of by flaring or otherwise. The invention of the internal-combustion engine in the 1860's was another revolutionary industrial development, one that was of immense significance to the petroleum industry. This new engine used oil fuels as the direct source of its power, and its wider application, as well as the invention of other types of engines based on similar principles, created new markets for the various kinds of petroleum products and gave a great impetus to the expansion of the industry. Thus, the remarkable development of the automotive industry since the turn of the century, especially in the United States, opened a rapidly expanding outlet for the use of gasoline in automobiles, buses, trucks, motorboats, tractors, and airplanes. The increasing use of diesel and semidiesel engines in recent years gave rise to a swiftly growing demand for distillate fuel oils in ships, locomotives, trucks, and tractors, as well as in furnaces employed for space heating. The conversion from coal to petroleum products in railways, ships, space heating, electric generating plants, and the mining and manufacturing industries pushed the utilization of residual fuel oils sharply upward. The demand for kerosene also grew steadily. It was used for illumination in lamps, and new markets were opened for it to be used in stoves for cooking and heating water and space, in certain types of internal-combustion engines, and, more recently, in jet engines. Increasing mechanization of industry, agriculture, construction, and transport greatly expanded the markets for lubricants. Intensive construction provided a very large outlet for the use of asphalts in paving, roofing, waterproofing, pipe-coating, etc. Also, recent years have witnessed a very sharp rise in the utilization of gas products; nevertheless, part of the natural gas associated with the production of crude oil is still wasted for lack of nearby outlets. In addition to the above, the very rapid development of the petro-chemical industry in recent years has created a new and rapidly rising demand for hydrocarbon products for the manufacture of a wide range of products, but such uses absorb only a small fraction of oil and gas production at the present time.

This widening application and the growing utilization of petroleum products, especially as a source of energy, were responsible for the phenomenal increase in production of crude petroleum in the world from 1 million tons (7 million barrels) in 1872 to 10 million tons (77 million barrels) in 1890, 100 million tons (766 million barrels) in 1921, and 1,000 million tons (7,663 million barrels) in 1960. The tendency to use petroleum fuels rather than coal in many competitive fields was due to their manifold advantages.[2] As a result, the relative importance of crude oil within the world output of commercial sources of energy (coal and lignite, crude oil and natural gas, and hydroelectric power) rose from 6 per cent in 1913 to 33 per cent in 1960, and that of natural gas increased from 2 to 14 per cent in the same period; while the share of coal declined from 90 to 51 per cent (see Table 1).

TABLE 1

WORLD PRODUCTION OF COMMERCIAL SOURCES OF ENERGY
(In Million Metric Tons Coal Equivalent and Per Cent)

Year	Coal and Lignite	Crude Petroleum	Natural Gas	Hydroelectricity	Total
I. (million metric tons coal equivalent)					
1929	1,412	276	76	14	1,778
1937	1,404	381	104	22	1,910
1949	1,476	627	225	38	2,365
1954	1,670	940	365	54	3,029
1960	2,204	1,399	622	86	4,311
II. (per cent)					
1913	90	6	2	2	100
1929	79	16	4	1	100
1937	74	20	5	1	100
1949	62	26	10	2	100
1954	55	31	12	2	100
1960	51	33	14	2	100

Sources: United Nations, *Statistical Papers Series J: World Energy Supplies*, No. 4: 1956-59 (New York, 1961); No. 5: 1957-60 (New York, 1962); "Review of Middle East Oil," *Petroleum Times* (London, June, 1948).

At present, solid (coal and lignite) and liquid and gas fuels (petroleum and natural gas) provide the major commercial sources of energy in the world. The relative importance of other sources of energy, including hydroelectric power, is not significant. In the coming decades, nuclear energy will probably become another major source of energy, after its costs of production have decreased sufficiently to enable it to compete with other fuels in certain fields.[3] The next decades will also undoubtedly witness the increasing utilization of other forms of energy, such as solar, geothermal, wind, and tidal energies;[4] however, they are unlikely to account for a significant proportion of the world output of energy in the foreseeable future.

B. Geographical Distribution

The changing geographical distribution of the total consumption of commercial sources of energy and the share of liquid fuels consumed in various areas are given in Table 2. The following points may be observed: First, the bulk of the world's energy consumption is concentrated in the developed and industrialized countries—i.e., North America and Europe, including the Soviet bloc—which together accounted for 93 per cent of the world's energy consumption in 1929 and 88 per cent in 1960. Second, there appears to be a close relationship

TABLE 2

GEOGRAPHICAL DISTRIBUTION OF CONSUMPTION OF COMMERCIAL SOURCES OF ENERGY

Region	Total Energy: Aggregate (Million Metric Tons Coal Equivalent) 1929[a]	1937[a]	1951	1960	Total Energy: Per Capita (Kg Coal Equivalent) 1937	1960	Liquid Fuels and Natural Gas, as Ratio of Total Energy Consumption (Per Cent) 1929	1960
North America	858	814	1,262	1,549	5,805	7,802	29	74
Caribbean America	10	15	35	78	305	893	69	92
Other America	17	19	36	61	245	519	49	85
Western Europe	624[b]	640[b]	638	837	2,120	2,565	3	32
Middle East	5	7	19	37	75	264	45	87
Far East	83	109	111	214	160	242	12	36
Oceania	15	20	32	46	1,835	2,947	16	35
Africa	15	20	38	59	155	310	9	25
Soviet bloc[c]	172	284	540	1,354	405	1,280	16	19
TOTAL WORLD	1,799	1,928	2,710	4,236	880	1,405	18	46

Sources: United Nations, *Statistical Papers Series J: World Energy Supplies*, No. 1: 1929-50 (New York, 1952); No. 5: 1957-60 (New York, 1962); *Demographic Yearbook, 1949-50* (New York, 1950).

[a]The data have been reclassified to be comparable in coverage with the figures of other years, but they have not been adjusted for stock changes.

[b]East Germany has been included in Western Europe.

[c]Data cover the present territory of the Soviet bloc countries; however, the figures for 1929 and 1937 do not include East Germany, North Korea, and North Vietnam.

between level of income and energy consumption; thus, North America has the highest per capita energy consumption in the world, followed by Oceania, Western Europe, the Soviet bloc (in Europe and Asia), Latin America, Africa, the Middle East, and the Far East. Third, the rate of increase in per capita energy consumption has been affected by both the rate of economic growth and the availability of sources of energy, especially petroleum resources. Thus, the increase for the Soviet bloc was 200 per cent in the period 1937–60 as compared with 250 per cent for the Middle East; 100–190 per cent for the Caribbean, other Latin American nations, and Africa; 30–60 per cent for North America, the Far East, and Oceania; and only 20 per cent for Western Europe. Fourth, there was a considerable shift toward the consumption of liquid fuels and natural gas in all regions. Fifth, areas endowed with abundant petroleum resources showed a higher ratio of liquid fuels and natural gas in their total energy consumption.

Up to this time, the rapidly increasing demand for petroleum products has been met by the natural crude petroleum extracted from deposits in the marine sedimentary strata of the earth. In addition, there is the possibility of producing petroleum from tar sands, oil shale, and coal, which are found in large quantities in many areas; however, because of the relatively high cost, output from these sources has not gone beyond the experimental stage except in a very few cases. Moreover, there are still large volumes of undiscovered natural petroleum reserves, and it seems safe to assume that their total volume is several times greater than that of present proved recoverable reserves.[5] Despite the increasing rate of withdrawal from these reserves to meet the growing demand, estimates of world proved oil reserves have continued to rise from 22 billion barrels in 1936 to 63 billion in 1944, 100 billion in 1952, and 266 billion at the beginning of 1961.[6] This sharp increase was due largely to the discovery of huge new oil deposits, particularly in the Middle East; partly to increased knowledge of reserves of existing fields; and partly to technological progress, which made possible the recovery of an additional volume of petroleum from existing reserves at competitive costs.

The proved petroleum reserves of the world are scattered among a large number of countries—55 countries in 1960—but the major portion is located in a few geologically favorable regions: the Persian Gulf area, the Gulf of Mexico and inland United States area, the Caribbean area, North Africa, the Caspian Sea region, and the East Indies archipelago. The volume of proved reserves of the Middle East, which had been estimated at 4.6 billion barrels in 1936, rose to 163 billion barrels at the end of 1960, and in relative terms increased from 21 per cent of the world's reserves to 61 per cent. Within the Middle East itself, Kuwait has the largest volume of proved reserves (60 billion barrels), followed by Saudi Arabia (51 billion), Iraq (24 billion), and Iran (22 billion). These figures compare with 32 billion barrels for the United States, 17 billion for Venezuela, and 8 billion for Indonesia. There are no reliable figures available for the proved reserves of the Soviet Union, Algeria, and Libya; estimates for the Soviet Union run from 23 to 60 billion barrels, for Algeria from 3 to 19 billion, and for Libya from 1.5 to 5 billion. Undoubtedly, these figures are subject to change. Large parts of the Middle East, North Africa, and many other favorable regions, especially the continental shelves in many oil-bearing areas, are far from being adequately explored, and there are good chances of finding considerable additional reserves. Moreover, petroleum exploration has spread in recent years to many less favorable regions; this process has been initiated or supported by many governments as a result of the increasing claim of rising oil imports on foreign exchange, and has led to the discovery of small oil reserves in a number of countries.

The production of crude petroleum is carried out in many countries, but most of the output is concentrated in a few: the United States, the Soviet Union, Venezuela, Kuwait, Saudi Arabia, Iran, Iraq, Canada, Indonesia, Mexico, and Roumania. These eleven countries accounted for 92 per cent of the world's crude oil production in 1960 (see Table 3). Algeria, Libya, and Argentina will, in the near future, be joining the list of major oil producers.

TABLE 3

PROVED OIL RESERVES AND PRODUCTION OF CRUDE PETROLEUM IN MIDDLE EAST AND OTHER COUNTRIES
(Millions of Barrels)

Country	Production					Cumulative Production to January 1, 1961	Proved Oil Reserves, January 1, 1961
	1913	1929	1937	1949	1960		
Middle East							
Abu Dhabi	—	—	—	—	—	—	300
Bahrein	—	—	7.8	11.0	16.5	246	225
Iran	1.9	42.1	77.8	204.7	390.8	4,159	22,000
Iraq	—	0.8	31.8	31.0	354.6	2,716	24,000
Kuwait	—	—	—	89.9	594.3	4,248	60,000
Neutral Zone	—	—	—	—	49.8	171	2,900
Qatar	—	—	—	0.8	63.9	452	2,300
Saudi Arabia	—	—	0.1	174.0	456.5	4,257	51,000
TOTAL	1.9	42.9	117.5	511.4	1,926.4	16,249	162,725
United States	248.4	1,007.3	1,279.2	1,841.9	2,574.9	65,447	31,613
Venezuela	—	137.5	186.2	482.3	1,041.7	13,875	17,354
U.S.S.R.	62.8	99.5	193.2	233.2	1,080.4	13,042	24,000
Canada	0.2	1.1	2.9	21.0	191.8	1,503	3,679
Indonesia	11.2	39.3	56.7	44.9	150.5	2,241	8,200
Mexico	25.7	44.7	46.9	60.9	99.0	3,361	2,458
Roumania	13.6	34.8	52.5	33.7	85.2	1,984	904
Argentina	0.1	9.4	16.4	23.0	62.9	808	1,550
Algeria	—	—	—	—	67.2	82	4,600
Libya	—	—	—	—	—	—	3,000
Other countries	21.4	69.4	87.7	147.0	383.2	5,575	6,167
TOTAL WORLD	385.3	1,485.9	2,039.2	3,399.3	7,663.2	124,167	266,250

Source: Gulf Publishing Company, *World Oil* (Houston, Texas, July 15, 1951, and August 15, 1961).

The pattern of geographic distribution of crude oil production, though greatly influenced by the availability of oil deposits, is also partly determined by demand and by government policies, and therefore differs substantially from that of the oil reserves. The discovery of huge reserves in the Middle East has made possible the sharp growth of crude oil production in this region—from 2 million barrels in 1913 to 118 million in 1937 and 1,926 million (261 million tons) in 1960.

On the other hand, despite this sharp rise in production, the Middle East, which accounted for 61.1 per cent of the world's proved oil reserves in 1960, produced only 25.1 per cent of the world's crude oil in that year, while the United States with 11.9 per cent of the reserves produced 33.6 per cent. The corresponding ratios for Venezuela are 6.5 and 13.6 per cent, respectively; for the Soviet Union, 9.0 and 14.1 per cent; and for Indonesia, 3.1 and 2.0 per cent. Hence, the Middle East is presently drawing on its oil reserves at a slower rate than other areas (except North Africa, where production has just started); these ratios, combined with the possibility of discovering additional reserves, indicate the huge potentialities that exist for expansion of crude production in the Middle East.

C. Production in the Middle East

The development of crude petroleum production within the Middle East is shown in Appendix Table 1, p. 183.[7] Among the major producers of the region, Iran was the first, with the discovery of oil at Masjid-i-Sulaiman, in southern Iran, in 1908 and commercial production in 1912. Iran continued to expand its production and to hold its long lead until the nationalization of its petroleum industry in 1951; in the interwar period, several important fields were discovered, including Haft Kel, Naft Safid, Gach Saran, Lali, and Agha Jari (see Table 27, p. 93). In 1951–54, Iran's oil production declined drastically from 242 million barrels in 1950 to 8 million in 1952. Since the settlement of the nationalization issue in October, 1954, output has resumed its upward trend but, although it has surpassed its previous records by attaining a level of 391 million barrels in 1960, Iran has fallen behind Kuwait and Saudi Arabia. The government has been pressing the consortium of oil companies for the restoration of Iran's traditional position, and the operating companies have launched a large-scale program aimed at appreciably increasing the capacity of crude oil production. In addition, in 1961, an Italian and an American oil company, both prospecting in other areas, announced the discovery of petroleum reserves and are expected to start production in the near future. The government-owned National Iranian Oil Company is also active in exploration and has succeeded in discovering three oil and gas fields in central Iran, but production is being held up until fuller information on the extent of the fields is available.

The second major producer of the region was Iraq, where a small oil field was discovered at Naft-Khaneh in 1923 and put into operation for local consumption, and a major field was discovered at Kirkuk in 1927; subsequently, another important field was struck at Ain Zalah. However, because these fields were so far inland, it was not until 1934 that oil production started in large quantities; oil flowed abroad after two pipelines, with diameters of 12 inches, were laid from Kirkuk to the Mediterranean ports of Haifa and Tripoli, at distances of 530 and 620 miles, respectively. In the following years Iraq's production was limited to its pipeline capacity, with a temporary drop of output during the war years. In 1946, the Iraq Petroleum Company began to construct two 16-inch pipelines to Haifa and Tripoli, parallel to the old ones, but the Arab-Israeli conflict of 1948 stopped the completion of the first line as well as the flow of crude oil to Haifa. The completion of the second line to Tripoli in 1949 and, more important, the opening of another major 30-inch line from Kirkuk to Banias in 1952—the latter at a cost of about $140 million—greatly raised the crude oil export capacity of Iraq from its northern fields. There was also large-scale development of Iraq's southern oil resources, located near the Persian Gulf, which resulted in production and flow of crude oil in 1951. These developments increased Iraq's crude oil output from 30 million barrels in 1936 to 50 million in 1950 and 251 million in 1955. Following the damage caused to the pipeline system during the Suez crisis, output declined to 163 million in 1957, but after the repair of the pipelines it began to rise again, to 355 million in 1960.

In Bahrein, oil was discovered in 1932. Production of crude oil started immediately, but was limited by the small size of the reserves; it rose only from 8 million barrels in 1937 to 11 million in 1955 and 16 million in 1960. However, as will be discussed later, Bahrein has become one of the major refining centers of the Middle East, using mainly imported crude oil. In 1938, petroleum reserves were discovered in Saudi Arabia, at Dammam, and subsequently at Abqaiq, while the outbreak of war retarded the development of the oil fields of the two sheikdoms of Kuwait and Qatar. The large-scale development of the petroleum industry undertaken in these areas during the postwar years, as well as in Qatar and in the Neutral Zone lying between Kuwait and Saudi Arabia, facilitated the sharp growth of crude oil production, particularly in Kuwait from the Burgan and Magwa fields and in Saudi Arabia from the Abqaiq and Ghawar fields. Also, in 1950, a 30–31-inch pipeline was completed from the Saudi Arabian oil fields to the port of Sidon, on the Mediterranean, at a distance of 1,068 miles. The project, which started with a crude capacity of 300,000 barrels per day, increased to 450,000 by 1958, absorbing an initial investment of

$230 million. The installation of petroleum-handling facilities, together with the shutdown of oil exports from Iran during 1951–54, made it possible to expand the petroleum output of these countries in the early 1950's, while in the latter half of the decade production increased very slowly in Saudi Arabia but sharply in Kuwait. As a result, the crude oil output of Saudi Arabia rose from 8 million barrels in 1944 to 456 million in 1960; Kuwait's output increased from 6 million barrels in 1946 to 594 million in 1960; and Qatar's output rose from 12 million in 1950 to 64 million in 1960. In 1953 oil was also discovered in the Neutral Zone, and production of crude oil started in the following year, rising gradually to 50 million barrels in 1960.

D. Natural Gas

As a by-product of crude petroleum and refined products, the Middle East produces large volumes of natural and refinery gas. Most of the refinery gas is utilized as fuel in refineries and local industries. Part

TABLE 4

ESTIMATED OUTPUT AND USE OF NATURAL GAS ASSOCIATED WITH PRODUCTION OF CRUDE OIL IN THE MIDDLE EAST AND SELECTED COUNTRIES, 1959 AND 1960
(Millions of Cubic Feet a Day)

Country	Output	Use		
		Reinjection	Other Uses	Surplus
Middle East, 1960				
Iran	723	—	97	626
Iraq	483	132	50	301
Kuwait[a]	793	—	91	702
Saudi Arabia	686	240	34	412
Other Middle East	310	—	71	239
TOTAL	2,995	372	343	2,280
Other countries, 1959				
Algeria	200	—	20	180
Venezuela	2,765	714	351	1,700
United States	11,479	3,883	5,496	2,100
TOTAL	14,444	4,597	5,867	3,980

Sources: Data for 1960 provided by the Arabian American Oil Company; other data obtained from the Arabian American Oil Company, *Natural Gas in Saudi Arabia: Economics, Sales, Utilization*, (Dhahran, Saudi Arabia, 1960), p. 11. Figures on "other uses" and "surplus" in the United States have been adjusted on the basis of information given in the text of the preceding source.

[a] In 1960, natural gas consumption in Kuwait averaged 91 million cubic feet a day; a plant scheduled for completion early in 1961 will inject a further 100 million cubic feet of gas a day into the oil reservoirs (see Kuwait Oil Company, *Annual Review of Operations*, 1960).

of the natural gas is used for reinjection into the oil reservoirs for repressuring, or for fuel; the major part is flared. Table 4 shows the estimated output and use of natural gas associated with crude oil production in the Middle East and other countries. In 1960 the Middle East produced 1,100 billion cubic feet of natural gas—with a heat value equal to that of 24 million tons of crude petroleum—three-fourths of which was wasted.[8] In Venezuela the ratio was two-thirds. In the United States, however, where most of the oil is produced by pumping, with little release of gas, and where there is a large internal market for natural gas, the ratio of waste is only 18 per cent. In the state of Texas, which has the most rigid conservation rules, wastage has been reduced to 8 per cent.[9] In recent years, increasing efforts have been made by both the oil companies and the governments of the Middle East to find outlets for these gases and to reduce the volume of waste. Gas has been offered for sale at the low price of 2¢ per thousand cubic feet at the wellhead in Kuwait and at 3.5¢ at the gas-oil separators in Saudi Arabia. Several petrochemical projects have been embarked upon in the region (see Chapter VII, Section F); however, they are not expected to absorb an appreciable part of the produced gases, and the complete elimination of waste would require much greater effort and larger investments.

E. Refining

In the past, petroleum refineries were, in general, resource oriented, i.e., most of them were located at the centers of crude oil production. This pattern of refinery location changed during the postwar years; most of the new refineries have been constructed at the major consuming centers, except where the crude-oil–producing countries have exerted pressure on the oil companies to refine more locally. The underlying economic, political, and strategic factors for this change are discussed in Chapter III, Section H. However, it may be pointed out here that the postwar refining development has drastically altered the geographical distribution of refining activities as compared with prewar years.

The Middle East, which exported the bulk of its oil output as refined products before the war and in the immediate postwar years, has become mainly an exporter of crude petroleum. Despite the fact that its refining capacity increased from 695,000 barrels per day in 1947 to 1,433,000 barrels per day in 1959, the ratio of crude oil delivered for refining to the total crude oil output of the Middle East declined from 66 per cent in 1937 to 55 per cent in 1949 and 21 per cent in 1960.

In Indonesia, also, the corresponding ratio declined from 143 per cent in 1949, when crude oil was imported for refining, to 58 per cent in 1960, but in recent years the government has imposed regulations on the oil companies for the export of an increasing share of their output in refined form. In Venezuela, where similar regulations have been imposed, the ratio of crude oil refined to total crude production rose from 11 per cent in 1949 to 32 per cent in 1960. Recently, the oil-producing countries of the Middle East have also attempted to expand refining operations by subjecting, in certain new concessions, the oil companies to conditions similar to those in Venezuela and Indonesia (see Chapter VIII, Section B).

Despite these efforts by the major oil-producing countries, refining capacity has continued to shift to the major consuming centers, such as the United States, Western Europe, the Soviet Union, Canada, Japan, Brazil, Argentina, Mexico, Australia, and India, where it has rapidly expanded (see Table 5). In 1959, North America accounted for 49 per cent of the world's refining capacity as compared with 13 per cent for the Caribbean and other American areas, 16 per cent for Western Europe, 10 per cent for the Soviet bloc, 6 per cent for the Middle East, and 5 per cent for the Far East.

Another major development in refining operations in recent years has been the construction of larger, better equipped, and more efficient refineries, in order to reduce refining cost. As a result, the average capacity of refineries has greatly increased in most countries, and the Middle East, with its large plants in Abadan, Bahrein, Ras Tanura, Kuwait, and Aden, had the highest average in the world in 1959. On the other hand, the ratio of cracking and reforming capacity to total refining capacity, though it increased in most countries, especially in the United States, actually declined in the Middle East, and was, in fact, the lowest among the major refining regions of the world. The structure of the demand for Middle Eastern refined oil was largely responsible for this development and for the existing product-mix pattern of Middle Eastern refined products, which is heavily weighted toward the production of lower priced heavy fuel oils, a substantial part of which is used as bunkers by tankers picking up crude oil from the Persian Gulf (see Table 6).

There are at present five major refineries in the Middle East. Abadan refinery, located in southern Iran, is the oldest in the region and the largest in the world. It has an estimated crude oil input capacity of about 500,000 barrels a day and a cracking capacity of 116,000 barrels a day. It manufactures a wide range of products including, in addition

TABLE 5

WORLD REFINING CAPACITY AND PRODUCTION, 1947 AND 1959, REGIONAL TOTALS AND MAIN COUNTRIES IN EACH REGION
(Thousands of Barrels Daily, Unless Otherwise Specified)

Region and Country	January, 1947			January, 1959			1959
	Number of Refineries	Capacity		Number of Refineries	Capacity		Crude Runs to Stills
		Crude Oil	Cracking and Reforming		Crude Oil	Cracking and Reforming	
Middle East	7	695	187	20	1,433	293	1,080
Aden	—	—	—	1	120	12	84
Bahrein	1	110	29	1	187	74	189
Iran	3	402	125	3	493	116	371
Iraq	2	8	—	6	56	25	35
Kuwait	—	—	—	2	220	—	143
Neutral Zone	—	—	—	1	50	—	30
Saudi Arabia	1	90	—	1	189	42	174
North America	444	5,533	3,187	356	10,827	9,229	9,153
Canada	33	245	78	45	872	659	739
United States	411	5,288	3,109	311	9,955	8,570	8,414
Caribbean and Other America	55	1,133	490	74	2,809	1,202	2,729
Argentina	13	94	56	15	222	108	216
Brazil	3	6	—	8	153	75	154
Mexico	6	179	28	8	447	55	287
Netherlands West Indies	3	580	303	2	650	523	745
Venezuela	9	131	53	13	820	163	819
Western Europe	63	364	115	124	3,633	1,138	3,165
France	14	150	58	13	713	277	619
Federal Republic of Germany	8	24	—	25	407	154	440
Italy	9	40	13	36	723	179	526
Netherlands	1	14	16	2	349	133	315
United Kingdom	15	97	17	14	918	245	778
Africa[a]	2	37	4	6	100	27	100
Far East	12	168	50	46	1,017	222	836
India	4	30	9	4	110	40	102
Indonesia	7	118	42	5	249	79	241
Japan	—	—	—	25	553	79	392
Oceania	2	8	—	7	212	85	207
Soviet bloc[b]	41	840	226	101	2,271	600	(2,270)
Roumania	15	190	47	15	240	—	...
U.S.S.R.	22[c]	638[c]	179[c]	70	1,950	600	...
TOTAL WORLD	626	8,778	4,259	734	22,302	12,796	19,540

Sources: American Petroleum Institute, *Petroleum Facts and Figures, 1959* (New York, 1959); United States Bureau of Mines, *World Petroleum Statistics 1959* (Washington, 1960).

[a]Including U.A.R. (Egypt).

[b]Excluding China, for which figures were not available.

[c]1941 figures.

TABLE 6

COMPOSITION OF REFINING OUTPUT (PRODUCT-MIX) IN MIDDLE EAST AND OTHER COUNTRIES
(Per Cent and Thousands of Barrels)

Country and Year	Percentage of Total Crude Oil Input					(In Thousands of Barrels)	
	Gasoline	Kerosene	Distillate Fuel Oils	Residual Fuel Oil	Total	Total output of major refined products	Total crude oil input
Aden							
1955	16.3	9.0	11.9	58.0	95.2	30,081	31,606
1960	10.7	8.0	19.8	48.9	87.4	27,119	31,024
Bahrein							
1950	27.1	9.9	17.6	43.9	98.5	56,059	56,900
1960	18.8	12.2	22.2	38.9	92.1	70,140	76,131
Iran							
1950	20.3	9.3	17.5	45.9	93.0	177,875	191,175
1960	18.5	15.4	14.7	39.3	87.9	124,956	142,089
Kuwait							
1950	1.6	0.5	21.2	74.2	97.5	7,599	7,794
1960	2.2	0.5	16.6	76.5	95.8	62,219	64,943
Saudi Arabia							
1950	21.3	7.7	27.5	36.3	92.8	35,616	38,364
1960	12.2	10.3	12.9	55.5	90.9	74,841	82,312
TOTAL ABOVE COUNTRIES							
1950	21.2	9.0	18.9	45.1	94.2	277,149	294,233
1960	14.0	10.7	16.5	49.4	90.6	359,275	396,499
1960							
United States	48.4	7.2	21.4	10.6	87.6	2,733,351	3,119,327
Mexico	25.9	10.3	12.1	34.7	83.0	89,001	107,278
Venezuela	11.5	3.8	16.0	59.0	90.3	298,032	330,105
France	23.2	4.4	22.5	29.3	79.4	194,561	244,973
Italy	15.9	3.5	25.3	37.4	82.1	194,142	236,513
United Kingdom	21.4	5.7	18.1	38.4	83.6	268,524	321,274
Indonesia	14.7	15.3	19.0	19.7	68.7	59,603	86,756
Japan	18.5	7.5	10.8	46.9	83.7	173,983	207,883

Sources: American Petroleum Institute, *Petroleum Facts and Figures* (New York, 1959); United States Bureau of Mines, *World Petroleum Statistics*, 1960 (Washington, D.C., 1961). See also Appendix Table 3.

to the major products, aviation gasoline, liquefied petroleum gas, and lubricating oil. In 1950, the refinery produced 177 million barrels of major products (gasoline, kerosene, distillate fuel oils, and heavy fuel oils), but output declined to 8 million barrels in 1953 and, following the settlement of the nationalization crisis, moved gradually up, reaching 114 million barrels in 1960—much below its 1950 level. The second oldest large refinery of the Middle East is the Bahrein refinery, which started operation in 1936 with a capacity of 10,000 barrels a day. By 1939 refining capacity had increased to 35,000 barrels a day; it rose to 65,000 barrels a day in 1945 and 186,500 barrels a day in 1959, with a reforming capacity of 73,700 barrels a day. Because of the small volume of crude oil output in Bahrein, this refinery imports the major part of its crude petroleum input from Saudi Arabia, through two 12-inch submarine pipelines. The third major refinery of the Middle East is located in Ras Tanura, Saudi Arabia. This plant was constructed during the war years and started operation in 1945 with a capacity of 50,000 barrels a day; by 1959, capacity had been increased to 189,000 barrels a day, with a reforming capacity of 41,500 barrels a day. Another important refinery, located at Mina al Ahmadi, Kuwait, began operation in 1949 with a capacity of 25,000 barrels a day and was expanded considerably in the period 1956–58, when its capacity rose to 220,000 barrels a day. However, this plant is designed mainly for production of fuel oils needed for bunkering of tankers and produces only small quantities of higher priced gasoline and kerosene. Finally, there is a large refinery in Aden, completed in 1954 with a daily capacity of 120,000 barrels of crude oil input and 12,000 barrels of reforming; it processes crude oil imported from the Persian Gulf and supplies much bunker fuel to ships stopping at Aden.

F. World Markets for Petroleum

The pattern of geographical distribution of petroleum consumption differs greatly from that of crude production and reserves; as a result, most countries depend on imports of crude oil or refined products to meet part or all of their domestic demand for oil. Table 7 has been constructed to compare production and consumption of petroleum in the major oil-producing and oil-consuming countries of the world, and to illustrate their surplus or deficit in 1937 and 1959.

It may be noted that the major part of the world's petroleum production is consumed in North America, Western Europe, and the Soviet Union, followed by such countries as Japan, Argentina, Brazil, and Australia. On the other hand, all the leading consuming countries, with the exception of the Soviet Union, are net importers of petroleum. The imports of these countries, as well as those of smaller importers in Latin America, Asia, and Africa, are supplied mainly from two major sources: the Persian Gulf and the Caribbean areas. In addition, the Soviet Union, Indonesia, and Roumania export appreciable amounts of petroleum and it is expected that North Africa, which started shipping

TABLE 7

PRODUCTION AND INLAND CONSUMPTION OF PETROLEUM IN MAJOR PRODUCING AND CONSUMING COUNTRIES, 1937 AND 1959
(Millions of Metric Tons)

Country	1937			1959		
	Production of Crude Petroleum	Inland Consumption of Refined Products (Crude Oil Equivalent)	Surplus or Deficit (–)	Production of Crude Petroleum	Inland Consumption of Refined Products (Crude Oil Equivalent)	Surplus or Deficit (–)
Major Exporting Countries						
Middle East						
Bahrein	1.07	0.11	0.96	2.26	0.62	1.64
Iran	10.33	1.19	9.14	45.01	4.16	40.85
Iraq	4.26	0.10	4.16	41.74	1.80	39.94
Kuwait	–	–	–	69.53	0.35	69.18
Neutral Zone	–	–	–	6.20	0.20	6.00
Qatar	–	–	–	7.99	0.07	7.92
Saudi Arabia	0.01	–	0.01	54.17	0.91	53.26
TOTAL	15.67	1.40	14.27	226.90	8.11	218.79
Venezuela	27.79	0.77	27.02	147.93	8.25	139.68
U.S.S.R.	29.10[a]	29.10	–	129.55	107.01	22.54
Indonesia	7.26	0.94	6.32	18.22	6.42	11.80
Roumania	7.15	1.12	6.03	11.44	4.75	6.69
Major Consuming-Importing Countries						
United States	177.66	148.38	29.28	347.93	439.35	–91.42
United Kingdom	–	9.87	–9.87	0.15	41.13	–40.98
Canada	0.38	5.77	–5.39	24.97	39.62	–14.65
Federal Republic of Germany	0.45	3.48	–3.03	5.10	24.19	–19.09
France	0.07	5.60	–5.53	1.62	22.89	–21.27
Japan	0.35	4.52	–4.17	0.40	20.36	–19.96
Italy	0.01	2.63	–2.62	1.70	20.02	–18.32
Mexico	6.73	3.11	3.62	13.96	15.08	– 1.12
Argentina	2.24	4.08	–1.84	6.38	14.06	– 7.68
Sweden	–	1.24	–1.24	0.11	11.88	–11.77
Brazil	–	1.11	–1.11	3.08	11.76	– 8.68
Netherlands	–	1.38	–1.38	1.78	11.48	– 9.70
Australia	–	2.17	–2.17	–	9.66	– 9.66
China	0.01	1.26	–1.25	3.70	8.01	– 4.31
India	0.30	1.85	–1.55	0.45	6.57	– 6.12

Sources: Production figures, 1937: United Nations, *Statistical Yearbook, 1948* (New York, 1949). Production figures, 1959: United Nations, *Monthly Bulletin of Statistics*, (New York, January, 1961). Consumption figures, 1937: United Nations, *Statistical Papers Series J: World Energy Supplies*, No. 1, 1929-50 (New York, 1952). Consumption figures, 1959: United Nations, *Statistical Papers Series J: World Energy Supplies*, No. 4: 1956-59 (New York, 1961).
[a]Revised data.

oil in 1958, will become an important exporter in the near future. The United States, the leading producing and consuming country, had through 1948 an exportable surplus, but since then the rise in production has lagged behind the increase in consumption, due to the rationing of production for conservation of local oil resources, and the country has now become the leading importer in the world. The Soviet Union, the second major consumer, has been able to expand its production at a higher rate than its consumption. As a result it has once more, since 1953, become an exporter of petroleum; it is aiming at regaining its traditional leading position as such. Another major consuming area, Western Europe, has enormously expanded its petroleum demand in the postwar period, partly because of conversion from coal to oil; owing to its negligible local production, however, it has relied on imports of petroleum from abroad. In the past, the bulk of Europe's petro-

TABLE 8

MAJOR WORLD PETROLEUM MOVEMENTS, 1938, 1947, AND 1959
(Thousands of Barrels Per Day)

Origin	Destination							
	North America	South America	Europe	Africa	Middle East	Far East and Oceania	Soviet Union	Total
1938								
North America	—	66	222	10	2	127	4	431
South America	161	—	321	44	—	1	—	527
Middle East	—	—	115	41	—	44	—	200
East Indies	—	2	12	11	2	52	—	79
TOTAL	161	68	670	106	4	224	4	1,237
1947								
North America	—	16	160	8	2	40	2	228
South America	548	—	382	35	1	3	—	969
Middle East	6	—	224	100	—	245	—	575
East Indies	—	—	—	—	—	—	—	—
Soviet Union	—	—	3	—	—	—	—	3
TOTAL	554	16	769	143	3	288	2	1,775
1959								
North America	—	30	50	—	—	—	—	80
South America	1,205	—	580	115	—	—	—	1,900
Middle East	405	90	2,420	155	—	900	—	3,970
East Indies	75	—	—	—	—	285	—	360
Soviet Union	—	20	243[a]	1	54	3	—	321
TOTAL	1,685	140	3,293	271	54	1,188	—	6,631

Sources: *The Petroleum Data Book* (Dallas, 1947 and 1948); Arabian American Oil Company, *Aramco Handbook* (1960); and United States Senate, Eighty-Seventh Congress, *Soviet Oil in the Cold War* (Washington, D.C., 1961).
[a]Includes 6,000 barrels daily to nonspecified destinations.

leum needs was supplied by the Western Hemisphere (the United States and the Caribbean area), but in the postwar years the Middle East became the main supplier of oil to Europe. In recent years the Middle East has been joined by the Soviet Union and North Africa; exports from both these areas to Western Europe, especially North Africa, are expected to rise rapidly. The other parts of the Eastern Hemisphere, namely, the Far East, Oceania, and Africa, rely for their petroleum needs mainly on imports from the Middle East and Indonesia, while the oil deficit countries of the Western Hemisphere depend largely on imports from the Caribbean area and to a smaller extent from the Middle East. Table 8 is presented to show the pattern of international trade of the world, by regions; it brings out the striking increase in the share of the Middle East during the last twenty years and the widening range of markets it supplies.

G. Transportation of Middle Eastern Oil

The crude petroleum and refined products entering world markets constitute nearly half of the total volume of international trade.[10] In the early years of petroleum development, when smaller quantities of oil products were involved, oil was stored and transported in cans and barrels. However, the rapid expansion of production and the development of bulk trading necessitated the devising of transportation facilities that would be more efficient, speedy, and economical. As a result, specialized means of transport were developed for carrying crude oil and refined products: tankers, tank barges, pipelines, rail tank cars, and motor tank trucks. While tankers and pipelines are utilized for the bulk movement of petroleum, other forms of transportation are used for carrying smaller volumes of oil products within a country.

The marketing of oil products within the Middle East, however, is still handicapped by transport difficulties. Recently the National Iranian Oil Company, faced with the rapid expansion of the demand for oil in Iran, started construction of a network of pipelines from the southern refineries to the northern centers of oil consumption. However, as already shown, the local demand for petroleum in the oil-producing countries of the Middle East absorbs only a small share of the domestic petroleum output, while exports account for some 96 per cent. These exports are moved by pipelines to the sea terminals and delivered to tankers for transport to the world markets. In general, the Middle Eastern oil fields so far discovered and exploited are located close to the Persian Gulf; the main exceptions are Kirkuk and Ain Zalah in northern

Iraq. In fact, wherever possible, the oil companies have concentrated their exploration activities around the Persian Gulf, and recently in the continental shelves of the Gulf as well, so that they could keep their transport costs to a minimum by the construction of shorter pipelines to the sea terminals. Since the major markets of Middle Eastern petroleum are located west of Suez, the greater part of the oil products to these markets have to move through the Suez Canal; this requires a 3,600-mile haul around the Arabian Peninsula and payment of Suez Canal dues.

Three major pipelines were constructed from the oil fields of Iraq and Saudi Arabia to the Mediterranean during the postwar years. Plans were under way for the construction of others, including the Middle Eastern pipelines from Iran and Kuwait to the Mediterranean; however, this project did not materialize owing to the refusal of Iraq to give transit rights, since it wished to have priority for the expansion of its own production. The demolition of the Iraqi pipeline pumping stations in Syria during the Suez crisis encouraged the exploration of an alternative route to the Mediterranean, through Turkey; a project for a pipeline, gathering oil from all the countries bordering on the Persian Gulf and transporting it to a Turkish port on the Mediterranean Sea, was given up owing to the political difficulties it raised. Another project for a pipeline from central Iran through Turkey to the Mediterranean was abandoned temporarily until it could be justified with sufficient proved reserves. On the other hand, the increasing volume of exports of petroleum to the countries west of Suez raises the question of the Suez Canal's capacity to handle an additional number of tankers. In order to facilitate these oil movements, the following steps have been taken or proposed. First, a project is underway for the deepening of the Suez Canal to permit the passage of larger tankers.[11] Second, plans have been prepared for the construction of pipelines parallel to the Suez Canal in the United Arab Republic (Egypt), and a pipeline has been laid from the port of Eilat in the Gulf of Aqaba to the Mediterranean by the Israeli government.[12] Third, large tankers are being constructed that will move oil around Africa at a cost not much higher than the present average cost of moving oil through the Canal. Table 9 shows the movement of petroleum exports from the Middle East through pipelines to the Mediterranean, through the Suez Canal and the Indian Ocean.

The great increase in the volume of oil entering intercontinental trade is shown in Table 8; the share of the Middle East in this trade rose from 10 million tons or 16 per cent in 1938, to 30 million tons or 32 per cent in 1947, and nearly 200 million tons or 60 per cent in 1959. This rise in world oil trade has required an expansion of the world ocean-going

TABLE 9

EXPORTS OF MIDDLE EASTERN PETROLEUM THROUGH MEDITERRANEAN PIPELINES, SUEZ CANAL, AND INDIAN OCEAN
(Millions of Barrels)

Year	Suez Canal (1)	Eastern Mediterranean Pipelines (2)	Indian Ocean (3)	Total (4)
1938	39	30	31	100
1948	214	26	151	391
1949	273	28	173	474
1950	352	55	199	606
1951	317	166	203	686
1952	340	228	174	742
1953	366	292	197	855
1954	422	303	242	967
1955	495	305	335	1,135
1956	487	280	443	1,210
1957	400	211	631	1,242
1958	699	305	493	1,497
1959	730	326	544	1,600
1960	847	343	634	1,824

Sources: Column (1): Suez Canal Authority, *Suez Canal Report, 1959*, p. 136. Column (2): Appendix Table 3. Column (3): Difference between Column (4) on the one hand, and Columns (1) and (2) on the other. Column (4): Estimated on the basis of exports of net crude petroleum (Appendix Table 3) plus exports of refined products calculated by deducting from production of refined products (Appendix Table 2), domestic consumption of petroleum products (see the sources of Table 43).

tanker fleet, whether in private or government ownership, from 16.5 million tons dead weight in 1938 and 24 million in 1947, to 62 million in October, 1959; at the latter date the volume of tankers under construction was 22 million tons. Almost all petroleum exports from the Middle East are transported by foreign vessels, most of which are owned or chartered by petroleum companies operating in the region. Until recently, the Middle Eastern oil-producing countries did not own ocean-going tankers, but in the last few years some of them have acquired a few vessels. In October, 1959, Saudi Arabia had one tanker of 46,500 tons and Kuwait one tanker of 46,000 tons; in 1961, Iran's tanker fleet consisted of four tankers aggregating 176,000 tons.

H. Organization and Control of the World Petroleum Industry

It may generally be stated that the legal ownership of petroleum resources either follows title to the surface land or is vested in the state—including the local or national governments, and the rulers of autocratic states and sheikdoms. These two different legal systems have given rise to two distinct institutional patterns for petroleum operations. The leading example of the first system is the United States, where private ownership of underground resources has led to the development of a competitive market for the acquisition of rights and for the exploration and exploitation of petroleum deposits, and to the establishment of a petroleum industry controlled by numerous small and large enterprises. Because of the multitude of landowners overlying a single oil field, this system has resulted in the drilling of thousands more wells than were necessary to adequately drain the fields under efficient production methods, and in the reduction of ultimate recovery from the reservoir.

The second system is to be found in most of the other oil-producing countries. For example, petroleum resources are owned by national governments in Iran, Iraq, Indonesia, North Africa, Mexico, Venezuela, and the Soviet bloc countries; they belong to the rulers in Bahrein, Kuwait, Qatar, Saudi Arabia, and Brunei; in Argentina and Libya they belong partly or wholly to provincial or state governments. The development of petroleum resources in these countries may be carried out by the grant of exploration and exploitation rights by governments either to their own agencies or to foreign or domestic private oil companies. Under this system a few petroleum enterprises, in most cases foreign oil companies (because local capital and technical skill were not available) have developed oil resources and established maximum efficient operation (see Chapter IV, Section G).

The rising demand for petroleum in industrialized countries and the lack or insufficiency of oil deposits in most of them stimulated petroleum exploration in a number of distant regions. Several petroleum interests, and in some cases their governments—particularly those of Germany, Great Britain, and the Netherlands—made attempts as early as the late nineteenth century to secure rights for the use of oil resources in geologically favorable areas through concessionary agreements with local governments. British interests obtained an important oil concession in Iran, and Dutch interests a few concessions in the East Indies; and British, Dutch, and German interests were promised a concession in the Ottoman Empire. American and British-Dutch interests also obtained concessions in Roumania, Russia, and Latin America.

The early attempts aimed at securing rights to foreign oil resources continued, with increasing intensity, during the interwar period. The Americans, fearing the early exhaustion of their oil reserves, made a determined effort and, with the backing of their government, succeeded in several instances in obtaining control of a considerable share of oil resources in promising areas, particularly the Middle East, the East Indies, and Latin America. The French also stepped in and, together with American, British, and Dutch interests (and partly at the expense of German interests), were granted the proposed concession in Mesopotamia and others in various areas formerly constituting provinces of the Ottoman Empire. British and Dutch interests also extended their control in favorable areas and secured additional concessions. On the other hand, Soviet Russia nationalized its petroleum resources immediately after the 1917 Revolution, and took over its petroleum industry from foreign and domestic private firms, as did the other Soviet bloc countries after World War II. American and British-Dutch interests in Mexico were also nationalized.

The pattern of petroleum operations outside the United States arising in this period has continued into the postwar years, with minor changes in underlying principles. This pattern was characterized by the emergence of a few international oil companies—five American, one British, one British-Dutch, and one French—which established virtual control over the world's major oil resources outside the United States and the Soviet Union. In most respects these companies enjoyed the support of their respective governments, the French and one of the British companies being partly owned and controlled by their governments. They not only engaged in the exploration of oil reserves and the production of crude petroleum, but became integrated companies—sometimes by absorbing or joining other companies—in order to control most of their refining, transportation, and marketing (see Chapter III, Section A). In most cases these companies organized joint producing companies; they were also able to reach an understanding with one another regarding production and marketing in defined areas. During the postwar period, the major oil companies intensified their operations and have succeeded in securing concessions in many new areas, including North Africa, Latin America, Canada, and Australia. A major development of this period has been the appearance, on the international scene, of oil companies from Italy and Japan, as well as independent oil companies from the United States and France. These companies have been able to secure petroleum concessions in South America, the Middle East, and North Africa; they have succeeded in developing substantial petroleum reserves, which enable them to produce considerable amounts of petroleum and to compete in world markets with the already established major international companies.

On the other hand, a trend has developed in the opposite direction, i.e., the control of petroleum resources by domestic enterprises. Some of the oil-producing countries, having reached a higher stage of development and being motivated by various political, social, and economic reasons, have organized their own enterprises to undertake petroleum operations on their own in the whole or in part of their territories. However, these enterprises, though growing in importance, have until recently played a relatively insignificant role in the international petroleum market. In addition to the Soviet bloc countries, Mexico, and Yugoslavia, where control of all phases of petroleum operations is given to government monopolies, there are other countries like Bolivia, Brazil, Chile, and Spain, where control of oil resources and their exploitation is granted to government-owned companies. Moreover, there are a number of countries that allow both public and private companies, including foreign ones, to engage in the development of oil resources, such as Argentina, Peru, Iran, Indonesia, India, Italy, and Turkey.

I. Concessionary Agreements in the Middle East

Petroleum operations in the Middle East have been developed and, until recently, completely controlled by foreign oil companies under concessionary agreements reached with the governments. In many countries outside the region (e.g., Argentina, Venezuela, Colombia, Indonesia, and Libya), either from the start or in recent years, such agreements have been concluded in conformity with the general mining or petroleum laws, while in the oil-producing countries of the Middle East the absence of such laws necessitated negotiations and bargaining for the formulation of the terms and patterns of the concessions. In 1947, the Iranian government organized a state-owned oil company and gave it the responsibility for developing Iran's petroleum resources, and in 1957 it introduced a general petroleum law, which has governed the recent oil agreements. The Iraqi government announced in 1961 that it will shortly take similar steps.

The concessionary agreements developed in the Middle East determine the rights and obligations of concessionaires and governments. The terms of the agreements vary from one country to another, and even from one agreement to another in the same country, but in general they have the following common features.[13] They determine the duration of the contract, which usually runs for 40 to 75 years (unlike the United States, where the lease is permanent); define the area under concession; exclude the operation of other enterprises within the defined area; grant rights of exploration drilling, production, refining, and transportation, as well as rights to install necessary facilities for these operations; and provide the right of eminent domain to the concessionaire so that his operations would not be impeded by owners of the land under concession. In addition, these agreements grant the privilege of importing capital goods and intermediate products used in oil operations without payment of import duties, and allow exports of petroleum without payment of export duties and without the obligation of surrendering the foreign exchange proceeds of the sales to the government. On the other hand, the concessionary agreements obligate concessionaires for the payment of royalties, rents, and certain taxes, in lieu of all forms of taxes and duties; impose obligations on concessionaires to undertake exploration and drilling activities within a certain stipulated period; include provisions for the employment and training of local workers and technicians; stipulate the supply of petroleum to the domestic market, in some cases, at lower prices; and provide for the settlement of disputes through arbitration rather than local courts.

These concessionary arrangements thus provide extensive rights and privileges to the oil companies and guarantee the continuation of their operations. Before the changes that took place in 1950–54, a United Nations report commented on the agreements of the oil companies as follows:

> The terms of their concessions . . . give the foreign companies a freedom of action which substantially insulates them from the economy of the Middle Eastern countries. Output is determined by considerations of world, rather than local conditions. Moreover, it is the companies which provide and own the means of transport, whether pipelines or tankers, to carry Middle Eastern oil to its markets, and it is they who secure these markets, both in Western Europe and in other parts of the world. . . . The foreign exchange derived from sales of oil accrues to the petroleum companies and is in large measure retained by them. Hence the impact of oil operations on Middle Eastern producing countries is mainly indirect and the benefits derived by them are limited. The benefits consist of royalties and other payments to governments, foreign exchange spent by oil companies in the course of their operations, employment provided for workers, technical skills acquired by nationals employed by the oil companies and fuel provided for local consumption at reasonable rates.[14]

Though the basic framework of the prewar agreements between the foreign oil companies and the governments has remained unchanged, especially in matters relating to the control of oil operations and marketing, there have been a number of important changes in the terms of original agreements in favor of the producing countries. These changes have been brought about by the rising pressure of local nationalistic feelings aimed principally at obtaining a larger share of benefits derived from their natural resources. As a result, the share of the governments in oil income has substantially increased (see Chapter VI, Section C). The foreign oil companies have agreed to other adjustments recognizing the changed conditions and local needs, and in most cases have provided a few seats in their Boards of Directors to government officials. In Saudi Arabia, the Arabian American Oil Company has moved the seat of its Board of Directors from New York to Dhahran. In certain cases, the governments have been given an option to take their royalties in kind and export directly. In Iran, Iraq, and Kuwait, the foreign oil companies have turned their local marketing activities over to the government-owned local oil companies, supplying them with crude oil or products at cost (see Chapter III, Section E). The concessionary companies have committed themselves to an intensification of their training programs and to the recruitment of an increasing share of their senior staff from among the nationals of the country in which they operate. Furthermore, the companies have substantially increased their local purchases as well as the construction of houses and the provision of other benefits for their employees.

No attempt will be made here to give a detailed account of the development of oil concessions in the Persian Gulf region, since several excellent studies are already available.[15] The following paragraphs merely list the various concessions that have been granted by the governments of the region and indicate briefly some of their outstanding features. Fuller details on the financial aspects of these concessions are given in Chapter VI, and a synopsis of all concessions at present in force will be found in the Appendix.

Iran. The first concession in the region, which covered banking, railroads, and other operations as well as oil mining, was granted in 1872 by the government of Iran to de Reuter, a British citizen, but was canceled almost immediately.[16] Another concession, of narrower scope, was also given to de Reuter in 1889, but its oil provisions were canceled ten years later owing to his failure to find petroleum. On May 28, 1901, a concession was granted to William D'Arcy, also a British citizen; it covered an area of 500,000 square miles and ran for 60 years.[17] Drilling under this concession started in 1902 and, following the discovery of oil on a commercial scale in 1908, the Anglo-Persian Oil Company, with a capital of £2 million, was formed in 1909. In 1914, the British government acquired a controlling interest in that company by subscribing £2.2 million.

Operations under this concession continued until 1932, but friction developed between the two parties and increased gradually. Iran complained about the sale of oil by the company to its subsidiaries and to the British Navy at lower prices, and about its charging investment expenditures outside Iran as costs of oil operations; it demanded a share in the profits of companies formed by the Anglo-Persian Oil Company but operating outside Iran. On the other hand, the company refused to pay the Iranian income tax introduced in 1930, claiming exemption from taxation under its concession agreement. On November 27, 1932, the government canceled the concession, but a new agreement was reached on April 29, 1933.[18] The latter increased substantially the revenues received by Iran, reduced the concessioned area to approximately 100,000 square miles, provided for greater supervision of company activities by government representatives, and extended the concession period by 32 years, i.e., to the end of 1993. After the Second World War, renewed tensions led to a series of unsuccessful negotiations and the abortive Supplemental Agreement of July 17, 1949.[19] In March, 1951, the Majlis announced the nationalization of the oil industry, and on May 1, 1951, a law was passed providing for the implementation of the principle of nationalization and for the establishment of the National Iranian Oil Company to undertake oil operations.[20] The crisis that ensued was followed by the agreement of October 29, 1954, between the government and a consortium of oil companies.[21] This agreement covered nearly all the area previously under concession to the Anglo-Iranian Oil Company, embodied the principle of nationalization, and turned over the assets of the Anglo-Iranian Oil Company in Iran to the National Iranian Oil Company. In settlement of compensation for the company's assets in Iran, and of the claims and counterclaims of both parties, Iran undertook to pay to the Anglo-Iranian Oil Company a sum of £76 million. As to the operations of the industry, Iran gave control of oil installations to two operating companies—an Exploration and Producing Company and a Refining Company—incorporated in the Netherlands and registered in Iran, and the National Iranian Oil Company took over the management of nonbasic facilities in the southern fields, domestic distribution facilities, and a small oil field and refinery in western Iran. The two operating companies agreed to operate the industry and to turn over crude oil and refined products, at cost plus a specified small fee, to the trading companies of the consortium members. The trading companies, in turn, agreed to take their share of oils at posted market prices of crude oil, plus a nominal fee for refining profits and minus a small discount as marketing allowance. The income realized from these activities, including the fees of the operating companies, was to be divided into two equal parts. Iran's share, together with the value of 12.5 per cent of royalty crude oil, payable to Iran at posted market prices, would amount to one-half of the oil income before payment of taxes to foreign governments.

The setting up of a consortium of oil companies to solve the Iranian oil question was in response to Iran's refusal to allow the return of the Anglo-Iranian Oil Company as the exclusive operator of the southern fields and refineries. As a result, the major oil companies organized Iranian Oil Participants, Limited, with the Anglo-Iranian Oil Company (renamed the British Petroleum Company in December, 1954) holding 40 per cent interest; the American companies, 40 per cent; Royal Dutch–Shell, 14 per cent; and the Compagnie Française des Pétroles, 6 per cent (see the Appendix). In return for turning over 60 per cent of its interest in Iran to other oil companies, the British Petroleum Company was to receive $600 million, of which $90,720,000 was paid in cash and the balance of $509.3 million at a rate of 10¢ per barrel of crude oil and products exported by the companies.[22]

In order to speed up the development of its other oil resources, the Iranian Parliament approved, in 1957, a law giving the right of exploration and exploitation of petroleum to the National Iranian Oil Company and authorizing it to make arrangements with other oil companies for participation in the development of Iranian oil deposits, subject to ratification by Parliament. This law reversed the policy of Iran adopted under the law of October 22, 1947, which had forbidden the granting of oil concessions to foreign interests.[23] Immediately after the passage of this law, three separate agreements were signed between the National Iranian Oil Company and three foreign companies: the Italian company, AGIP Mineraria Company (August, 1957); Pan American Petroleum Corporation (April, 1958); and the Canadian company, Sapphire Petroleum, Limited (1958). The agreement with the last of these was canceled later because of lack of progress in oil exploration and drilling.

The terms of these oil agreements are more or less similar; the following gives a summary of the agreement between the National Iranian Oil Company and Pan American.[24] The agreement covers an area of 6,176 square miles in the continental shelf of the Persian Gulf, and extends over a period of 25 years, after production and sale of oil in commercial quantities, with an option of three five-year extensions. The area will be reduced in size by 25 per cent at the end of the first five years and by another 25 per cent at the end of the second five years; finally, it will be limited to the area under exploitation at the end of 12 years. The operations will be carried out by a joint company, owned equally by the National Iranian Oil Company and Pan American, each nominating half of the members of its Board of Directors. The exploration cost will be financed exclusively by Pan American, while the exploitation investment will be made jointly by the National Iranian Oil Company and Pan American. The latter has agreed to spend within 12 years a minimum of $82 million from its own resources on exploration, and, if it succeeds in discovering oil in commercial quantities with less expenditure, the savings will have to be divided with the government. In addition, the agreement provides for the payment of $25 million in cash to the government one month after it is signed. The income derived from oil operations will be divided equally between the National Iranian Oil Company and Pan American; in addition, the Iranian government is entitled to 50 per cent of the income of the latter, thus raising the total share of Iran from oil operations under this agreement to 75 per cent of the oil income. This new pattern will undoubtedly have repercussions in other oil-producing countries.[25]

Iraq. The history of petroleum concessions in Iraq dates back to that obtained by the Deutsche Bank in 1890, which included mining rights. But no effective steps to set up a company for the exploitation of oil were taken until the formation of the Turkish Petroleum Company in 1912, with a capital of £80,000. In 1914, the "Foreign Office Agreement" was reached, raising the capital to £160,000, with the following participation: Deutsche Bank, 25 per cent; Anglo-Persian Oil Company, 47.5 per cent; Anglo-Saxon Petroleum Company, 22.5 per cent; and Calouste Gulbenkian, 5 per cent.[26] One of the most important features of this agreement was its self-denying clause (Article 10), which was later incorporated in the "Red Line" agreement of July 31, 1928;[27] in it the participating groups undertook, "on their behalf and on behalf of companies associated with them not to be interested directly or indirectly in the production or manufacture of crude oil in the Ottoman Empire," except in Egypt, Kuwait, and the transferred territories on the Turkish-Persian border.

The First World War was followed by much diplomatic negotiation and pressure culminating in the "Red Line" agreement, which changed the pattern of ownership, giving 23.75 per cent of the shares to each of the following: Anglo-Persian Oil Company, Anglo-Saxon Petroleum Company, Compagnie Française des Pétroles, and Near East Development Company;[28] and 5 per cent to C. Gulbenkian.[29] Previously, in return for the relinquishing by Turkey of its claims to Mosul, the Iraqi government had agreed to turn over to it 10 per cent of the royalties it received from the Turkish Petroleum Company or any subsidiaries it might form.[30]

The "Red Line" agreement made the Turkish Petroleum Company, or other operating companies to be set up, nonprofit crude producing enterprises. All crude oil produced or purchased by them was to be offered at seaboard terminals, to the partners in the agreement according to their respective shares in the capital of the companies, at a price equal to the cost of production and transportation (including payments to governments) plus a fixed fee not exceeding 5*s*. per ton (Article 13); in 1934 the actual fee was fixed at 1*s*. By 1928, the capital of the Turkish Petroleum Company had increased to £2 million.

While these negotiations were proceeding, the Turkish Petroleum Company had obtained a concession from Iraq on March 14, 1925.[31] The concession was to run for 75 years and covered 192 square miles (in 24 rectangular blocks of 8 square miles each) to be selected by the company within 32 months from an area of about 78,000 square miles. The company undertook to start drilling in three years; it was exempted from payment of taxes and the government was entitled to a royalty of 4*s*. gold per ton (see Chapter VI, Section C). This agreement was modified by the Supplemental Agreement of March 24, 1931, which extended the concession area to 32,000 square miles, abandoned the plot system, and relieved the company from its drilling obligations. In return, the company (which was renamed the Iraq Petroleum Company in 1929) agreed to construct by the end of 1935 a pipeline to the Mediterranean, raise its rent payments to the government, and supply the government with oil products at agreed prices (see Chapter III, Section F and Chapter VI, Section B). The company started drilling in April, 1927, and struck oil, near Kirkuk, in October, 1927.

In addition to the above concession, the Iraqi government validated, on May 24, 1926, the concession rights of the Anglo-Persian Oil Company in the territories that had been included in the D'Arcy concession of 1901 in Iran, but transferred to Turkey in 1914. The concession, which had been granted for 60 years, was extended to 1996. Oil had been discovered in this area at Naft Khaneh in 1923, and the Anglo-Persian Oil Company developed the field to meet local demand through its subsidiary, the Khanaqin Oil Company.

The Iraqi government also granted an exclusive concession to the British Oil Development Company, Limited, in 1932. The terms of this concession were similar to the one granted to the Iraq Petroleum Company, except that, in addition to other payments, the government was entitled to receive 20 per cent of the petroleum produced and saved, either in value or in kind. It comprised an area of about 46,000 square miles, west of the Tigris, and was to run for 75 years from May 25, 1932. By the end of the year, the control of the British Oil Development Company had passed to Mosul Oil Fields, Limited, a corporation set up by Italian, British, and German interests to acquire the shares of the British Oil Development Company. However, because of their interests in Iraqi oil, the parent companies of the Iraq Petroleum Company formed Mosul Holdings and between 1937 and 1941 acquired all the shares of Mosul Oil Fields and the British Oil Development Company and set up the Mosul Petroleum Company, Limited, in 1941 to take over the British Oil Development Company concession. Oil was discovered at Ain Zalah in 1939, but because of the outbreak of the war and the higher royalty provisions, the field was not developed until 1952.

The remaining part of Iraq, not covered by the previous concessions, was leased in November, 1938, for oil exploration to the Basrah Petroleum Company, Limited, an affiliate of the Iraq Petroleum Company on terms similar to those of the British Oil Development Company.[32] There was very little activity in this area until the end of the war, but in 1949 the company discovered Zubair oil field, near the Persian Gulf, and oil started flowing out of Fao terminal in December, 1951.

The slower development of the Iraqi oil industry than that of other Persian Gulf countries brought about strong criticisms from the government and demands for higher oil production and revenues. Negotiations between the government and the Iraq Petroleum Company and its affiliates resulted in a 50 per cent rise in royalty rates in August, 1950, retroactive to January, 1950; and in February, 1952, a new agreement was reached, retroactive to January, 1951. This provided for equal sharing of profits, a guarantee of greatly increased oil production, and the supply of crude oil at cost to a government refinery to be built to meet local consumption. The agreement fixed oil prices at Iraqi borders, which for the oil flowing to the Mediterranean were substantially lower than posted prices at sea terminals minus pipeline costs, and allowed considerable discount from posted prices to offtakers of Iraqi oil. The modifications made at the end of 1954 removed the bulk discount. The new government of Iraq started negotiations with the Iraq Petroleum Company group in 1958 for other changes in the terms of agreements as regards the concession area, capital participation in the companies, and changes in the equal profit-sharing formula; but no agreement had been reached by the end of 1961 (see Chapter VIII, Section B).

As to the concession in the "transferred territories," the Iraqi government made arrangements in 1952 for the purchase of the Khanaqin Oil

Company and its refining and distribution facilities in Iraq. The British Petroleum Company, the previous concessionaire, was to run operations for ten years, but in 1958 the government terminated the concession.

The "Red Line" agreement of 1928 was also brought under discussion among its members before the war and in the immediate postwar years. The ensuing dispute between the American partners and some other members led the French company to take its complaints to British courts and in November, 1948, an agreement was reached outside the court freeing members from the restrictive provisions, providing for expansion of production in Iraq, and enabling members to acquire oil from Iraq in excess of their respective shares.[33]

Bahrein. In 1914 the Sheik of Bahrein undertook not to grant an oil concession to any party without the consent of the government of the United Kingdom. On December 2, 1925, an oil concession was given to a British company, Eastern and General Syndicate, Limited, and on November 30, 1927, the Eastern Gulf Oil Company, a subsidiary of Gulf Oil Corporation, entered into an option contract with the Syndicate to purchase the Bahrein concession. But since Gulf Oil Corporation had signed the "Red Line" agreement in 1928, it was precluded from exercising its right under the option, and the Turkish Petroleum Company also declined to assume the obligations of Gulf Oil under the option. Consequently, Eastern Gulf Oil Company transferred its Bahrein rights to Standard Oil Company of California on December 21, 1928, for a sum of $50,000.

The Standard Oil Company of California took immediate steps to exercise its option and formed the Bahrein Petroleum Company, incorporated in Canada with a capital of $100,000. The acquisition of this concession by an American company brought about a controversy with the British government that was not settled until 1930, after which the Bahrein Petroleum Company was granted an exploration license. The company started drilling in October, 1931, and discovered oil in May, 1932. Subsequently, on December 29, 1934, the Bahrein Petroleum Company obtained an exclusive concession covering an area of 100,000 acres, valid for 55 years, and providing for a royalty of 3 rupees 8 annas per long ton of oil produced, with a minimum yearly payment of 75,000 rupees.[34] With the revision of the concession, on June 19, 1940, the duration was extended for five years, and the area was enlarged to include the Sheik's present and future domains; the minimum annual payment was also raised to 1,250,000 rupees.

Since Standard Oil Company of California did not have marketing facilities outside the United States, it was soon faced with the problem of disposing of its production from Bahrein, as well as its expected output from Saudi Arabia. In 1936, it entered into negotiations with The Texas Company, which had extensive markets in the Eastern Hemisphere supplied from the United States, and on July 1, 1936, an agreement was reached giving Standard Oil Company of California a 50 per cent interest in The Texas Company's marketing facilities east of Suez and The Texas Company a 50 per cent interest in Bahrein.

In 1950, royalty was raised to 10 rupees per ton, and in December, 1952, the equal profit-sharing formula was introduced in Bahrein, retroactive to January, 1952; at the same time the concession was prolonged to 2024. This profit-sharing agreement did not cover refining operations, but later Bahrein imposed a duty of 5¼¢ a barrel on imports of crude oil for the local refinery.

Saudi Arabia. The history of oil concessions in Saudi Arabia dates back to 1923, when the Eastern and General Syndicate, Limited, secured oil exploration rights covering the province of al-Hasa; but since these rights were not exercised, the concession was canceled four years later.

The discovery of oil in Bahrein in 1932 aroused the interest of Iraq Petroleum Company members and Standard Oil of California in the eastern parts of Saudi Arabia. In the competition that followed, the latter outbid Iraq Petroleum Company by a relatively small sum and won an exclusive concession in eastern Saudi Arabia, on May 29, 1933.[35] The agreement was to run for 66 years, covered an area of 360,000 square miles, and included preferential rights to additional concessions in Central and Western Najd. The company agreed to advance loans repayable from future royalties, which had been fixed at 4*s.* gold per ton, to build a refinery, and to supply the government with gasoline and kerosene free of charge (see Chapter III, Section F).

Following the agreement between Standard Oil of California and The Texas Company regarding Bahrein (see above), a further agreement was concluded in December, 1936, giving The Texas Company a one-half interest in the Saudi Arabian concession in return for the payment of $3 million in cash and $18 million in deferred payments from future production in Saudi Arabia. The two companies organized California Texas Oil Company (Caltex) to undertake marketing activities; the latter bought the marketing facilities of The Texas Company in Europe for $28 million in 1946.

The California Arabian Standard Oil Company, the operating company in Saudi Arabia, began drilling in 1935 and by March, 1938, discovered oil in commercial quantities in the Dammam area. This led several companies to seek concessions, including Iraq Petroleum Company and German, Italian, and Japanese interests. The California Arabian Standard Oil Company was again successful and concluded a supplemental agreement with the government in 1939 for 60 years, which enlarged its concession area by about 80,000 square miles and included the Saudi Arabian half-interest in the two Neutral Zones on its borders with Iraq and Kuwait. In return, it agreed to pay bonuses and a rental.

During the war years the company, renamed Arabian American Oil Company (Aramco) in January, 1944, continued its exploration and drilling and constructed substantial facilities for the production and export of crude oil and refined products, but the marketing facilities available to its parent companies remained limited. Negotiations were therefore started with other American companies that had marketing facilities as well as access to additional capital. The results of these negotiations were embodied in eight agreements, signed in 1947, which became effective in December, 1948, following the dissolution of the "Red Line" agreement.[36]

In return for the acquisition of a 40 per cent interest in Aramco, 30 per cent by Standard Oil of New Jersey and 10 per cent by Socony-Vacuum, these two companies agreed to pay $76.5 million and $25.5 million, respectively, to Standard Oil of California and The Texas Company. In addition, they agreed not to receive dividends until Standard Oil of California and The Texas Company had received specified amounts.[37] The total cost of the 40 per cent interest in Aramco to Standard Oil of New Jersey and Socony was about $450 million, but most of this was from the future income of Aramco.

During the postwar years a controversy arose between the Saudi Arabian Government and Aramco over the question of the rate of conversion of royalty payments; it was resolved by the March, 1948, agreement (see Chapter VI, Section C). In October, 1948, another agreement raised royalty on oil produced from the offshore area by 5¢ a barrel; at the same time Aramco surrendered its rights in the Kuwait-Saudi Arabian Neutral Zone and agreed to pay an annual rental of $2 million on the offshore area until oil was produced in commercial quantities, after which a minimum royalty of $2 million would be paid. Aramco also obligated itself to gradually relinquish portions of its concession area.

On December 27, 1950, the government of Saudi Arabia imposed an income tax of 50 per cent on the net operating income (i.e., after payment of taxes to foreign governments) of companies engaged in petroleum production. From this 50 per cent, companies could deduct all such payments to the Saudi Government as royalties, rentals, and other taxes. On December 30, 1950, an agreement was reached whereby the company submitted to the income tax decree, thus introducing the equal profit-sharing formula in the Middle East.

Several issues were raised in the following years in the application of this agreement. The first was the question of bulk discount given on offtake of oil to parent companies of Aramco. This was solved in October, 1954, when Aramco agreed to eliminate such discount and to pay to the government, in settlement of claims, an amount of $70 million for the period from December 31, 1951, to October 6, 1953. Second, the provision for a 50 per cent Saudi share in oil income, which was applicable to the net income of the company, was revised, and the government levied its income tax on gross income. This change affected mainly the United States Treasury, since foreign government taxes are deductible from the income tax liability of American companies. Finally, in June, 1956, Aramco agreed to submit to the application of equal profit-sharing on the operation of Ras Tanura refinery and to the elimination of marketing allowance and the volume discounts allowed from posted prices. In the meantime, an understanding was reached to the effect that, if the actual sales of crude oil and refined products to third parties (i.e., customers other than the parent companies of Aramco) were at prices lower than the published prices, the government may then accept the actual sales receipts. With regard to the marketing allowance, the parties concerned agreed to accept the actual audited marketing expenses. The 1956 agreement was made retroactive to October, 1953, and the Saudi Arabian government received an additional amount of $75 million for the settlement of previous claims.

Kuwait. As in Bahrein, the Sheik of Kuwait undertook, on October 27, 1913, not to grant an oil concession without the consent of the United Kingdom government. In 1928, Gulf Oil Corporation, acting through the Eastern and General Syndicate, sought a concession in Kuwait, from which it was not debarred since the territory lay outside the "Red Line" area. However, the Anglo-Persian Oil Company also put in an application and, after the two competitors had enlisted the support of their respective governments, a compromise was reached in 1933; this was followed by the granting of a concession on December 23, 1934, to the Kuwait Oil Company, a company with a capital of £200,000, equally owned by Gulf Oil Corporation and the Anglo-Persian Oil Company.[38] Neither party was to dispose of its interest therein without the consent of the other, and each would abstain from action damaging to the other's marketing position. Oil would be produced to an extent demanded by either, Anglo-Persian being allowed, if it wished, to substitute Iranian for Kuwaiti oil in fulfillment of its sales contracts.[39] The concession covered the whole of Kuwait, about 6,000 square miles; ran for 75 years; and provided for a bonus of 470,000 rupees, an annual rental of 95,000 rupees, and a royalty of 3 rupees per long ton, with a minimum of 250,000 rupees per annum, plus 4 annas per ton in lieu of taxes.

Drilling started in 1936; in 1938 Burgan oil field, the largest in the world, was discovered. Development was discontinued in 1942 and was resumed in 1946. In order to ensure markets for the rapidly expanding production, agreements were concluded, in 1947 and 1948, between the Anglo-Iranian Oil Company and Standard Oil of New Jersey and Socony-Vacuum, and between Gulf Oil Corporation and Royal Dutch–Shell, for the long-term supply of several hundred million barrels of crude oil (see Chapter III, Section D). On November 30, 1951, the equal profit-sharing formula was applied to Kuwait and at the same time the concession was extended by seventeen years, to 2026. In subsequent years various modifications were introduced, eliminating quantity discounts.

On January 15, 1961, a concession was granted to Kuwait Shell Petroleum Development Company, Ltd., covering about 1,500 square nautical miles off the shore of Kuwait and running for 45 years.[40] In addition to profit sharing (Article 6), the concession provides for a bonus of £7 million, payable on signature; for further bonuses of £23 million, partly dependent on the rate of growth of production; and for an annual rental of £1 million, until the discovery of oil in commercial quantities, and thereafter of £2 million until exports begin (Article 5). The government may take part or the whole of its 12.5 per cent royalty in kind (Articles 5 and 9) and is entitled free of charge to all the natural gas which the company does not utilize, sell, or "put to some other economic use" (Article 18). After the discovery of petroleum the government may purchase, for itself or on the behalf of a Kuwaiti company controlled by it, an interest of up to 20 per cent in the company (Article 23). Three years after the discovery of oil in commercial quantities, and at five-year intervals thereafter, 20 per cent of the unexploited area is to be relinquished to the government (Article 10).

Qatar. Following the entry of Standard Oil of California into Bahrein, the Iraq Petroleum Company made attempts to secure exclusive oil concessions in other parts of the "Red Line" area. In September, 1932, the Anglo-Persian Oil Company obtained a license from the Sheik of Qatar for a geological survey of the peninsula. In view of its obligations under the "Red Line" agreement, the Anglo-Persian Oil Company agreed to act in Qatar as the nominee of the Iraq Petroleum Company. On May 17, 1935, it obtained a 75-year exclusive oil concession, which covered an area of about 4,100 square miles. This provided for the payment of a 400,000-rupee bonus, an annual rental of 150,000 rupees for the first five years and 300,000 rupees thereafter, and a royalty of 3 rupees per ton. Subsequently, Iraq Petroleum Company formed the Petroleum Developments (Qatar), Ltd., and on February 5, 1937, took over the Anglo-Persian Oil Company concession.[41] Drilling began in October, 1938, and resulted in the discovery of Dukhan oil field in December, 1939; however, because of the outbreak of World War II and slow progress in the development of the oil field in postwar years, exports did not start until December, 1949. The terms of payment under the concessionary agreement of 1935 were revised in 1951 from 3 rupees per ton to 10 rupees, and in the following year an equal profit-sharing formula was adopted. The company was renamed Qatar Petroleum Company, Limited, in 1953.

Another concession was granted, in 1949, by the Sheik of Qatar to the International Marine Oil Company (owned by Superior Oil Company and Central Mining and Investment Corporation), covering regions off the shore of Qatar, beyond a three-mile limit. This concession was relinquished in 1951, and the Shell Overseas Exploration Company obtained an exclusive concession in the same area in December, 1952; this covered an area of about 10,000 square miles for a period of 75 years and provided for the payment of £260,000 as bonus and the application of the equal profit-sharing formula upon the discovery of oil.[42]

Neutral Zone. Interest in the Neutral Zone dates to 1924, when the Eastern and General Syndicate was granted exploration rights by the rulers of Saudi Arabia and Kuwait with an option for a future concession. This permit, however, was allowed to lapse, and no further action was taken until 1946, when Kuwait invited bids for concessions by competitive auction. On June 28, 1948, the American Independent Oil Company (a group of independent companies; see the Appendix), the highest bidder, obtained exclusive rights covering Kuwait's undivided half-interest for 60 years. The terms of payment offered by the company were by far the highest hitherto seen in the Middle East: a royalty of $2.50 a ton, a bonus of $7.5 million, a rental of $625,000 a year until the discovery of oil, and a 15 per cent "carried interest," or share of net profits. The agreement was modified by the supplemental agreement of July, 1961, which provided for payment of 57 per cent of the company's realized profits, or 50 per cent of the profits based on posted prices, whichever is higher. In October, 1948, Aramco relinquished its claims on the Neutral Zone (see above), and on February 20, 1949, the Pacific Western Oil Company secured a 60-year concession covering Saudi Arabia's undivided half-interest. This provided for a royalty of 55¢ a barrel, a bonus of $9.5 million, an annual rental of $1 million until discovery, and a 25 per cent "carried interest," or share of net profits. In April, 1956, the name of the latter company was changed to the Getty Oil Company.

The American Independent Oil Company, designated as the operating company, began drilling in 1949. After the expenditure of nearly $40 million on concession dues and investments by the end of 1952, the company discovered oil at Wafra in March, 1953; export began in 1954. Thereafter, each of the two partners produced oil from a specific horizon, not used by the other, and each had its own pipelines, terminals, tankage, and camps.[43]

A concession covering the area off the shore of the Neutral Zone was granted to the Arabian Oil Company on December 10, 1957, by Saudi Arabia and in May, 1958, by Kuwait.[44] The duration of the Saudi concession, including exploration, is 44 years; that of the Kuwaiti is 44½ years. In neither is the right of renewal assured; if a Kuwaiti or Saudi rival should present himself, he is to be given preference. The Saudi government is to receive 56 per cent of the profits made by the company at all stages of operation, i.e., crude oil production, refining, transport, and marketing; the corresponding figure for Kuwait is 57 per cent, calculated separately for crude oil production based on posted prices, and for other activities as a whole (Article 6). Both agreements provide for an annual dead rent of $1.5 million to each government, for refining obligations, for the transfer of 10 per cent of the shares to the governments if oil is found in commercial quantities, and for the progressive surrender of parts of the concession area. Both governments also have the option of taking up to 20 per cent of the oil in kind. Drilling began in 1959, and in January, 1960, oil was struck off the shore of Khafji.

Other Arabian Peninsula Areas. In 1937, agreement was reached between Petroleum Concessions, Ltd., a company with a shareholding identical to that of the Iraq Petroleum Company, and the rulers of Dubai and Sharjah for concessions over their territories in return for small immediate payments and annual dead rents. In the same year, similar agreements were reached by the same company with the Sultan of Masqat and Oman covering the whole of his territory, including Dhofar, and in 1938 and 1939 with the rulers of Ras al Khaima and Kalba. All these concessions ran for 75 years and provided for a royalty of 3 rupees a ton. Exploration in this area started in 1938 and drilling in 1949, but so far oil has not been discovered in commercial quantities by either Petroleum Concessions or Dhofar Cities Service Petroleum Corporation, which in 1953 acquired a concession over Dhofar, surrendered in 1951 by the former. Petroleum Concessions also surrendered its concession for Sharjah in 1959 and for Ras al Khaima in 1960.[45]

In August, 1952, a 60-year concession for an area of about 1,200 square miles off the shore of Dubai was granted to Dubai Marine Areas, Ltd., a company with a two-thirds Anglo-Iranian Oil Company and a one-third Compagnie Française des Pétroles ownership. In March, 1953, a 65-year concession for an area of 12,000 square miles off the shore of Abu Dhabi was granted to Abu Dhabi Marine Areas, Ltd., with the same ownership. Drilling started in 1953; by 1958, oil in commercial quantities had been discovered near Abu Dhabi. Present plans call for the construction of a 20-mile submarine pipeline to Das Island, from where export is scheduled to begin in 1962.[46] In 1960, oil was also discovered in commercial quantities at Murban, on the mainland of Abu Dhabi.[47]

Except for the operations of the Aden refinery, opened in 1954, other parts of the Arabian Peninsula lie outside the scope of this study. A list of concessions in force at the beginning of 1960 in these areas is given in the Appendix.

II. Investment[1]

A. Investment in World Oil Industry

The rapid growth of the petroleum industry during the last century, to its present scale, has been made possible by the investment of enormous amounts of capital. The greater part of this investment has taken place since the Second World War. At the beginning of 1960, the total value of gross fixed assets in the petroleum industry of the world, excluding the Soviet bloc for which no data are available, was estimated at $97,250 million, at historical costs, and the value of net fixed assets at $53,150 million.[2] At the beginning of 1947, the estimated value of gross fixed assets had stood at $24,600 million and that of net fixed assets at $12,150 million. Although the rise of capital expenditures in the petroleum industry has been spectacular during the postwar period, the above figures tend to understate the investments made prior to 1947. Moreover, these data underestimate the present value of total investments, because they are based on annual investment figures given at historical costs and do not reflect the changing value of the dollar; thus the data have not been adjusted to take into account the increase in price of labor and material inputs in investments, resulting from inflationary tendencies all over the world.[3] Furthermore, the figures refer only to fixed assets and do not include the liquid assets of the petroleum industry, which would have to be added to the net fixed assets in order to arrive at the total net assets employed.

The geographical distribution of the fixed assets is given in Table 10. The Western Hemisphere accounted for 77 per cent of net fixed assets (excluding foreign flag tankers) at the beginning of 1960, most of this being located in the United States; the Eastern Hemisphere, excluding the Soviet bloc, contained only 23 per cent of such assets. There have been basic changes in the geographical pattern of investment in the petroleum industry in the postwar years, which have been due to the following: the discovery and development of prolific oil fields outside the United States, especially in the Middle East, the Caribbean area, and North Africa; the increasing cost of exploration activities and

TABLE 10

ESTIMATED VALUE OF GROSS AND NET FIXED ASSETS IN WORLD PETROLEUM INDUSTRY (EXCLUDING SOVIET BLOC), 1947, 1956, AND 1960, BEGINNING OF PERIOD
(Millions of Dollars)

Area	Gross Fixed Assets			Net Fixed Assets		
	1947	1956	1960	1947	1956	1960
United States	17,700	40,400	54,700	8,500	20,900	27,500
Canada	425	2,525	4,815	175	1,700	3,350
Venezuela	1,150	3,450	6,125	600	1,500	3,450
Other Countries, W.H.	1,250	2,440	4,850	650	1,275	2,800
TOTAL WESTERN HEMISPHERE	20,525	48,815	70,490	9,925	25,375	37,100
Middle East	900	2,750	4,125	525	1,625	2,375
Western Europe	1,125	4,060	8,475	625	2,425	5,225
Africa	175	425	1,875	125	300	1,400
Far East	550	1,950	3,575	300	1,175	2,050
TOTAL EASTERN HEMISPHERE	2,750	9,185	18,050	1,575	5,525	11,050
Foreign flag tankers	1,325	5,300	8,710	650	2,825	5,000
GRAND TOTAL	24,600	63,300	97,250	12,150	33,725	53,150

Sources: The Chase Manhattan Bank, *Investment Patterns in the World Petroleum Industry* (New York, December, 1956); *Capital Investments by the World Petroleum Industry* (New York, October, 1960).

Note: The figures include the cost of drilling dry holes and lease-concession acquisitions but exclude geological and geophysical expenses and lease rentals.

the diminishing return from such expenditures in the United States; the rapidly rising consumption of petroleum products in the Eastern Hemisphere, especially Western Europe; and a trend toward the construction of refineries in petroleum consuming centers. As a result, while investment in the petroleum industry continued to grow in major petroleum producing, refining, and consuming areas, the share of the United States in yearly investments declined from 68 per cent in 1948 to 48 per cent in 1959; hence their share in the total net fixed assets of the industry declined from 74 to 47 per cent between 1947 and 1960. On the other hand, there was a considerable increase in the share of Western Europe, Canada, Venezuela, and the Far East; there was only a slight rise in that of the Middle East—from 4.6 to 4.9 per cent—during the same period.

B. Investment in the Middle East

Compared to its part in world petroleum activities, the share of the Middle East in the total fixed assets of the oil industry is relatively low. While in 1960 the Middle Eastern petroleum industry represented 68 per cent of the world's proved crude petroleum reserves (excluding the Soviet bloc), 26 per cent of its crude oil production capacity, and 7 per cent of its refining capacity, its share in the total fixed assets of the petroleum industry (excluding foreign flag tankers) was only 5 per cent. Part of this advantage is offset, however, by lower prices for Middle Eastern petroleum. Moreover, it should be remembered that the bulk of Middle Eastern oil is exported in the form of crude and that heavy investments are required outside the region for its transport, refining, and marketing.

The relatively low capital requirement in the Middle East, as will be seen later in this chapter, is essentially attributable to the exploration and extraction of crude petroleum rather than to other petroleum activities, i.e., refining, transport, and marketing. In petroleum exploration and extraction, this advantage has been due to several factors. Among these are the exceptionally favorable geological formations, with a high probability of discovering petroleum deposits at a low unit cost; the extremely high productivity of the oil wells; and the lowness of wages. The last of these, however, is partly offset by lower labor productivity (see Chapter IV, Section H).

However, despite the relatively low share of the Middle East in the total investments of the world oil industry, the absolute magnitude of such investments in the region has been considerable and is rising rapidly. The value of gross fixed assets in the petroleum industry of the Middle East, at historical costs, increased from the equivalent of \$100 million in 1926 to \$350 million in 1935, \$900 million in 1947, and \$4,125 million in 1960—compared to an increase in the value of net fixed assets from \$525 million in 1947 to \$2,375 million in 1960 (beginnings of the years).[4] The total net assets of the Middle Eastern oil industry, defined as the sum of net fixed assets and liquid assets, is estimated to have increased from \$630 million in 1947 to \$2,850 million in 1960 (see Table 11).

These levels of investment were achieved as a result of the combination of several highly favorable factors. The discovery of extremely rich and prolific petroleum deposits provided natural resources on the basis of which a large-scale petroleum industry could be established. The lower investment requirements for the development of oil fields (in relation to the level of output) and the prospect of a very high rate of return from investments stimulated the influx of foreign capital from abroad for initial development. This high profitability, in turn, supplied capital for later development of the industry. The rapidly expanding demand for petroleum products, especially in Western Europe during

TABLE 11

VALUE OF FIXED ASSETS AND ESTIMATED TOTAL ASSETS IN THE PETROLEUM INDUSTRY OF THE MIDDLE EAST, 1946-61
(Millions of Dollars)

Beginning of Year	Gross Fixed Assets	Net Fixed Assets	Estimated Total Net Fixed and Liquid Assets
1946	795	455	545
1947	900	525	630
1948	1,110	695	835
1949	1,470	1,005	1,205
1950	1,825	1,295	1,555
1951	2,000	1,390	1,670
1952	2,150	1,450	1,740
1953	2,325	1,530	1,835
1954	2,490	1,590	1,910
1955	2,610	1,600	1,920
1956	2,750	1,625	1,950
1957	3,010	1,750	2,100
1958	3,325	1,915	2,300
1959	3,725	2,155[a]	2,585
1960	4,125	2,375	2,850
1961	4,175	2,400	2,880

Sources: Figures on gross and fixed assets for the years 1947, 1956, 1959, and 1960 have been obtained from: The Chase Manhattan Bank, *Investment Patterns in the World Petroleum Industry* (New York, 1956); *Capital Investments by the World Petroleum Industry* (New York, 1959, 1960, and 1961). The other data on fixed assets have been estimated on the basis of the figures for the above years and the annual investment figures given in the former publication. Account has been taken of retirements and transfers. The data on total assets have been estimated by raising the figures on net fixed assets by 20 per cent—i.e., by approximately the same percentage as in Saudi Arabia, in 1956, when the value of net fixed assets amounted to $339.3 million and the amount of net working capital to $67.7 million. It should be added that Aramco also had other assets, amounting to $64.3 million and consisting mainly of long-term loans and advances. However, this type of asset is not to be found on such a scale among other companies operating in the region; moreover, such assets pertain in large measure to activities outside the petroleum industry. See United States Senate, Eighty-Fifth Congress, *Emergency Oil Lift Program and Related Oil Problems* (Washington, 1957), Part 4, Appendix B, pp. 2838-39. The same proportion also holds in the Venezuelan oil industry; in the United States it is 16 per cent.
[a]Revised data.

the postwar period, provided a growing market for the increasing supply of petroleum from the Middle East; the concessionary agreements between the local governments and the foreign oil companies insured a favorable institutional framework for oil operations. In addition, such inherent features of the petroleum industry as exploration risks and the long gestation period of investment were generally less disadvantageous in the Middle East than elsewhere, because of the high probability of finding oil, particularly in the Persian Gulf area, and, as already mentioned, because of the lower investment requirements in relation to productive capacity.[5]

Though the rise in petroleum investments has been spectacular in the Middle East during the past decades, the capacity of the region's oil industry to absorb additional capital remains very great, especially when its output-reserve ratio is compared with that of other major petroleum producing countries (see Chapter I, Section B). The factors limiting the expansion of the petroleum industry in the Middle East are neither the scarcity of oil deposits nor the shortage of capital and lack of technical and entrepreneurial skills; the growth of the industry has been influenced more by market availability and political risks. Sales of Middle Eastern oil have been restricted in the United States partly by a quota system imposed on imports of foreign oil, under which Venezuela receives a somewhat better treatment than the Middle East (see Chapter III, Section A). In addition, the rate of growth of petroleum consumption in the Eastern Hemisphere has slowed down (mainly owing to a decline in the rate of increase in petroleum consumption in Western Europe), and part of this market is being gradually taken over by oil exports from the Soviet Union and North Africa (see Chapter VIII, Section A). Furthermore, the serious risks of dependence on Middle Eastern oil—in view of local political developments, the geographical location of the area, and the present world tension—have led the oil companies and petroleum consuming countries to reduce this dependence by encouraging the development of petroleum resources in other areas, especially in North Africa, which, having been recently opened to exploration, has naturally attracted much competitive bidding for oil development. Despite these unfavorable factors, investments in the Middle Eastern oil industry are expected to grow in the coming years, but, perhaps, at a lower rate.

The value of annual gross fixed investment in the petroleum industry of major producing countries of the region for the period 1948–58 is given in Table 12. It may be noted that total investments, after reaching high levels in the early postwar years—owing to large-scale expansion of oil-handling facilities, refineries, ports, and especially pipelines and social overheads—declined considerably in the period 1950–55, but recovered thereafter. By 1959, the current value of investments had passed the earlier high levels—reaching $425 million as compared with $395 million for 1949. Such a fluctuation in investments has also occurred in the past, with investments rising in the early 1920's, the first half of the 1930's, and the latter part of the 1940's, and declining in the intervals.

TABLE 12

ANNUAL GROSS FIXED INVESTMENTS AND BREAKDOWN OF TOTAL INVESTMENT IN MIDDLE EASTERN PETROLEUM INDUSTRY BY COUNTRY, 1948-58
(Millions of Dollars)

Period or Sector	Iran[a]	Iraq[b]	Kuwait	Neutral Zone	Qatar	Saudi Arabia[c]	Total	Other Oil Invest-ments[d]	Grand Total
I. Annual investments									
1948	72.8	55.6	48.7	0.2	14.4	90.3	282.0	108	390
1949	96.0	57.2	52.9	2.3	18.4	101.2	328.0	67	395
1950	38.7	30.3	10.6	3.9	4.2	31.8	119.5	106	225
1951	24.1	42.7	10.6	4.2	3.6	55.2	140.4	65	205
1952	—	40.3	14.7	4.0	7.9	99.7	166.6	68	235
1953	—	28.8	16.9	2.9	9.6	72.4	130.6	104	235
1954	—	19.9	14.3	5.0	14.8	55.9	109.9	85	195
1955	6.9	24.4	10.2	5.6	8.4	64.5	120.0	100	220
1956	17.2	28.0	27.7	5.5	7.9	88.8	175.1	125	300
1957	35.3	23.0	66.5	7.5	5.0	75.5	212.8	137	350
1958	83.7	26.3	63.8	10.0	6.7	81.9	272.4	178	450
TOTAL 1948-58	374.7	376.5	336.9	51.1	100.9	817.2	2,057.3	1,143	3,200
II. Breakdown of total investment									
Exploration	19.2	51.9	8.4	25.7	4.8	...	110.0[e]	...	...
Production	130.8	134.4	109.2	11.5	49.9	...	435.8[e]	...	...
Refining	50.7	—	28.9	—	—	...	79.6[e]	...	...
Transport	45.0	160.0	62.9	13.9	28.4	...	310.2[e]	...	...
Others	129.0	30.2	127.5	—	17.8	...	304.5[e]	...	...
TOTAL 1948-58	374.7	376.5	336.9	51.1	100.9	...	1,240.1[e]	...	...

Sources: Data on specified countries are actual figures obtained from the Department of Economic and Social Affairs of the United Nations. Data on "Grand Total" are estimates published by: The Chase Manhattan Bank in *Investment Patterns in the World Petroleum Industry* (New York, December 1956) and in *Capital Investments by the World Petroleum Industry* (New York, November, 1959, and November, 1961). Figures on "Other Oil Investments" are the difference between the data on "Grand Total" and "Total."

[a]Data refer to investments by the Anglo-Iranian Oil Company between 1948 and 1951, and by the Iranian Oil Participants, on behalf of the National Iranian Oil Company, since 1955. Investments by the National Iranian Oil Company and three foreign oil companies, which recently obtained operating rights in Iran, are not covered.

[b]Excluding investments by the Iraqi government in Durah Refinery and the expansion of local marketing facilities.

[c]Excluding investments by the Trans-Arabian Pipeline Company.

[d]Includes investments in Aden, Bahrein, Israel, Jordan, Lebanon, Syria, Turkey, other Arabian Peninsula sheikdoms, and those not covered by the figures for Iran and Iraq.

[e]Excluding Saudi Arabia.

C. Geographical Distribution of Investment in the Middle East

During the postwar period, investment has been the greatest in Saudi Arabia, followed by Iran (including the investments of the National Iranian Oil Company and three foreign petroleum companies), Iraq, Kuwait, Aden, and Qatar. This pattern of investment has drastically changed the prewar and immediate postwar geographical distribution of investments.

Iran accounted for the greater part of the total assets of the petroleum industry of the Middle East during the prewar period. But the discovery of huge oil reserves in other areas of the region and the implementation of plans for their large-scale development reduced considerably Iran's share in investments; in addition, the nationalization of the petroleum industry disrupted capital expenditures in the industry for the period 1951–54. The value of the gross fixed assets of Anglo-Iranian Oil Company in Iran, at the end of 1950, was £90.1 million; this had been written down by depreciation to net assets of £28.7 million.[6] Since an appreciable part of these investments had taken place before the Second World War, at lower costs, their replacement costs at current prices would be much higher than the indicated figures. These assets were taken over by the Iranian government in 1951, and in September, 1954, an agreement was reached between the latter and the Anglo-Iranian Oil Company for the settlement of all claims and counterclaims of the parties against each other. The agreement provided for the transfer of all the Anglo-Iranian Oil Company's assets in Iran to the government, and, in consideration of this transfer and of the claims and counterclaims of both parties, the government agreed to pay the company an amount of £76 million, of which £51 million was paid in cash (out of the additional payments due to the government under the Supplemental Agreement of July, 1949, with the company); the balance of £25 million was to be paid in ten yearly installments of £2.5 million each, beginning January 1, 1957.[7] The government, in addition, agreed that the consortium of oil companies "should undertake the operation and management of certain of the oil properties (but not all of them) of the Government of Iran and the National Iranian Oil Company, including the Abadan Refinery."[8] The net value of these assets appears to have been estimated at £67 million, as the agreement with the consortium of oil companies accepted the depreciation and amortization charges of 10 per cent a year for fixed assets and provided for setting aside £6.7 million annually, for ten years, as the fixed assets charge of the above assets. Of the £67 million, the refineries accounted for £41 million and the facilities for producing and handling of crude oil for the balance.[9] The other assets, including investments in the small oil field and refinery in western Iran (Kermanshah) and the domestic distribution facilities, were kept under the direct control of the National Iranian Oil Company. From the conclusion of the consortium agreement in September, 1954, until the end of 1958, an amount of $143 million was invested for the expansion of petroleum facilities, of which $84 million was financed from the funds set aside for depreciation and amortization. These figures do not include an additional investment of about $100 million made by the National Iranian Oil Company and three foreign oil companies in other parts of the country outside the consortium area.

In Saudi Arabia, the gross fixed assets of the Arabian American Oil Company in 1958 were $699 million, and those of the Trans-Arabian Pipeline Company were $177 million, making a total of $876 million; net fixed assets were about $400 million. This figure does not include investments made recently by the Japanese oil concern off the shore of the Neutral Zone. The growth in investments in this country has been very rapid, as evidenced by the fact that the operating company started its activities there in 1933 with an original capital of $500,000, which was raised in 1936 to $700,000. By the end of 1946, Aramco had invested an amount of $115 million, by using its accumulated surplus and reserves of $23.5 million and borrowing $91.8 million from its parent companies.[10] In 1947, agreements were reached between the parent companies—Standard Oil of California and The Texas Company—and Standard Oil of New Jersey and Socony-Vacuum, whereby the latter two companies acquired, respectively, 30 and 10 per cent shares in the company, in return for a total sum of $102 million. These agreements paved the way for the rapid development of the Saudi Arabian oil industry and the construction of the Trans-Arabian pipeline, which was completed in December, 1950 (see Chapter I, Section I).

By the end of 1956, the total value of gross fixed assets of Aramco had gone up to $608.7 million, which, after the deduction of $269.4 million for depreciation and amortization, represented a net value of $339.3 million. In addition, the company had a net working capital of $67.7 million plus other assets of $64.3 million, which raised its total assets at the end of 1956 to $471.4 million. These assets, in turn, had been financed by $106.2 million received from the parent companies, and $365.2 million from earnings retained in the business.[11]

In Iraq, the Turkish Petroleum Company started investing in petroleum development in 1925, and by 1928 had raised its capital to £2 million from £160,000 in 1914; by 1934, when Iraqi petroleum began to flow to world markets, total capital expenditures had reached about $62 million.[12] In 1951, investment by oil companies in the petroleum industry of Iraq was estimated at £90 million,[13] and an additional investment of nearly $300 million has since been made in the industry (including the construction of a government refinery at Dorah), raising the value of gross fixed investments in the Iraqi oil industry to over $650 million at the beginning of 1959; net fixed assets may be put at nearly half that amount.

Kuwait, presently the largest crude petroleum producer of the Middle East, occupied the fourth rank in gross fixed assets of the region's oil industry and accounted for approximately $350 million at the beginning of 1959. The original capital of the Kuwait Oil Company had been £200,000, and it had invested very little in the development of Kuwait's petroleum resources prior to the end of World War II. Large-scale investments were made during the postwar period, and by the end of 1950 the company had borrowed about £33 million in interest-free loans from its parent companies and had invested all of this in the expansion of its oil operations.[14]

In Aden, Qatar, and the Neutral Zone, nearly all the investment in the oil industry has taken place during the postwar years;[15] the value of gross fixed assets in these territories amounted, respectively, to $150 million, $110 million, and $50 million[16] at the beginning of 1959. While in the latter two areas the investments have been made for the development of crude oil production and oil-handling facilities, in Aden they were confined to petroleum refining and storage facilities. Another area with appreciable investments in its petroleum industry is Bahrein, for which no reliable data could be obtained for recent years. However, according to officials of the Bahrein Petroleum Company, operations in Bahrein started in 1929 with an original capital of $100,000; by the end of 1946 an amount of $92.4 million had been earned from this original capital, and all of it had been reinvested in the expansion of the oil industry there, raising the total assets of the company to $92.5 million.[17] On the basis of information available on physical assets, the value of gross fixed assets in Bahrein may be estimated at well below $200 million at the beginning of 1959.

D. Distribution of Investment by Branches

Investments in the petroleum industry cover, in general, four major branches of economic activity: mining, refining, transport, and marketing. In addition, further investments are required, especially in underdeveloped countries, for the development of economic and social overhead—such as roads, ports, housing, water supplies, sewage systems, schools, hospitals, and other community facilities. Very often, investments in all these fields are made in vertically integrated oil operations, particularly by the major petroleum companies outside the United States. Integration has been induced by such factors as the nature and characteristics of petroleum, which requires specialized equipment and facilities for processing, transportation, and marketing, and the desire of oil companies to guarantee steady sources of supplies and outlets; the high risks involved in exploration; the geographical distribution of reserves and the international character of the industry; the high capital expenditures required; and the large economies of scale inherent in the industry.

The pattern of investments by major branches of petroleum operations has shown very little change, between 1947 and 1960, for the world petroleum industry as a whole (see Table 13). Exploration and production of crude petroleum have continued to absorb the major part of investments—accounting for nearly one-half of the gross fixed assets of the industry—followed by refining, transportation, and marketing. The relatively high share of crude oil production in investment has favored a shift in investment toward regions where capital requirements in production are comparatively low.

However, there has been a sharp difference between various regions in the pattern of petroleum investments; also, the structure of investments has changed considerably within each region since 1947. The share of exploration and production facilities in total investments has been much lower in the Middle East than in Venezuela, mainly because of the former's lower ratio of capital to productive capacity. On the other hand, the shares of pipelines as well as social overhead have been higher in the Middle East than in other regions, owing to the greater necessity of developing infrastructure and community facilities. In Western Europe, the largest petroleum market outside the United States, the pattern of investment in the petroleum industry is drastically different from that of the major oil-producing areas, the share of production being relatively low while that of refining and marketing are rather high. This pattern of investment reflects the fact that Western Europe is essentially a petroleum consuming area, producing very small quantities of crude petroleum but importing a large volume of crude oil and refining it locally for domestic consumption and re-export to nearby areas.

TABLE 13

DISTRIBUTION OF VALUE OF NET FIXED ASSETS, BY BRANCHES OF PETROLEUM ACTIVITIES, IN SELECTED AREAS, BEGINNING OF 1947 AND 1960
(Per Cent of Total Investment, Unless Otherwise Specified)

Branch and Date	Middle East	United States	Canada	Venezuela	Western Europe	Africa	Far East	Total World[a]
January 1, 1947								
Production of crude oil	50.5	51.8	20.0	87.5	4.8	8.0	25.0	46.9
Pipelines	11.4	8.2	2.9	4.2	1.6	—	—	6.9
Tankers	—	7.1	—	—	—	—	—	10.3
Refineries and chemical plants	23.8	14.1	20.0	5.8	37.6	12.0	23.3	15.5
Marketing facilities	9.5	15.3	48.5	1.7	52.0	76.0	50.0	17.2
Others (including social overhead)	4.8	3.5	8.6	0.8	4.0	4.0	1.7	3.2
TOTAL	100.0	100.0	100.0	100.0	100.0	100.0	100.0	100.0
TOTAL (millions of dollars)	525	8,500	175	600	625	125	300	12,150
January 1, 1960								
Production of crude oil	48.4	56.7	51.3	73.9	11.0	45.7	24.4	44.9
Pipelines	15.8	8.4	11.0	9.1	3.1	10.7	1.9	7.3
Tankers	0.6	2.4	0.6	0.4	0.4	0.4	0.5	10.8
Refineries	18.9	14.1	16.7	12.0	41.6	6.8	32.9	17.0
Chemical plants	—	3.5	1.6	—	6.4	—	1.5	2.6
Marketing facilities	7.4	12.6	16.6	2.8	34.4	32.1	37.3	14.9
Others (including social overhead)	8.8	2.3	2.1	1.7	3.1	4.3	1.5	2.5
TOTAL	100.0	100.0	100.0	100.0	100.0	100.0	100.0	100.0
TOTAL (millions of dollars)	2,375	27,500	3,350	3,450	5,225	1,400	2,050	53,150

Sources: The Chase Manhattan Bank, *Investment Patterns in the World Petroleum Industry* (New York, 1956); the figures for January 1, 1960, have been obtained directly from the Chase Manhattan Bank.

[a]Excluding the Soviet bloc, but including other countries of the Western Hemisphere and foreign flag tankers.

Note: Because of rounding off, the percentages do not add up to totals.

Basic changes have also taken place in the pattern of petroleum investments within various regions since 1947. In the Middle East, the shares of pipelines and social overhead in fixed assets increased considerably as a result of the construction of major pipelines from the oil fields of Iraq and Saudi Arabia to the Mediterranean ports, as well as of the development of "company towns" in the newly developing oil fields, refining centers, and oil terminals (see Tables 13 and 14). On

TABLE 14

VALUE OF FIXED ASSETS OF MIDDLE EASTERN PETROLEUM INDUSTRY BY BRANCHES OF ACTIVITIES, 1947, 1956, AND 1960

(Millions of Dollars)

Beginning of the Period	Exploration and Production	Pipelines	Refineries	Marketing	Tankers	Others	Total
Gross fixed assets							
1947	350	115	300	100	—	35	900
1956	950	590	655	190	—	365	2,750
1960	1,750	835	815	310	15	400	4,125
Net fixed assets							
1947	265	60	125	50	—	25	525
1956	575	310	355	130	—	255	1,625
1960	1,150	375	450	175	15	210	2,375

Sources: The Chase Manhattan Bank, *Investment Patterns in the World Petroleum Industry* (New York, December, 1956); the figures for 1960 have been obtained directly from The Chase Manhattan Bank.

the other hand, a lower rate of increase in expansion of refineries and the small volume of regional consumption of petroleum products—as compared with the rapidly rising crude oil production—were responsible for the drop in the share of refining and marketing in the total fixed assets of the Middle Eastern petroleum industry between 1947 and 1956. In the United States, increasing costs of petroleum exploration and production and the building up of a relatively large excess crude oil producing capacity raised the share of production in total investments, while the shares of tankers and marketing declined in the corresponding period. In Venezuela, Western Europe, and the Far East, the large-scale expansion of petroleum refineries brought about a considerable increase in the share of refining in the value of total fixed assets in these areas.

E. Investment-Capacity Ratios

Reference has already been made to the low ratio of capital to capacity in the petroleum industry of the Middle East as compared with other areas. This point requires further elaboration. First, it should be mentioned that physical investments of comparable specifications have higher costs in the Middle East than in the United States and most of the other major oil-producing areas. This is due to the fact that nearly the entire petroleum industry has been implanted from the outside world into the region, necessitating the import of equipment, machinery, construction materials, and other capital goods, as well as technical and managerial skills, from long distances at high costs, and requiring the development of a costly infrastructure, including "company towns" in desolate deserts (see Chapter IV, Section D). Such disadvantages as high costs of development, however, have been more than compensated for by economies of scale and by higher oil output per well. Therefore, the important question to the industry is not so much the higher cost of a specific investment—e.g., the cost of drilling an oil well—as it is the relative cost of output and return from that investment. Second, in order to analyze this factor in greater detail, it is necessary to distinguish between various stages of petroleum operations in the region, and to compare their ratios of capital to capacity with those of other areas, separately.[18]

In exploration and production of crude petroleum, the ratio of investments to capacity is extremely low in the Middle East as compared with other areas (see Table 15). In fact, the attractiveness and competitiveness of the Middle Eastern petroleum industry are essentially due to the advantages of this sector of oil operations. However, in comparing the data, it should be noted that they refer to the value of gross fixed assets divided by capacity for crude petroleum output and do not take into account the size of discovered petroleum reserves, which are very large in the Middle East. The same conclusion may be drawn from Table 16, which shows unit costs of maintaining and expanding crude petroleum production in various areas.

Another point of great importance in this connection is that, while the marginal investment-capacity ratio has increased sharply in the United States, Venezuela, and several other petroleum producing areas, it has, so far, declined in the Middle and Far East.[19] This may be due to the fact that in the latter regions, initial costs of petroleum development have been relatively high, while additional development of out-

TABLE 15

VALUE OF GROSS AND NET FIXED ASSETS IN PRODUCTION OF CRUDE PETROLEUM, TOTALS AND PER BARREL OF PRODUCTIVE CAPACITY BY AREAS, END OF 1946 AND 1959

Area	Total Fixed Assets Crude Oil Production (Millions of Dollars)			Fixed Assets Per Barrel of Daily Crude Oil Capacity (Dollars)		
	End of 1946 (1)	End of 1959 (2)	Increment in 1946-59 (3)	End of 1946 (4)	End of 1959 (5)	Increment in 1946-59 (6)
I. Gross Fixed Assets						
United States	9,525	33,175	23,650	1,880	3,190	4,450
Canada	85	2,380	2,295	3,890	2,380	2,350
Venezuela	1,050	4,700	3,650	880	1,340	1,590
Other Western Hemisphere	720	2,050	1,330	1,900	2,410	2,860
Western Europe	40	900	860	1,130	3,330	3,400
Africa	15	855	840	610	2,850	3,050
Middle East	350	1,750	1,400	420	290	270
Far East	150	985	835	2,200	1,450	1,370
TOTAL	11,935	46,795	34,860	1,560	2,030	2,280
II. Net Fixed Assets						
United States	4,400	15,600	11,200	870	1,500	2,110
Canada	35	1,720	1,685	1,600	1,720	1,725
Venezuela	525	2,550	2,025	440	730	880
Other Western Hemisphere	365	1,125	760	960	1,320	1,630
Western Europe	30	575	545	840	2,130	2,320
Africa	10	640	630	410	2,130	2,290
Middle East	265	1,150	885	320	190	170
Far East	75	500	425	1,100	740	700
TOTAL	5,705	23,860	18,155	750	1,040	1,190

Sources: The Chase Manhattan Bank, *Investment Patterns in the World Petroleum Industry*, (New York, December, 1956); *Capital Investment by the World Petroleum Industry*, (New York, October, 1960); American Petroleum Institute, *Petroleum Facts and Figures, 1959* (New York, 1959); Kenneth E. Hill, *Outlook for Oil Stock* (New York, Eastman Dillon, Union Securities and Company, June, 1960).

Note: The data on fixed assets per barrel of daily crude production capacity (Columns 4, 5, and 6) have been calculated by dividing the value of total fixed assets (Columns 1, 2, and 3) by the estimates of daily crude oil production capacity in the corresponding areas. For the year 1946, it has been assumed that the figures on output of crude oil in 1947 represent roughly the productive capacity in the beginning of that year, i.e., the end of 1946; while for the year 1959, in view of existence of large unused capacity, the published estimates on maximum efficient productive capacity (instead of actual production figures) have been used.

put has benefited from economies of scale and has required relatively lower investment; while in the former areas, investment requirements have gradually increased because of the extension of oil development into less promising or less accessible districts, resulting in a decline in marginal output. It should be noted, however, that in the last few years

TABLE 16

UNIT COSTS OF MAINTAINING AND EXPANDING CRUDE PETROLEUM PRODUCTION IN MIDDLE EAST AND OTHER AREAS, 1950-60[a]
(Dollars Per Barrel of Crude Oil Production)

Year	Middle East	United States	Venezuela	Canada	Far East	Other Areas
1950	0.13	1.18	0.30	6.99	0.70	0.45
1951	0.11	1.32	0.37	4.83	0.75	0.51
1952	0.17	1.58	0.42	5.47	0.88	1.03
1953	0.11	1.69	0.41	4.02	0.79	1.25
1954	0.11	1.86	0.39	4.01	0.83	1.21
1955	0.12	1.88	0.41	3.28	0.86	1.25
1956	0.16	1.94	0.81[b]	2.85	0.84	1.53
1957	0.17	1.95	0.95[c]	2.61	1.07	2.05
1958	0.21	1.73	0.58	2.51	0.86	2.31
1959	0.19	1.69	0.41	2.70	0.75	2.62
1960	0.15	1.63	0.24	2.53	0.62	2.23
AVERAGE	0.16	1.68	0.51	3.15	0.82	1.67

Sources: The Chase Manhattan Bank, *Capital Investments by the World Petroleum Industry* (New York, October, 1960, and November, 1961).
[a]Including the cost of drilling dry holes and lease-concession acquisitions, geological and geophysical work, and lease rentals.
[b]Including $0.35 per barrel for acquiring new petroleum concessions.
[c]Including $0.38 per barrel for acquiring new petroleum concessions.

there has been much investment in Canada and North Africa that has not yet led to full production.

Investment-capacity ratios vary much less between the different regions in the fields of refining and transportation than in the fields of exploration and production. Since the Middle East relies on the import of capital goods and technical skills from abroad for development of these facilities, and since output is not affected by natural advantages, as it is in the production of crude oil, it is to be expected that the above ratios for the region would be somewhat higher—15 to 30 per cent for similar equipment and installations—than in the developed countries, despite lower labor cost in the Middle East. It is difficult, however, to find comparable published data to show the extent of variation in investment-capacity ratios between different areas. This lack of comparability is due mainly to variation in the size of plant or transport facilities (pipelines and tankers); differences in equipment, reflected largely in greater utilization of catalytic cracking or other specialized machinery in refining processes; and the rising trend in the price of capital goods. However, an attempt has been made here to indicate the order of magnitude of investment-capacity ratios in refining for various areas during 1947–60, without adjusting the results for the foregoing limitations (see Table 17). It will be seen that the investment-capacity ratio in refining in the Middle East was lower than in other areas. This was partly due to the

TABLE 17

REFINING CAPACITY AND VALUE OF GROSS AND NET FIXED ASSETS IN PETROLEUM REFINING, BY AREAS, 1947-60

	Million Barrels Daily		Millions of Dollars		Dollars: Fixed Assets per Barrel of Daily Refining Capacity		Ratio of Cracking & Reforming Capacity to Total Refining Capacity Beginning 1960
Country or Region	Increase in Refining Capacity, 1947-60	Refining Capacity, Beginning 1960	Increase in Fixed Assets, 1947-60	Fixed Assets, Beginning 1960	Increment in 1947-60	Beginning 1960	
I. Gross fixed assets							
United States	4,962	10,250	5,175	8,175	1,043	798	87
Canada	675	920	795	910	1,178	989	77
Venezuela	755	886	680	725	901	818	16
Other W. Hemisphere	954	1,956	1,040	1,365	1,090	698	52
Western Europe	3,413	3,978	3,160	3,460	926	870	29
Africa	80	117	105	125	1,313	1,068	26
Middle East	740	1,435	515	815	696	568	21
Far East	1,199	1,375	1,035	1,150	863	836	24
TOTAL	12,778	20,917	12,505	16,725	979	800	60
II. Net fixed assets							
United States	4,962	10,250	2,675	3,875	539	378	87
Canada	675	920	525	560	778	609	77
Venezuela	755	886	380	415	503	468	16
Other W. Hemisphere	954	1,956	630	800	660	409	52
Western Europe	3,413	3,978	1,940	2,175	568	547	29
Africa	80	117	80	95	1,000	812	26
Middle East	740	1,435	325	450	439	314	21
Far East	1,199	1,375	605	675	505	491	24
TOTAL	12,778	20,917	7,160	9,045	560	432	60

Sources: Refining capacity: American Petroleum Institute, *Petroleum Facts and Figures, 1959* (New York, 1959); *The Oil and Gas Journal* (December 28, 1959). Fixed assets: The Chase Manhattan Bank, *Investment Patterns in the World Petroleum Industry* (New York, December, 1956); the data for the beginning of 1960 have been obtained directly from The Chase Manhattan Bank.

large size of plants in the Middle East, which required lower investments per unit of capacity, and partly to simpler equipment and processing in refining, as reflected in the lower ratio of cracking and reforming capacity to total refining capacity (see Table 5, p. 14). It has recently been estimated that a simple refinery in Western Europe, equipped with a distillation unit with catalytic reforming and capable of producing up to 20 per cent gasoline and 10 per cent kerosene from typical Middle Eastern oil, will cost $22 per ton annual capacity for a plant with a one million ton output and $10 per ton for a plant with a seven million ton output. The corresponding costs for a refinery with a catalytic cracking plant and with a gasoline yield of up to 40 per cent, would be $42 and $20 per ton annual capacity for one million and seven million ton plants, respectively. As for pipelines, they are estimated to require an investment amounting to $50,000 per mile for an 18-inch pipeline with a five million ton annual throughput capacity, as compared with $110,000 per mile for a 30-inch pipeline with a fifteen million ton capacity.

The last category of fixed assets to be considered here is "other" investments, which consist largely of capital expenditures in social and economic overheads. In this field, the Middle East, as compared with some of the major petroleum producing areas, appears to have been in an unfavorable position in the past, since initial investments there for the development of basic facilities and "company towns" have been heavy. At the beginning of 1960, "other" investments represented 8.8 per cent of the net fixed assets of the petroleum industry in the Middle East, as against 2.3 per cent in the United States, 1.5 per cent in the Far East, and 1.7 per cent in Venezuela. This ratio is expected to decline in the Middle East in the future, since the greater part of the required basic facilities in the fields has already been constructed.[20] Moreover, part of these investments, especially those in housing and community facilities, may be considered as compensation for the lower cost of local labor. Even if such investment be added to investments in exploration and production facilities, the resulting investment-capacity ratio for the Middle East would still be far below that of other areas.

The foregoing analysis shows that the situation of the petroleum industry of the Middle East, compared to that of other areas, has been highly advantageous with respect to the requirement of capital for its development. This has been due to the lower investment-capacity ratio in exploration and production activities; the handicaps from which investments in other fields of oil activity have suffered have not appreciably offset this advantage. However, it should be emphasized that in making the above analysis, attention has been paid only to the existing industry in each region, without considering the extensions of that industry into other areas. For instance, Middle Eastern crude petroleum is mainly exported abroad and refined and marketed in other countries, but investments in such activities have not been included in the above analysis. In order to give an idea of the order of magnitude of such investments, Table 18 has been constructed; it shows that these investments were very roughly three times as large as those within the region.

TABLE 18

INVESTMENT IN GROSS AND NET FIXED ASSETS IN RELATION TO MIDDLE EASTERN OIL, WITHIN AND OUTSIDE THE REGION, BEGINNING 1960
(Millions of Dollars)

Item	Gross Fixed Assets			Net Fixed Assets		
	Within the Region (1)	Outside the Region (2)	Total (3)	Within the Region (4)	Outside the Region (5)	Total (6)
Production	1,750	–	1,750	1,150	–	1,150
Pipelines	835	280	1,115	375	125	500
Refineries	815	3,555	4,370	450	1,950	2,400
Marketing facilities	310	3,090	3,400	175	1,895	2,070
Tankers	15	6,185	6,200	15	3,360	3,375
Others	400	–	400	210	–	210
TOTAL	4,125	13,110	17,235	2,375	7,330	9,705

Sources: For sources for Columns (1) and (4), cf. Table 14. The data in Columns (2) and (5) are, respectively, the difference between Columns (3) and (1), and the difference between Columns (6) and (4). The figures in Columns (3) and (6) have been arrived at on the basis of data given in The Chase Manhattan Bank, *Capital Investments by the World Petroleum Industry* (New York, October, 1960), as follows: for refineries and marketing facilities, average net and gross fixed assets per barrel of oil refined and consumed were calculated for the world as a whole and multiplied by the volume of oil production in the Middle East; for tankers, average net and gross investment per barrel of oil moved in ocean trade was computed and was multiplied by the volume of exports of oil from the region; for pipelines, a rough estimate was made on the basis of pipeline investments in Western Europe; and for production and "others," it was assumed that all net or gross fixed assets relating to the Middle Eastern oil industry are located in the region.

Within the Middle East region itself, there are also considerable variations in investment-capacity ratios, and marginal investment-capacity ratios have declined with the expansion of the industry. This decline is attributable to economies of large-scale output, but is not expected to continue beyond certain levels of production, which would differ from one country to another.

F. Source and Ownership of Investment

Until recently, nearly the entire investment in the petroleum industry of the Middle East had been financed and controlled by the eight major international oil companies—five American, one British, one British-Dutch, and one French. Practically no national capital participated in the development of the region's oil industry either directly or indirectly. This was due partly to the shortage of capital in the region, especially capital in large blocks, willing to take large risks; partly to the absence of even elementary knowledge of the oil business; and partly to the lack of opportunity to buy stocks of the operating companies in the Middle East, since all such stocks were owned by the parent companies of these operating companies and were not available to the public (the only exception being the Anglo-Iranian Oil Company, which operated in Iran until 1951). However, the shares of the parent companies, which engage in world-wide activities, are of course traded in the leading stock exchanges of the world. This situation began to change in the late 1940's. First, smaller independent oil companies—of American, Canadian, Italian, Japanese, and German nationality—have undertaken oil operations in the Middle East, have invested considerable sums, and in a few cases have achieved remarkable success. Second, the governments of several countries, notably Iran, Iraq, Israel, Turkey, and the United Arab Republic, have begun to mobilize local resources for the development of their petroleum industry. Third, all the assets of the Anglo-Iranian Oil Company in Iran were legally transferred to the ownership of the Iranian government in 1954, following arrangements for the payment of compensation and the settlement of other issues arising from the nationalization of the petroleum industry; the government, in turn, agreed to the use of its assets in southern Iran by the consortium of oil companies.

These factors have brought about considerable changes in the pattern of distribution of ownership and control of the Middle Eastern petroleum industry by the various national interests (see Table 19). British interests, which had accounted for about 44 per cent of gross fixed assets in the region's oil industry in 1947, represented only 18 per cent in 1959; on the other hand, the share of American companies (including both major oil companies and independent petroleum concerns) increased from approximately 40 to 50 per cent during the corresponding period. The share of interests of "other" countries, i.e., other than American, British, Dutch, or French, which was negligible in 1947,

TABLE 19

ESTIMATED DISTRIBUTION OF GROSS FIXED ASSETS IN THE PETROLEUM INDUSTRY OF THE MIDDLE EAST, BY NATIONAL OWNERSHIP AND CONTROL, BEGINNING OF 1947 AND 1959
(Millions of Dollars and Per Cent)

	Millions of Dollars		Per Cent	
Country	1947	1959	1947	1959
United States	360	1,850	40	50
United Kingdom[a]	400	680	44	18
France	70	200	8	5
Netherlands[a]	70	125	8	3
Others	—	870	—	24
TOTAL	900	3,725	100	100

Sources: The data have been estimated on the basis of the gross fixed assets in the petroleum industry of various countries of the Middle East (for the actual data and their sources see the text) and the legal ownership of operating oil companies in those countries. Investments in Iran, located within the operating area of the Iranian Oil Participants, are owned legally by the National Iranian Oil Company, and have been included under "others."

[a] The investments of Royal Dutch-Shell have been allocated as 40 per cent to the United Kingdom and 60 per cent to the Netherlands.

jumped to 24 per cent in 1959; a great part of this was represented by the assets turned over by the Anglo-Iranian Oil Company to the National Iranian Oil Company.

The initial costs of petroleum development in the Middle East were financed by imports of capital from abroad, while later development, i.e., development after the production and export of petroleum in commercial quantities, has been carried out by the utilization of depreciation funds and part of the net income. The original capital brought into the region as a whole by foreign oil companies may be estimated at about $600 million at the beginning of 1960; of this, Saudi Arabia accounted for one-third; Iran for one-fourth; Iraq and Kuwait each for over one-tenth; and the other countries for the remaining two-tenths. This original capital should be compared with the estimated total assets of $2,850 million at the beginning of 1960, of which $2,375 million represented the value of net fixed assets. Hence, the original capital accounted for about one-fifth of the capital employed in the region's oil industry, and the remaining four-fifths was financed by the use of depreciation and amortization funds and by the utilization of part of the net income of the oil companies. In other words, the companies reinvested their profits in the industry, rather than distributing them to their stockholders and raising on the money market the fresh capital required for expansion.

III. Prices and Receipts

A. The Structure of the Petroleum Market

The sectors of the world petroleum market, namely the United States, the Soviet bloc, and the rest of the world, have one important feature in common: In recent decades they have not generally corresponded to textbook definitions of a competitive market, and their domestic output and imports of petroleum are not at present allowed to vary freely and to determine prices. The Soviet bloc market is, of course, state controlled, and the volume of imports and exports does not seem to be determined by the relation between domestic and foreign costs. It is worth noting that costs of crude oil production in the Middle East, together with transport charges, are probably lower than the cost of Soviet or Roumanian oil in a large part of the Soviet bloc, but practically no Middle Eastern oil is marketed in those areas. In the United States, despite the presence of a large number of competing oil producers, petroleum prices have been sustained since the 1930's at an artificial level by restrictions on domestic output and on imports. Under a conservation policy, the system of prorationing practiced in almost all oil-producing states has kept domestic output well below the level it would otherwise have attained. As for imports into the United States, in addition to a small duty levied since 1932, there has been a quota system. This was introduced for the first time in the 1940's for a short period on a country basis. In 1955 the leading importers initiated voluntary controls on foreign oil, and since March, 1959, the government has imposed mandatory quotas on oil imports.[1]

The outstanding feature of the oil markets of the rest of the world has been the predominance of the seven major international oil companies: Standard Oil Company of New Jersey, Standard Oil Company of California, Socony-Vacuum Oil Company, Gulf Oil Corporation, The Texas Company, Royal Dutch–Shell Oil Company, and British Petroleum Company (formerly Anglo-Iranian Oil Company); to these may be added an eighth, Compagnie Française des Pétroles. Table 20 shows the extent of their control over the reserves, production, refining, and transport of oil. In addition, and not of least importance, it would appear that the seven international oil companies are dominant forces in marketing in most countries;[2] a detailed analysis, however, cannot be given because of the scarcity of statistical information.

TABLE 20

PERCENTAGE SHARE CONTROLLED BY SEVEN MAJOR INTERNATIONAL PETROLEUM COMPANIES

<table>
<tr><th>Object Controlled and Year</th><th>U.S.</th><th>Other Western Hemisphere</th><th>Eastern Hemisphere[a]</th><th>World[a]</th></tr>
<tr><td>Reserves</td><td></td><td></td><td></td><td></td></tr>
<tr><td>1949</td><td>34</td><td colspan="2">82</td><td>65</td></tr>
<tr><td>1958[b]</td><td>33</td><td>71</td><td>90</td><td>80</td></tr>
<tr><td>Production of crude oil</td><td></td><td></td><td></td><td></td></tr>
<tr><td>1949</td><td>32</td><td>81</td><td>96</td><td>55</td></tr>
<tr><td>1959</td><td>33</td><td>73</td><td>84</td><td>60</td></tr>
<tr><td>Refining[c]</td><td></td><td></td><td></td><td></td></tr>
<tr><td>1950</td><td>44</td><td>76</td><td>79</td><td>57</td></tr>
<tr><td>1959</td><td>43</td><td>76</td><td>65</td><td>56</td></tr>
<tr><td>Major pipelines</td><td></td><td></td><td></td><td></td></tr>
<tr><td>1950</td><td>44</td><td>100</td><td>100</td><td>57</td></tr>
<tr><td>Private tankers</td><td></td><td></td><td></td><td></td></tr>
<tr><td>1950[d]</td><td>...</td><td>...</td><td>...</td><td>(67)</td></tr>
</table>

Sources: 1949 and 1950 figures: United States Federal Trade Commission, *International Petroleum Cartel* (Washington, 1952), pp. 23-28. 1958 figure on reserves: P. H. Frankel and W. L. Newton, "The State of the Oil Industry," *National Institute Economic Review* (London, 1960). 1959 figures on production and input to refineries: *Moody's Industrials* (New York, 1960).

[a] Excluding Soviet bloc.

[b] Data for 1958 include Compagnie Française des Petroles.

[c] Data for 1950 refer to capacity; data for 1959 refer to crude oil input.

[d] Ownership or chartering. In 1959, the companies owned 43 per cent of the world tanker fleet and chartered a further fleet, estimated at between 29 and nearly 47 per cent of the total.

The next point that must be raised is the degree of competition among these companies. On this question, not surprisingly, opinions differ sharply. On the one hand, a report by the United States Federal Trade Commission prepared in 1952 claims to have "shown that these major oil companies, through the high degree of concentration of control, through direct ownership, through joint ownership, through purchase and sales contracts, and through production and marketing agreements, have been able to limit production, divide up markets, share territories and carry on other activities designed to stabilize markets and control production."[3] On the other hand, the companies have strenuously maintained that they compete with each other and do not engage in any form of collusion.[4] And various intermediate explanations have been offered. For instance, it has been stated that "Price competition in the international oil industry is . . . massive rather than hysterical. It is the type of competition suited to an industry consisting mainly of large scale mature enterprises keenly aware of the importance of self-discipline and stability."[5] The fact is that the problems raised by the behavior of firms in an oligopolistic market, where there may or may not be "competition among the few," are far from having been solved. Thus a distinction has been drawn between "true" agreements between firms, based on direct contact, and "tacit" agreements, based on "spontaneous coordination."[6] Again the phenomenon of "price leadership" has been attributed to explicit or implicit collusion on the one hand, or of competition on the other.[7] Similarly, the system of "basing point pricing," which is used in the oil and other industries, has been diversely interpreted as a result of collusion and as a manifestation of imperfect competition.[8]

With oil, the matter has been further complicated by the political and strategic aspects of the industry and the vital importance of petroleum as a source of energy. In fact, in at least two crises, the Iranian nationalization crisis of 1951–53 and the Suez crisis of 1956–57, the government of the United States, notwithstanding its antitrust legislation, and that of the United Kingdom urged the oil companies to coordinate their activities, and set up an agency to assist them in doing so. However, at least this much is clear: The major international oil companies have not practiced active price competition and have not energetically invaded each other's markets.[9] The following is a fair summary of the situation:

> First, with all the international companies engaged in the Middle East, and about half of them also controlling almost all Venezuelan production, the quantities drawn from each of the producing countries settled into a workable pattern. The pattern tended to be determined by the respective market share of each of the companies in the consuming countries. In the aggregate these shares tended to remain reasonably constant. Secondly, these conditions permitted a price policy which made crude oil production in Venezuela and in the Middle East exceedingly profitable.[10]

To this may be added the following appraisal:

> The separate "groups" are often closely associated through joint ownership of subsidiaries and through long-term supply or marketing agreements; but they are also in competition with each other, the competition largely taking

> the form of attempts to maintain or increase their shares in the market for final products, or to obtain a position in new markets, through strategic acquisition of raw material supplies and refinery and distribution facilities, through improvement in products and service, and through advertising. Price competition is avoided as far as possible and market-sharing arrangements have not been unknown.[11]

It should, of course, be remembered that the companies have had to meet the competition of other fuels and have been subjected to many pressures from the governments of producing and consuming countries. Moreover, in very recent years, the above-mentioned pattern has been significantly changed by the emergence of new oil competitors, including the Soviet Oil Trust, as will be described in detail in the last chapter.

B. Elasticity of Demand

Another factor affecting prices, in addition to the degree of competition among sellers, is demand. As regards petroleum, the following points may be noted. In the first place, the demand for crude oil is a derived one, since it is the refined products that are directly consumed. Second, long-term income elasticity of demand for oil products seems to be high up to a certain point. This is partly because some products are essential for the provision of certain services the demand for which increases sharply as incomes rise (e.g., gasoline for motor and aviation travel), and partly because refined oil is cleaner and easier to handle than its main rivals, coal and lignite (but not natural gas or electricity), and is therefore increasingly demanded when incomes rise and cheapness can be readily sacrificed to convenience. Third, the price elasticity of demand for different petroleum products varies greatly, depending on the availability of acceptable substitutes, the urgency of the needs served, and the importance of the cost of the oil product relative to the total cost of the service rendered, i.e., the question of joint demand.

Thus, the demand for gasoline seems to be highly inelastic with respect to price because, in an industrial society, it is a necessity for which there are no acceptable substitutes and the purchase of which is nonpostponable, and also because gasoline costs represent only a small part of the total costs of operating a motor vehicle.[12] The same is true, to an even greater extent, of lubricating oils. The demand for kerosene also seems to be inelastic, whether it is used as the principal domestic fuel and illuminant, as in underdeveloped countries, or whether it provides jet fuel. On the other hand, the demand for distillate fuel oil seems to be much more elastic, since substitutes for it may be used by replacing equipment. The demand for residual fuel oil is even more elastic than that for distillate fuel oil: "The former is in much the same category as the latter in terms of available substitutes; however, in addition, in certain uses substitute products can be utilized immediately through the use of change-over equipment."[13]

Last, government taxes form a sizable, and in some countries the greater, part of the price of certain products, especially gasoline and kerosene, to the consumer; consequently, changes in the prices of these products, especially crude, may have very little effect on the consumer price. This, of course, decreases the price elasticity of demand as regards the producer.

It may be concluded, therefore, that the demand for most products is inelastic, but that some fuels, notably residual fuel, are more vulnerable to competition from other fuels in certain fields and are therefore more likely to react by price changes. Demand for crude oil is also likely to be inelastic with respect to price, since a relatively large change in the price of crude is likely to lead to a proportionately smaller change in the wholesale price of most of the products and, owing to the presence of the government taxes, to a still smaller change in their retail prices.

C. Pricing System

The pricing of crude oil and petroleum products has rested on the basing point system.[14] In the early 1920's, when the United States (mainly in the Gulf Coast states) and Mexico were the two leading exporters of petroleum, it was natural that oil prices in the Gulf of Mexico should influence the prices of minor exporters in the world market. This gave rise to the establishment of a "basing point" system for the world oil industry. In other words, prices all over the world were calculated as if the oil had come from the Gulf, irrespective of its point of origin, and buyers were charged the equivalent of Gulf prices and freights from the Gulf to the point of delivery.[15] Thus, if oil were supplied in Bombay from Abadan, the buyer would pay the Gulf of Mexico price of the given product plus the equivalent of the freight rate from the Gulf of Mexico to Bombay; since the latter was much higher than the freight rate from Abadan to Bombay, the buyer was being charged a "phantom" freight in addition to the base price and actual freights. If, on the other hand, oil were shipped from Abadan to London, in which case freight rates (Abadan to London) would be higher than from the Gulf of Mexico to London, the supplying company would have to "absorb" the difference between Gulf-London and Abadan-London freight rates. Thus, "prices increased geographically outward from the Gulf of Mexico until they reached a maximum on the opposite side of the world. This maximum price-line is called price-shed, akin to the watershed concept of physical geography. Before World War II the price-shed was located in the Indian Ocean, usually south of Burma, and ran approximately in a north-south direction."[16] It may be added that this system applied to both crude oil and refined products. The emergence of Venezuela as a major producer in the late 1920's did not disturb this pattern. Since the bulk of Venezuelan exports went to the Atlantic seaboard of the United States and Europe, and since the Venezuela-Atlantic seaboard and Gulf-Atlantic seaboard freights are virtually identical, it was logical that Venezuelan crude should be priced at the Gulf price minus the import duty collected in the United States on foreign oil, and that refined oil products should be priced similarly. The establishment in the 1930's of a base point in Constantsa, for Roumanian exports, did not disturb the existing system, except occasionally in the Mediterranean and Central Europe. This was because, on the one hand, Roumanian exports never constituted more than a small fraction of total world trade, and on the other hand, since the international companies had a large interest in Roumanian production, "even the Constantsa quotations were in fact not wholly independent of the United States prices, and followed in general price movements at the United States Gulf."[17]

The factors underlying this system underwent important changes during and after the Second World War, for the relative importance of the Western Hemisphere, which had been the main supplier of the world market, declined, and that of the Middle East greatly increased. This shift was bound to affect the "basing point" system.

During the Second World War, when shipments of oil from the Middle East expanded, the British Government became increasingly concerned over the "phantom" freight being charged.[18] Negotiations with oil companies led to the establishment, by 1945, of a new basing point, the Persian Gulf, with prices practically identical to Gulf of Mexico prices. In other words, buyers of Middle Eastern oil would henceforth pay the posted price of oil in the Gulf of Mexico plus the freight from the nearest source of supply. With this system, Middle Eastern oil could compete with Western Hemisphere oil wherever freight rates from the Middle East were lower than those from the Western Hemisphere, i.e., east of Suez and in the Mediterranean as far west as Italy. Thus a new price-shed was established in the west, near Malta, and in the east, west of Hawaii.

In the early postwar period, the discovery of additional huge reserves in the Middle East, increasing concern over the exhaustion of United States reserves, and the growing fuel needs of Europe made it expedient to raise Middle Eastern production. For this it was necessary that the *relative* price of Middle Eastern crude oil should fall so as to enable it to compete with Western Hemisphere oil in Western Europe. Hence, when in 1945–47 Gulf of Mexico prices of crude were raised by $1.32 per barrel (to $2.68 for crude oil of 34 degrees API), Persian Gulf prices were raised by only $1.17 (to $2.18).[19] By March, 1948, all major Middle Eastern producers had established a uniform Persian Gulf price of $2.18 per barrel (34 degrees), at which price existing freight rates equalized Middle Eastern and Gulf of Mexico based prices in London. In May, 1948, Persian Gulf prices were reduced to $2.03. This was intended to make Middle Eastern oil competitive with Venezuelan oil in Western Europe. Since Venezuelan prices continued to equal Gulf of Mexico prices (minus the above-mentioned import duty into the United States), while Venezuela–Western Europe freight rates were some 15¢ per barrel lower than United States–Western Europe rates, it was necessary to bring the price of Middle Eastern oil slightly below that of Venezuelan oil.

In 1949, with weakening markets resulting in cutbacks in production in the United States and Venezuela, and under pressure from the Economic Cooperation Administration, which was financing the supply of crude oil to Europe, Middle Eastern prices of crude were reduced by 15¢ in April to $1.88 a barrel. A further reduction of 13¢ took place in July, enabling the Middle East to compete with Venezuelan crude oil on the United States Atlantic seaboard by equalizing prices in New York at existing freight rates, which had appreciably declined in late 1948 and early 1949. This principle has remained in force since that time, but the delivered and realized prices have been affected by change in freight rates, and in some cases by the granting of discounts.

At this point, mention should be made of other basing points. After the Persian Gulf basing point was established, the small amounts of crude oil flowing from Iraq through the pipelines to the Mediterranean were priced so as to be competitive with Persian Gulf oil, i.e., their price was higher by the amount corresponding to freight rates from the Persian Gulf to the Mediterranean, including Suez Canal tolls. The same pricing system was applied to the oil transported through the Trans-Arabian pipeline and the large Kirkuk-Banias pipeline. Another basing point is Indonesia, where prices of crude oil and products are generally set in "such a manner as to equalize their delivered price with that of the major supply stream from the Middle East,"[20] but the supply of Indonesian oil is small and its influence is strictly limited. As for Algerian oil, a price was established in 1959 lowering the existing one "by about five per cent compared with the present price, which is based on the Persian Gulf price plus freight to this part of the Mediterranean."[21] Soviet pricing is touched on in Chapter VIII.

Table 21 shows subsequent price movements. The gap in posted prices between United States and Persian Gulf oil has widened steadily since 1953, while that between the Persian Gulf and Venezuela changed little over the period. Price increases in the Persian Gulf in 1953 and 1957, during the Suez crisis, accompanied similar movements in the United States and Venezuela, but were slightly smaller. The price reduction of February, 1959, immediately followed one in Venezuela, which may have been provoked by the Venezuelan Government's modification of its income tax schedule late in 1958 to raise its share of oil income (see Chapter VI, Section A). But the oil companies maintained that these reductions were designed to meet increasing competition from the Soviet Union and independent oil companies (see Chapter VIII, Section A).[22] However, the further small reduction in Venezuelan prices (5¢ to 10¢ per barrel) that took place in April, 1959, was not followed by one in the Middle East until August, 1960. These price declines were sharply criticized by the governments of the oil producing countries, which thereupon established the Organization of Petroleum Exporting Countries (OPEC), in September, 1960 (see Chapter VIII, Section A).

It should also be noted that the gap between Mediterranean and Persian Gulf prices for Middle Eastern oil narrowed in 1953 and 1954, when the price increases in the latter were not accompanied by corresponding increases in the Mediterranean. A contrary movement occurred during the Suez crisis, but by 1959 the gap between the two sets of prices was much narrower; for Saudi 34-degree crude it was 39¢ a barrel, compared to 66¢ in 1952. Delivered prices to customers were affected not only by changes in posted prices but also by fluctuations in tanker freight rates, which will be discussed later. The decline of such rates has increased the competitiveness of Middle Eastern oil, especially in distant markets. The changes in tanker freights have also affected the differential between Mediterranean and Persian Gulf posted prices for Middle Eastern oil.

As for refined products, after the war the Persian Gulf refineries, like

TABLE 21

ANNUAL AVERAGE POSTED PRICES OF CRUDE PETROLEUM, F.O.B. MIDDLE EASTERN, UNITED STATES, AND VENEZUELAN PORTS, 1948-61
(Dollars Per Barrel)

Country:	Iran	Iraq		Kuwait	Neutral Zone	Qatar	Saudi Arabia		United States	Venezuela
Outlet:	Persian Gulf	Persian Gulf	Mediterranean	Persian Gulf	Persian Gulf	Persian Gulf	Persian Gulf	Mediterranean	Gulf Coast	Caribbean Sea
Ports:	Bandar Mashur	Fao	Tripoli and Banias	Ahmadi	Mina Saud	Umm Said	Ras Tanura	Sidon		Puerto la Cruz
API gravity of crude petroleum:	34 degrees	36 degrees	36 degrees	32 degrees	24 degrees	39 degrees	34 degrees	34 degrees	34 degrees	36 degrees Oficina
1948	(2.04)	—	(2.76)	(1.85)	—	—	2.06	—	2.68	2.65
1949	(1.79)	—	(2.51)	(1.60)	—	(1.91)	1.81	—	2.68	2.65
1950	(1.69)	—	2.41	(1.50)	—	1.81	1.71	2.37	2.68	2.65
1951	(1.69)	1.73	2.41	(1.50)	—	1.81	1.71	2.37	2.68	2.65
1952	—	1.73	2.41	(1.50)	—	1.81	1.71	2.37	2.68	2.65
1953	—	1.80	2.41	1.67	—	1.95	1.81	2.37	2.98	2.90
1954	1.91	1.90	2.41	1.72	1.50	2.08	1.93	2.37	2.98	2.90
1955	1.91	1.90	2.41	1.72	1.50	2.08	1.93	2.37	2.98	2.90
1956	1.91	1.85	2.41	1.72	1.50	2.08	1.93	2.46	2.98	2.84
1957	1.97	1.93	2.67	1.80	1.58	2.14	1.99	2.63	3.38	3.05
1958	2.04	1.98	2.51	1.85	1.63	2.21	2.06	2.47	3.28	3.05
1959	1.88	1.82	2.33	1.69	1.51	2.05	1.90	2.29	3.28	2.84
1960	1.84	1.78	2.28	1.65	1.49	1.98	1.87	2.24	3.28	2.80
1961	1.78	1.72	2.21	1.59	1.48	1.91	1.80	2.17	3.28	2.80

Sources: *Platt's Oil Price Handbook and Oilmanac* (New York: McGraw-Hill Book Co.); United States Federal Trade Commission, *International Petroleum Cartel* (Washington, 1952); *Petroleum Press Service* (London, January-December, 1959); United States Senate, Eighty-Fifth Congress, *Emergency Oil Lift Program and Related Oil Problems, Joint Hearings Before Subcommittees of the Committee on the Judiciary and Committee on Interior and Insular Affairs* (Washington, 1957), Part 3, p. 2223.

Note: The figures in brackets have been estimated on the basis of published prices for Saudi Arabia. Prices have been weighted to arrive at annual average prices.

those of the Caribbean, quoted f.o.b. prices equal to "Platt's Low," f.o.b. Gulf of Mexico (see Table 22). In 1957, however, Persian Gulf refineries began to post prices slightly below those of the Gulf of Mexico for gasoline and below those of the Caribbean for heavy fuel oil, while other products tended to be priced higher. But, mainly because of the low cost of Persian Gulf crude, the gross refining margins in the region were probably among the highest of the major oil centers of the world (see Table 37, p. 120), even though the "product mix" was unfavorable in that the share of gasoline was low and that of heavy fuels high (see Table 6, p. 15).[23]

TABLE 22

ANNUAL AVERAGE PRICES OF REFINED PETROLEUM PRODUCTS, F.O.B. PERSIAN GULF PORTS, 1948-61

(Dollars Per Barrel)

Year	Gasoline	Kerosene	Distillate Fuel Oils	Residual Fuel Oils
1948	3.78	3.78	3.36	2.42
1949	4.10	3.23	2.84	1.43
1950	4.39	3.43	2.97	1.63
1951	4.62	3.59	3.26	1.75
1952	4.62	3.78	3.36	1.64
1953	4.76	3.79	3.41	1.70
1954	4.35	3.81	3.48	1.85
1955	4.41	3.78	3.60	2.01
1956	4.37	3.97	3.71	2.14
1957	4.49	3.95	3.91	2.40
1958	4.28	3.95	3.91	2.15
1959	4.10	3.90	3.86	1.82
1960	4.07	3.88	3.49	1.75
1961	3.94	3.68	3.19	1.65

Sources: *Platt's Oil Price Handbook and Oilmanac, 1958, Prices* (McGraw-Hill Book Co., New York, 1959); *Petroleum Press Service* (London, January-December, 1959-61).

Note: The data for 1957 to 1961 represent the posted prices of major petroleum products at Ras Tanura, Saudi Arabia. The figures for other years refer to the prices of major petroleum products at the United States Gulf Coast, to which the prices of refined products of the Middle East are linked. These prices refer to the annual average "low" prices of the products. Gasoline prices are for regular 87 octane gasoline; kerosene prices are for 41-43-gravity white kerosene; distillate fuel prices are for Number 2 fuel; and residual fuel oils prices are for bunker C fuel.

In the meantime, however, a more fundamental change was taking place in the pricing of Middle Eastern crude. With sharply falling tanker freight rates (see Chapter IV, Section J) and mounting pressures of supplies from new exporting companies, it became increasingly customary to offer Middle Eastern crude to large buyers in Latin

America, Japan, and elsewhere at prices that implied either a discount from posted prices or the forgoing of any profits—sometimes even the incurring of losses—on tankers owned or chartered by the oil companies. This trend was temporarily reversed in 1956–57 by the Suez crisis, but was resumed thereafter and accentuated by the sharp increase in competition from independent, Soviet, and other suppliers (see Chapter VIII, Section A). By 1960, discounts were being "offered openly by just about all major companies with unlimited supplies at the Persian Gulf"; the practice was even more widespread in Venezuela, where in 1959, Creole Petroleum Company, the largest operator, sold some two-thirds of its entire production at discounts.[24] "Reduction in posted prices ranged from 15 cents to 35 cents per barrel . . . Additional concessions on transportation charges and other handling costs further lowered the revenues realized."[25] In 1960, such discounts applied to about 18 per cent of Aramco's sales that were sold to customers other than its parent companies. The situation seemed to have improved slightly in 1961 as a result of the weakening of downward pressure on prices.

As a result of these changes in posted prices and freight rates, and to a lesser extent in discounts, imported crude has occasionally been delivered on the Atlantic seaboard in recent years at about $1.00 a barrel below the United States posted prices, and the link between prices in the United States on the one hand, and the Middle East or Venezuela on the other, has become extremely tenuous (see Chapter IV, Section J). However, the quota system established in the United States in 1959 has restricted the expansion in imports of such oils.

D. Marketing

One of the basic features of the Middle Eastern petroleum industry is that the oil companies operating in the region are, in general, producing enterprises, with no marketing facilities of their own outside the countries in which they have concessions. Marketing of Middle Eastern oil is carried out by their parent companies, which have world-wide transport, refining, and marketing facilities.[26] Thus the Iraq Petroleum Company and its affiliated companies deliver their oil exports to their parent companies at cost plus a fee of 1*s* per ton.[27] Similar arrangements apply to the production and exports of the Kuwait Oil Company. In Iran, the operating companies sell their output of crude and refined oil at cost plus a small fee to the National Iranian Oil Company and the trading companies participating in the consortium. On the other hand, Aramco was set up as a profit-making enterprise selling its crude exports to its parent companies at posted prices, minus certain discounts, while its refining operations were carried out at cost plus a fee of $2 million. In recent years these arrangements have changed and the company has also started selling directly to outsiders.

The parent companies that take such oil either market it through their facilities or sell it in intercompany transactions. Both types of transaction raise problems in the determination of the value of Middle Eastern shipments, f.o.b. points of export.[28] In the first type, oil passes through many operations before it reaches the final consumer, most of which are undertaken by the parent companies directly or through their subsidiaries. At each of these stages, the prices charged represent merely transfer prices set in operations between the various departments of the oil companies.[29]

In the second type, oil is sold under long-term supply contracts well below market prices.[30] Thus, in 1947, a contract was signed between the Anglo-Iranian Oil Company and Standard Oil Company (New Jersey) by which the former undertook to deliver to the latter 800 million barrels of crude oil, over 20 years, from its production in Iran and Kuwait. Two similar contracts with Socony-Vacuum covered 500 million barrels. These contracts came into effect in 1952. The second contract with Socony fixed the price at actual cost (including payments to governments) plus one-third of the gross profit realized by Socony on the crude oil. The other two contracts fixed the prices at actual cost plus a fixed sum per ton, the result being not less favorable to the seller than the second Socony contract. Earlier, another agreement had been signed between the Gulf Oil Corporation and Royal Dutch–Shell, covering a total of 1,250 million barrels over 22 years. No price was stipulated, but the terms provided for the equal sharing of profits realized on the production, transport, refining, and marketing of the oil. And under the agreement reached in November, 1948, among the parent companies of the Iraq Petroleum Company group, these companies were allowed to acquire oil from the Iraqi concession in excess of their pro-rata share at a price halfway between cost-plus-1*s*. and the current world market price; the other half was to go to those companies that drew less than their share of oil.

E. Posted Prices

These intracompany and intercompany transactions show that the actual receipts of the companies operating in the Middle East do not correspond to the market values of the oil exported by them. Since figures on actual receipts have not been published, the only alternative is to calculate "pro-forma" receipts on the basis of the volume of exports and posted prices of crude oil and petroleum products.[31]

Such posted prices have been denounced from opposite sides as being too high or too low. On the one hand, some Middle Eastern governments maintain that posted prices are unduly low and thus make it possible for the companies to earn huge profits in the later stages of operation, viz., transport, refining, and marketing. Thus, it has been claimed that the equalization of prices in New York, a marginal market for Middle Eastern oil instead of London, the area east of which constitutes the main European market, has underpriced Middle Eastern crude by 50¢ to 60¢ per barrel, involving a total discount during the period August 1, 1953, to August 8, 1960, of $5,065 million. It has also been claimed that the equalization of Middle Eastern and Venezuelan prices in New York on the basis of freight rates higher than those actually paid (viz., United States Maritime Commission *minus* 30 to 35 per cent, instead of USMC *minus* 50 per cent) resulted in a discount during the period June 1, 1957, to August 8, 1960, of 8¢ per barrel, or a total of $409 million. The sum of these two items is $5,474 million.[32]

On the other hand, the companies claim that the present level of posted prices of crude petroleum reduces profits on subsequent stages of operation to very small amounts, and that the large profits earned in the production of crude have to be used to finance, in various countries, other operations that are necessary for the expansion of the oil industry. Thus, a study of the net profits for 1953–58 of the seven major oil companies operating in the Eastern Hemisphere showed that, whereas net profits on production rose from $602 million in 1953 to $1,237 million in 1958, profits on other operations were never higher than $165 million, and there was actually a loss of $260 million in 1958.[33] And in his Statement for 1960, the Chairman of British Petroleum declared that:

> Payments to the Middle Eastern countries under the "fifty-fifty" agreements are based on posted prices and the total sum included in our 1960 accounts for such payments was £128 million. Our own Group profits, which last year amounted to just over £62 million, are related to the price we realize for the oil when we sell it; and these profits represent the net result of all the operations involved, and not merely those related to production.

Finally, a study by the United Nations Economic Commission for Europe, representing the viewpoint of consuming countries, criticized posted prices as being unduly high in relation to costs of production.[34]

It is outside the scope of this study to enter into the above controversy. It may be pointed out, however, that United States tax legislation has made it more profitable for American oil companies to set higher posted prices for crude and thus to attribute a larger share of profits to production of crude oil than to subsequent stages. This is because the higher the posted price, the greater the value of the depletion allowance granted to oil companies, since this is equal to 27.5 per cent of *gross* income from production.[35] In addition, income taxes paid by American oil companies to foreign governments on profits of crude oil production (see Chapter VI, Section C) can be credited against United States tax liability, and this, in turn, does not discourage high prices and profits on foreign crude oil. In recent years, British oil companies have been allowed a similar credit for foreign income taxes paid by them. Moreover, high prices for crude mean high profits on sales of crude to outsiders and reduce their margin in refining and marketing.[36] On the other hand, high prices of crude mean higher producing profits and larger payments to Middle Eastern governments under profit-sharing arrangements; it may be presumed that these arrangements should induce the companies to reduce posted prices except insofar as they are willing to pay larger amounts to these governments in order to maintain good relations with them. Another consideration would be that if they do not share such profits with the governments of producing countries, they will be subjected to income taxes of consuming countries.

For our purposes, however, it is sufficient that, during the period under review, both the companies and the Middle Eastern governments accepted posted prices as a basis for calculating gross receipts, profits, and payments to governments, even for the oil that is sold at lower prices through long-term intercompany contracts.

The early profit-sharing agreements did not touch upon the question of discounts granted to parent companies. Aramco used to apply such discounts, a process that was subsequently followed in most of the other producing countries for calculation of the government's share of profits. These discounts, which ranged between 15 and 20 per cent, were later eliminated; the governments concerned received back payments in settlement of this issue, which in Saudi Arabia amounted to $145 million for the period 1952–55. However, in order to stimulate output, some of the governments agreed to bulk discount if production exceeded a certain limit. For instance, in Iran such discounts ranged between 5 and 10 per cent for production beyond 35 million cubic meters; in Kuwait the discount was 18 per cent for production above

500,000 barrels a day, provided the over-all discount did not exceed an average of 5 per cent for total production. There were no quantity discounts in Iraq and Saudi Arabia, and that in Kuwait was recently eliminated. Another form of discount that appeared in these agreements was a 2 per cent discount designated as an allowance for marketing expenses; later this was reduced in Iran and Iraq to 1 per cent and in Saudi Arabia to actual sales expenses.

Another point of contention regarding pricing is the question of border value for the oil moving from Iraq and Saudi Arabia to the Mediterranean through pipelines. In Saudi Arabia, such values have been fixed on the basis of Persian Gulf and not eastern Mediterranean posted prices, and in Iraq, at levels substantially below eastern Mediterranean posted prices.

Finally, a new form of discount has appeared in the last few years: the granting of discounts on sales to third parties, i.e., to other than parent companies. Recently Saudi Arabia has agreed to accept actual realization prices received from such sales for calculation of the government's share of income; for oil transfers to parent companies, posted prices are used. As mentioned earlier, in 1960, sales to third parties amounted to 18 per cent of the volume of exports and the average discount was 15 per cent, giving a total average discount of 2.7 per cent.

F. Receipts from Local Sales

The constituents of the estimated "pro-forma" gross receipts are shown in Table 23. It will be noticed that local sales of crude oil and products by the oil companies covered in this study accounted for only a small fraction of their total receipts, partly because of small volume and partly because of the low prices charged, and that this fraction declined from a high of 4.6 per cent in 1949 (including cost of local transport) to about 1.6 per cent in 1960; the balance represented the value of exports of crude oil and refined products. The most striking change is the sharp drop in the value of local sales in 1951 and 1952. This was mainly due to the effects of the Iranian nationalization crisis, which cut off sales by the Anglo-Iranian Oil Company in Iran, where, excluding refinery consumption, half the products were consumed.[37] In subsequent years, however, a more important factor was the reduction in the oil prices charged by the companies to the governments following the agreements made in 1950–54. This reduction more than offset the rise in total consumption (see Chapter VII, Section F).

Most of the earlier Middle Eastern concession agreements contained

TABLE 23

GROSS REÇEIPTS OF THE PETROLEUM INDUSTRY IN THE MIDDLE EAST AND VENEZUELA, 1948-60
(Millions of Dollars and Per Cent)

	Middle East					Venezuela	
	Millions of Dollars				Per Cent	Millions of Dollars	Per Cent
Year	Local Sales of Crude and Refined Products	Exports of Refined Products	Exports of Crude	Total Gross Receipts	Refined Products as Proportion of Total Gross Receipts[a]	Total Gross Receipts	Refined Products as Proportion of Total Gross Receipts
1948	34.4	682.5	313.9	1,030.8	69.8	1,143.6	9.9
1949	46.7	578.2	392.9	1,017.8	61.4	1,010.9	10.6
1950	50.9	674.2	566.6	1,291.7	56.1	1,212.7	16.5
1951	28.2	561.4	852.5	1,442.1	40.9	1,425.6	19.3
1952	9.0	376.9	1,097.2	1,483.1	26.0	1,513.5	20.0
1953	12.3	425.4	1,379.4	1,817.1	24.1	1,583.1	23.1
1954	13.9	488.0	1,570.4	2,072.3	24.2	1,727.2	23.0
1955	30.0	614.1	1,798.9	2,443.0	25.8	1,901.1	25.7
1956	35.7	719.3	1,883.3	2,638.3	28.0	2,209.8	26.6
1957	39.8	801.9	1,946.7	2,788.4	29.6	2,738.5	26.0
1958	48.3	845.9	2,463.6	3,357.8	25.9	2,478.8	28.7
1959	53.8	840.8	2,450.5	3,345.1	25.9	2,414.1	(29.6)
1960	58.9	865.7	2,740.8	3,665.4	24.3	2,500.0	(30.0)

Sources: For sources and notes see Appendix Table 4.
[a]Calculated as the ratio of local sales plus exports of refined oil products to total gross receipts. Adjustments have been made to exclude local sales of crude petroleum.

a provision regarding the supplying of the oil requirements of the country concerned. Thus, the 1933 agreement between Iran and the Anglo-Iranian Oil Company (Article 19) stipulated that the company should supply oil products for internal consumption in Iran, the price to be fixed on the basis of average f.o.b. prices of oil products either in Roumania or the Gulf of Mexico, whichever was lower. The government was entitled to a discount of 25 per cent from this basic price, on its own needs, and other consumers in Iran to a 10 per cent discount. In Iraq, under the 1925 agreement with the Turkish Petroleum Company (Article 15), the company agreed to refine for local consumption up to 40,000 tons per annum and to sell the products at 35 per cent less than the wholesale price of the nearest similar product in Swansea, England. Under the Amendments of March 24, 1931, the basis was shifted to that of Gulf of Mexico prices.[38] And both the concession granted to the British Oil Development Syndicate (Article 12) in 1932 (and transferred by it in 1941 to the Mosul Petroleum Company) and the one granted to the Basrah Petroleum Company in 1938 (Article 14) specified that the companies were obligated to put at the disposal of the government up to 20 per cent of the crude oil produced by them free of charge, but that the government would not receive royalties on those amounts that were actually taken by it. Both agreements also provided for the delivery by each company to the government of up to 3,000 tons of asphalt per annum, free of charge. However, since production under these concessions did not start until the 1950's and since the government did not build refineries until 1955, no advantage was taken of these provisions, and the bulk of local needs continued to be met by the Alwand refinery of Khanaqin Oil Company, a subsidiary of the Anglo-Iranian Oil Company, or was imported from Iran at world posted prices.[39] In Saudi Arabia, on the other hand, Article 16 of the 1933 Concession Agreement stipulated that the company would give the government, for its own use each year, 200,000 American gallons of gasoline (about 700 tons) and 100,000 gallons of kerosene, free of charge. Under the Supplemental Agreement of 1939 (Article 8), the quantity of gasoline was to be gradually increased to 2,300,000 gallons (about 7,000 tons). No discounts were provided for other customers. In Qatar, a letter of May 17, 1935, following the 1935 Concession Agreement with the Anglo-Iranian Oil Company, stipulated that specified quantities of gasoline and kerosene would be provided to the Sheik free of charge; on September 1, 1952, the quantities were slightly altered to 40,000 British gallons of gasoline (about 150 tons) and 20,000 gallons of kerosene.[40]

Thus, it will be seen that internal prices for products sold were based essentially on foreign prices and not on domestic cost levels. The addition of heavy transport charges and of the large excise duties and other taxes levied by Middle Eastern governments also considerably raised the price to local consumers. Hence, in 1950, the retail price of gasoline in Iran was 56.1¢ per United States gallon, in Baghdad 23.3¢, and in Jedda 24¢, as compared with 11.3¢ in Caracas, 25.6¢ in New York, and 35.0¢ in London.[41]

The agreements concluded between 1950 and 1954 resulted in terms much more favorable to the governments. In Saudi Arabia, Article 6 of the 1950 agreement raised the annual quantities supplied free of charge to the government to 2,650,000 American gallons of gasoline (nearly 9,000 tons), 200,000 gallons of kerosene, and 7,500 tons of asphalt. Under the Collective Agreement of 1952 in Iraq (first schedule, paragraph 5), it was agreed that if the government should set up a refinery in Baghdad and connect it by a pipeline to K-2 pumping station, on the Kirkuk pipeline, the company would deliver crude oil at that station at a fixed charge of £63,000 per annum plus 5*s*. 6*d*. per ton, i.e., 10.3¢ a barrel, unless the cost of Kirkuk oil field production differed from this figure by more than 10 per cent, in which case delivery prices would be adjusted accordingly. This arrangement came into effect when the government refinery of Dorah, near Baghdad, was opened late in 1955. In Iran, Article 14 of the 1954 agreement stipulated that the operating companies shall supply the government-owned National Iranian Oil Company with refined products needed for internal consumption; charges for such deliveries are to cover the cost of extracting and refining the oil.

These revisions have sharply brought down the prices of oil products delivered in Iran and Iraq for public or private consumption. Moreover, some improvement has been made in reducing the cost of transport. In Iran, a 940-kilometer products pipeline from Abadan to Tehran was opened in 1957, and a 234-kilometer branch to Isfahan in 1958; other branches were laid to major consuming centers in the north. By 1959, 51 per cent of the oil consumed internally in Iran was moved by pipeline.[42] However, retail prices of petroleum products in most Middle Eastern countries have changed little in the past decade. Thus, in 1958, the price of regular gasoline in Iran was 22.6¢ a gallon, including taxes of 11.8¢, and of kerosene 11.8¢ a gallon, including taxes of 4¢; in Iraq the corresponding figures were 25.7¢, including 12.8¢ taxes, for gasoline and 6.5¢, including 0.8¢ taxes, for kerosene.[43]

G. Exports of Refined Products

Two striking features may be noted in Table 23: the over-all increase in the total value of refined products exported, and the sharp drop in their relative value to total receipts; this movement presents a contrast to that which took place in Venezuelan exports. Table 24 gives a breakdown by country.

Table 22 shows that price changes in refined products have been relatively small and have not been in the same direction for all products.[44] Thus, between 1948 and 1960, gasoline and distillate fuel oil prices rose significantly and then declined, showing an over-all increase of 7.7 and 3.8 per cent, respectively, and kerosene showed a small rise of 2.6 per cent. On the other hand, the price of residual fuel oils, which had been meeting increasing competition from coal and other fuels, fell sharply, recovered, and dropped again, showing an over-all decline of 31.8 per cent. Taking all the products together, there has been a very slight over-all fall in prices. But the determining factor in the movements

TABLE 24

ESTIMATED VALUE OF EXPORTS OF REFINED PRODUCTS FROM THE MIDDLE EAST AND VENEZUELA, 1948-60
(Millions of Dollars)

Year	Aden	Bahrein	Iran	Kuwait	Saudi Arabia	Total Middle East	Venezuela[a]
1948	–	150.8	404.6	–	127.1	682.5	113.0
1949	–	127.2	340.6	1.9	108.5	578.2	106.9
1950	–	155.6	405.4	14.3	98.9	674.2	199.6
1951	–	184.9	203.9	16.5	156.1	561.4	274.5
1952	–	195.5	–	17.7	163.7	376.9	303.4
1953	–	209.3	–	20.0	196.1	425.4	365.3
1954	21.3	221.4	18.8	20.4	206.1	488.0	397.0
1955	85.3	208.9	108.9	21.9	189.1	614.1	489.2
1956	96.6	207.1	208.1	22.3	185.2	719.3	587.0
1957	95.6	203.9	297.4	21.8	183.2	801.9	711.9
1958	81.4	210.1	288.7	109.9	155.8	845.9	712.6
1959	80.1	196.2	319.3	103.1	142.1	840.8	714.0
1960	72.8	200.1	280.0	119.3	171.5	865.7[b]	750.0

Sources: For sources and notes see Appendix Table 4.
[a]Data refer to total sales of refined products, including both exports and local sales.
[b]Including $22 million for the Neutral Zone.

of gross receipts from exports of products has been quantity rather than price. As Appendix Table 2, p. 184 shows, output of refined products dropped sharply during the Iranian nationalization crisis and recovered rapidly thereafter, partly because of the resumption of production in Abadan on a gradually increasing scale and partly because of the expansion of capacity and output in other countries.

As regards changes in relative value, exports of major refined products accounted for 66.1 per cent of total receipts in 1948 but only 23.6 per cent in 1960. This relative decline, despite a 26.8 per cent rise in the total estimated value of refined oil exports, is, of course, due to the much greater increase in exports of crude oil from the Middle East.

H. Exports of Crude Petroleum

As Table 21 shows, the great increase in the value of exports of crude was achieved despite slight reductions in price. As already mentioned, prices were cut in November, 1948, and again in July, 1949, and although they subsequently rose again, the level of early 1948 was not regained until July, 1957, in the aftermath of the Suez crisis. Prices were once more reduced, by about 8 per cent, in February, 1959, and again, by about 5 per cent, in August, 1960. However, these price fluctuations were completely swamped by the more than fivefold increase in the volume of exports of crude petroleum (see Table 25 and Appendix Table 3, p. 187).

This huge increase was a response to the unprecedented upsurge in the world economy that took place after 1945. This has been particularly marked in Western Europe and Japan, the main clients for Middle Eastern oil. As a result of this boom, energy consumption in Western Europe increased by 57 per cent between 1948 and 1960, and in Japan by 77 per cent between 1949 and 1960.[45] The increase in demand for energy could not be met by coal or other domestic sources of energy, since their output could not be speedily raised and imported coal was almost everywhere more expensive than imported oil.[46] A gap was thus left for oil, and consumption of oil by Western Europe rose by 394 per cent in 1948–60 and that of Japan by 1,550 per cent in 1949–60, and has continued to increase. Almost all this increase in consumption was met by imports.

The Middle East was the main beneficiary of this increased demand for oil. In the first place, the producing companies had outlets in Europe, to which Middle Eastern oil could flow. Second, there were the price adjustments discussed above, which made Middle Eastern oil more competitive. Third, there was the dollar shortage that prevailed throughout most of this period. The fact that United States and Venezuelan oil was dollar oil, whereas oil from Iran, Iraq, Qatar, and Kuwait could be paid for largely in sterling, helped to direct European demand toward it. The importance of this factor became clear during the 1949 sterling crisis, when output in the United States and Venezuela sagged while in the Middle East it continued to expand.[47] So did such factors as French ownership of nearly a quarter of the shares of the companies operating in Iraq; this caused France to become the leading customer for Iraqi oil and in some years to take half of Iraq's oil exports.

Another important factor was the policy of the companies operating in the Middle East in exporting crude oil, and the fact that they were not under any great pressure from the Middle Eastern governments to refine a large portion of their output in the area. In this they had a slight advantage over companies operating in Venezuela, which, under Article 5 of the Law of Hydrocarbons of 1943, were obligated to refine locally at least 10 per cent of the petroleum produced locally; in 1956 the minimum figure was raised to 15 per cent. As a result, only 10 per cent of the increase in crude oil production between 1948 and 1960 was refined locally in the Middle East, while the corresponding ratio for Venezuela was 52 per cent. This freedom from refining obligations

TABLE 25

ESTIMATED VALUE OF EXPORTS OF CRUDE PETROLEUM FROM THE MIDDLE EAST AND VENEZUELA, 1948-60
(Millions of Dollars)

Year	Exports							Imports			Net Exports of the Middle East	Exports of Venezuela
	Iran	Iraq	Kuwait	Neutral Zone	Qatar	Saudi Arabia	Total Exports	Aden	Bahrein	Total Imports		
1948	52.8	70.3	83.4	—	—	195.8	402.3	—	88.4	88.4	313.9	1,004.1
1949	44.5	68.5	138.0	—	0.2	223.7	474.9	—	82.0	82.0	392.9	868.7
1950	82.2	108.9	171.5	—	20.8	262.4	645.8	—	79.2	79.2	566.6	989.8
1951	44.4	139.1	288.6	—	31.8	442.1	946.0	—	93.5	93.5	852.5	1,121.0
1952		294.1	388.1	—	44.1	472.1	1,198.4	—	101.2	101.2	1,097.2	1,180.1
1953		462.1	495.9	—	58.0	475.1	1,491.1	—	111.7	111.7	1,379.4	1,180.5
1954	6.7	503.9	566.9	8.4	73.0	557.4	1,716.3	15.6	130.3	145.9	1,570.4	1,290.6
1955	115.6	539.7	651.3	12.3	83.2	573.4	1,975.5	54.0	122.6	176.6	1,798.9	1,373.8
1956	198.1	487.5	658.8	16.9	90.2	607.4	2,058.9	58.1	117.5	175.6	1,883.3	1,573.4
1957	273.8	345.1	714.8	35.2	105.5	641.1	2,115.5	58.6	110.2	168.8	1,946.7	1,968.0
1958	357.0	575.6	843.8	40.4	136.8	674.4	2,628.0	50.3	114.1	164.4	2,463.6	1,709.3
1959	391.8	617.4	748.7	48.8	123.0	671.9	2,601.6	51.0	100.1	151.1	2,450.5	1,650.0
1960	444.1	712.2	852.6	56.5	121.1	714.2	2,900.7	50.7	109.2	159.9	2,740.8	1,700.0

Sources: For sources and notes see Appendix Table 4.

made it easier for the companies to adjust production to market demand. Thus in Iran, Bahrein, and Saudi Arabia, which are large suppliers of the Middle Eastern, Asian, and African markets, refineries were built or expanded, though the rate of increase in refining was much smaller than in crude production (see Table 6, p. 15). In 1960, crude oil input to refineries equaled 36 per cent of the crude oil production in Iran, 18 per cent in Saudi Arabia, 21 per cent in the Neutral Zone, and 460 per cent in Bahrein, which operates chiefly on imports of crude oil.[48] On the other hand, in Iraq, Kuwait, and Qatar, whose exports are directed chiefly to Europe and North America, relatively little oil is refined locally; the corresponding figures for these three countries are 5 per cent, 11 per cent, and none, respectively.[49] The Venezuelan figure in 1960 was 32 per cent.[50]

The fact that Middle Eastern oil could be exported in its crude form made it more attractive to European and other consumers, who preferred to have the refining done at home for a variety of reasons, strategic, political, financial, and economic.[51]

In the first place, governments of consuming countries insist, for political and strategic reasons, on setting up refineries at home, thus becoming independent of imports of refined oil. As the Iranian nationalization crisis showed, it is much easier to develop alternative sources of crude oil than to build new refineries. Such an argument has particular force for an area like the Middle East, which borders on the Soviet Union and is racked by inner tensions and upheavals.

In the second place, for financial and economic reasons, most consuming countries have sought to reduce their foreign exchange disbursements on petroleum by refining the crude oil within their borders; this trend has been accentuated by the increasing gap between the value of a barrel of crude and that of the refined products derived from it.[52] Even without this gap, however, the trend would have persisted, since the value added in refining, no matter how small, represents a foreign exchange saving.

By the same token, domestic refining creates new jobs for nationals, and it may be noted that refining is a much more labor-intensive branch than crude production. Thus, it has been calculated that, in the Middle East, it takes roughly 3.5 times as many man-days to produce a ton of refined products as a ton of crude oil.[53] Refining also opens new opportunities for domestic investment. Another factor working in the same direction is the greater ability to use petroleum by-products and refinery gases—until quite recently mere nuisances—in the rapidly growing petro-chemical industry, especially in the highly industrialized countries. It may be noted in passing that in the postwar years petroleum has replaced coal as the main basis of the chemical industry. It is a fact that before the Second World War either the relatively low level of demand in Europe or the nature of product-mix precluded the building of refineries in that continent, while now both factors favor local refineries in Europe. Furthermore, many refineries are now being built for "market protection of crude oil outlet."[54]

Another economic reason for refining near the consuming centers should be noted. As mentioned above, prices of refined products in the Persian Gulf have remained about equal to those of corresponding products in the United States Gulf, while the price of crude has continued to decline. The widening gap between the prices of Middle Eastern crude oil and products has acted as a further stimulant to the location of oil refineries in consuming areas, particularly those east of Suez, which have become the main markets for Middle Eastern products.

Finally, there are certain handicaps under which the Middle East suffers, such as the lack of skilled labor and the absence or poor quality of public utilities and of servicing and repair facilities. These factors undoubtedly raise the cost and increase the inconvenience of refining in the area.[55] Against these, of course, must be set the economies made possible by the establishment of refineries near sources of supply, and by these refineries' large size.

In addition to the above considerations applying to oil crossing international frontiers, there are more general reasons for the construction of refineries at the consuming centers; these relate to transport, refining, and marketing. It is due to these factors that after 1951, all Soviet refineries were built at consuming rather than producing centers, and that in the United States the proportion of refineries in centers of production fell from 77 per cent in 1920 to about 60 per cent in 1955, the fall being particularly rapid since the Second World War.[56] A more recent study concludes that, "taking the United States as a whole, the bulk of the refinery capacity is located at or on the way to the principal markets rather than at the source of the crude."[57]

As regards transport, it should be noted first that tanker freights are lower for "dirty" cargo than for "clean," i.e., for crude oil than for refined products, since the expense of cleaning a tanker is considerable once it is dirty. Second, giant tankers operate at a much lower unit cost than small tankers (see Chapter IV, Section A); such tankers are more suitable for large volume crude transport than for refined products, since the latter seldom move in quantities sufficient to provide a full cargo for a supertanker, and the carrying of more than one kind of product on the same ship or having to make discharges at more than one port raises the cost of transport.[58] Third, there is the difficulty of pumping heavy fuel oil through a pipeline; this has led refiners in both Europe and the United States to locate their plants at the centers of consumption, pumping the crude to it by pipeline from the ports.[59]

As for refining, two developments should be noted. First, losses and waste in refining have been greatly reduced and are now negligible; evidently the greater the loss, the stronger the inducement to refine near the source of production in order to reduce transport costs. Second, refineries have become increasingly flexible and can vary their product-mix more easily to suit demand patterns. This, too, removes an advantage of resource location. If the product-mix cannot be varied, some of the products of a market-located refinery may be produced in excess of local market needs and therefore require much cross or back transportation—unless, of course, the refinery is very small, in which case the economies of scale are forgone. In a resource-located refinery, on the other hand, products can be more easily shipped directly to their ultimate destination, and this limitation on size does not operate. And, by the same token, greater refinery flexibility has increased the advantage of having the management near the market and able to follow more closely its fluctuations and needs.

Such are the main factors that have determined the location of new refineries and have offset the advantages of resource location in the Middle East. It may be added that, in recent years, the example of Europe has been followed by many other important consumers of Middle Eastern oil, notably India, Pakistan, Japan, Australia, and several other countries, who have insisted on being supplied with crude oil and refining it at home.[60] Furthermore, until quite recently, the consumption of oil products in many of these countries was too small to justify the construction of a refinery, but it has now grown to the point where the output of fairly large plants can be absorbed.

As a result of all this, whereas in 1939, excluding the United States and the Soviet bloc, 63.3 per cent of refining capacity was "resource located" and 36.7 per cent "market located," by 1960 the figures were 30.3 and 61.1 per cent, respectively, and the completion of projects under way should change them further to 24.1 and 68.1 per cent by 1963.[61]

VI. Costs and Outlays

The petroleum industry is, generally speaking, characterized by three main economic features: economies of scale, large initial investments, and the high proportion of fixed costs to total costs. The first two features, but not the third, are to be found in the Middle East. However, the outstanding characteristic of the region is its exceptionally low costs of crude oil production.

A. Economies of Scale

Economies of scale are substantial in all stages of the industry. In the production of crude oil, large-scale operation makes it possible for a big company to assume risks that would be beyond the capacity and resources of a small firm, and to apply more advanced technological methods and research to exploration and development;[1] it also makes it possible to exploit large oil resources more efficiently, a matter discussed more fully below.

In refining, investment per unit of capacity falls sharply with increase in scale up to a fairly high level. Thus, in the United States in 1950, it was estimated that investment per barrel of capacity fell from $1,300 for a 10,000-barrel-a-day refinery to $833 for a 30,000-barrel-a-day refinery, $610 for a 100,000-barrel-a-day refinery, and $545 for a 200,000-barrel-a-day refinery.[2] In Western Europe in 1960 the investment per barrel of capacity for a simple refinery was estimated to be $1,460 for a 10,000-barrel-a-day refinery, and $600 for a $100,000-barrel-a-day refinery. The corresponding figures for cracking refineries were $2,670 and $1,125, respectively. Another estimate is that "The cost of any plant, per barrel of capacity, will be only about 80 per cent of one half that size."[3] Moreover, total operating costs per barrel of refined oil also fall sharply with a rise in scale, mainly because of the drop in unit fixed costs, such as depreciation and insurance, but also because of lower labor requirements.[4]

In transport, also, both tankers and pipelines show large economies of scale. With tankers, it is estimated that "as compared with the war-built T-2's [16,600-ton tankers], the saving in transport cost per ton is about 40 per cent for a 45,000 tonner, 50 per cent for an 85,000 tonner and 60 per cent for a monster such as the Universe Apollo of over 100,000 tons d.w."[5] An authoritative study on tankers concludes that "The largest tanker is the cheapest to operate on a per-ton basis" because building costs per ton decrease with size; power requirements and fuel consumption increase less than proportionately with size; and "costs do not increase in proportion to size. It does not take a larger operating crew for an 84,740 ton ship than a T-2. The larger ships have somewhat larger crews only because they need additional men for deck maintenance."[6] It has been estimated that the relative investment cost per dead-weight ton in tankers declines from $100 for a 16,000 tonner to $55 for a 45,000 tonner, and $45 for an 85,000 tonner.

As for pipelines, an increase in diameter results in a much larger proportionate increase in volume with a consequent sharp fall in unit costs; thus a 24-inch pipeline can carry thirty times as much as a 6-inch line.[7] In the United States in 1950, it was calculated that in order to earn a 7 per cent return on investment, a 1,000-mile, 10-inch pipeline with a throughput of 45,000 barrels of crude oil a day would have to charge about 37¢ a barrel, whereas a 30-inch pipeline of equal length with a throughput of 350,000 barrels a day would have to charge just over 10¢.[8] And in Western Europe in 1960, costs per ton-mile fell from 1*d.* for a 1,000,000 ton throughput pipeline working at full capacity to less than 0.25*d.* for a 6,000,000 ton pipeline and 0.15*d.* for a 20,000,000 ton pipeline also working at full capacity.[9] The comparable costs in the underdeveloped countries, including the Middle East, were expected to be 20 per cent higher.

B. Large Initial Investment

Owing to its economies of scale, its capital intensive nature (see Chapter II, Section A), and to the uncertainties encountered in oil exploration, the petroleum industry requires very large initial investments before output can begin in commercial quantities. This is particularly true in the production of crude oil, where vast amounts had to be invested in certain countries before oil was discovered and additional larger amounts before production became possible—for example, $21 million and $39 million, respectively, in Colombia and a total of some $370 million in Libya.[10] Indeed, in several countries the expenditure of tens of millions of dollars has not yet resulted in the discovery of appreciable reserves—for example, in Netherlands New Guinea, Papua, parts of Turkey, and the Western Desert of Egypt (where $35 million was invested fruitlessly by one company)—and some of these concessions have been abandoned. For pipelines, an investment of several tens of millions, or even of hundreds of millions, of dollars is required; for refineries, investment runs into tens of millions and is constantly rising with the introduction of more complex methods of processing; tankers require investments of several millions; this figure, too, is rising with the ever-growing size of the ships. Further large investment has to be made in other forms of transport, in storage, and in distribution outlets before the oil reaches the consumer. A recent report estimates the present average cost of finding new oil, outside the United States and the Soviet bloc, at almost $2,000 for every barrel per day of production, i.e., about $100 million for 2.5 million tons a year. To this should be added "the investment for transportation, refining etc., which could add up to $150 million."[11] Of course, these figures vary greatly between regions (see Chapter II and Tables 15, p. 53, and 17, p. 55.)

C. High Fixed Costs

Generally speaking, and partly because of high initial investment and economies of scale, fixed costs account for a large proportion and variable costs for a small proportion of total costs in the petroleum industry, and the additional cost incurred by a small increase in output is very low. In other words, the short-term average cost curve falls rather sharply, and the marginal cost curve drops to a very low level after a certain volume of output is reached.

This statement holds for crude oil production, refining, and transport by pipeline. In production, large outlays have to be made in exploration and development. And even when the extraction of oil begins, variable costs are low. It has been estimated that the cost of lifting oil in the United States averaged 13¢ a barrel in 1940, 31¢ in 1950, and 45¢ in 1956, while the cost of discovery and development was 43¢, 92¢, and $1.42, respectively.[12] A more recent estimate puts variable costs in the United States at 20–29 per cent of total costs of crude; the remainder represents costs of discovery and development.[13] In refining, initial investment is very high per unit of output and labor costs are relatively low, amounting in the United States in 1943 to only 10–15 per cent of total operating costs.[14] Hence, according to a study made in the early 1950's, in United States refineries of 10,000–20,000-barrels-a-day output working at full capacity, fixed costs accounted for 73 per cent of total operating costs and variable costs for 27 per cent.[15] Similarly, a study of French refineries showed that fixed costs amounted to about one-half of total costs and labor costs to 17 per cent.[16] The fixed costs tend to decline with the increase in sizes of refineries. For example, in Western Europe they fell from 57 per cent of total cost (including fuel) for a 10,000-barrel-a-day refinery to 43 per cent for a 140,000-barrel-a-day refinery. In storage, the bulk of expenditures is incurred in setting up installations, whereas their operating costs are relatively low. In pipelines, which demand huge initial investments, labor and other variable costs are of minor significance. In the United States, fixed costs have been estimated at 65 per cent of the total for crude pipelines and 75 per cent for products pipelines.[17] In Western Europe they were estimated to be 65 per cent for 30-inch pipelines and 55 per cent for 18-inch pipelines, operating at full capacity. The average total costs fall very sharply until full capacity is reached and marginal costs are very low; conversely, unit costs rise very sharply if output is below full capacity. Hence, for the petroleum industry more than for most others, stability is a primary consideration, a fact which, as has often been pointed out, has promoted the spread of monopolistic practices.

D. Conditions in the Middle East

The description given above fits the Middle East only partially. In the Middle East, as elsewhere, there are substantial economies of scale, and large initial investments have generally been necessary before oil was discovered and produced. But the huge size of Middle Eastern reserves and the very low costs of production have meant that capital investment per unit of reserves and output has been relatively very small; consequently, fixed costs have formed a smaller proportion of total costs in crude oil production than in other regions, and variable costs a higher proportion. With respect to other branches of oil activities, the situation has been essentially the same in the Middle East as elsewhere.

The existence of substantial economies of scale is indicated by the decline in unit costs of crude oil production in Kuwait between 1946 and 1956–58, from over 14¢ to under 10¢ per barrel, as production rose from 6 million a year to an annual average of 442 million barrels. Similarly, in Iraq costs fell from 45¢ to 20¢ between 1949 and 1955–56 as output rose from 31 million to 242 million barrels, and in Qatar from 36¢ to 26¢ in 1950–58 as output rose from 12 million to 64 million barrels.[18] This would seem to show that the long-term supply curve slopes downward, i.e., unit costs decline as capacity is expanded. As regards the short-term supply curve, i.e., the one showing unit cost at different levels of output with a given capacity, it seems to fall sharply, at least until full capacity is reached. Thus in the February 3, 1952, agreement between Iraq and the Iraq Petroleum Company group (Article 9), cost per ton was put at about 23*s.* for 1951, about 17*s.* 6*d.* for 1952, and about 13*s.* for subsequent years; this decline in costs was expected to accompany the use to capacity of oil-producing facilities and pipelines.

Costs of *initial* investments, therefore, seem to be generally high in the Middle East. This is because, on the one hand, all the necessary equipment and much of the technical personnel have to be imported from more developed countries, and on the other, there are certain factors that raise local costs, particularly in production of crude. Among the latter are the scantiness of geological or even geographical information, the lack of security prevailing in certain areas at the time operations began, the scarcity of water, and the complete absence of such facilities as railways, roads, ports, airports, and electricity, not to mention housing, hospitals, and schools.[19] Some of these difficulties have also been encountered in refining and in pipeline installation. As a consequence, investment in social overheads is particularly high in the Middle East (see Chapter II). It was doubtless such considerations that the Vice-President of the Arabian American Oil Company had in mind when he stated that "Nothing we do in Saudi Arabia that I know of costs us less than it costs us in the United States, and 99 per cent of the things cost us more. If it is a well, it costs about twice as much to drill."[20]

In some Middle Eastern countries, large outlays were made before production began or reached a scale that made it possible to earn significant revenues. In Iran, the expenditure incurred before oil was struck in 1908 seems to have been nearly £1 million, and a further £1 million had to be invested before oil could flow to outside markets.[21] In Iraq, the total capital expenditure before export began in 1934 amounted to $62 million; this included the construction of two pipelines to the Mediterranean. "Some $8 million were invested in Saudi Arabia before the discovery of commercial oil,"[22] and a total expenditure of $100 million was incurred by 1945, at which time output was still very small; half of this sum was spent on building a refinery. Similarly, in Kuwait, where oil was quickly discovered, the Kuwait Oil Company had borrowed from its parent companies £33 million by 1950, all of which was used for development. On the other hand, initial investment in Bahrein and Qatar seems to have been relatively small and expansion appears to have been financed mainly from retained earnings (see Chapter I, Section I and Chapter II, Section C).

But in all these countries, reserves proved to be so huge and costs of production so low that investment per barrel of reserves or output is much smaller than in other parts of the world (see Chapter II, Section E). Actual expenditures on exploration in the countries covered by this study, excluding Saudi Arabia, amounted to $110 million in 1948–58 while the estimated addition to their proved oil reserves was about 80 billion barrels, resulting in an exploration cost of a little over one-tenth of a cent per barrel.[23] Consequently, the share of total costs imputable to capital has generally been relatively low in the Middle East, and that of variable costs correspondingly high. No exact breakdown is available, but Tables 26, p. 90, and 31, p. 107, would seem to show that, for the Middle Eastern oil industry as a whole, wages and salaries have been of the same order of magnitude as, or even slightly larger than, amortization of capital; this situation is very different from the one prevailing in the United States, or even in Venezuela, in spite of the fact that wage rates in both countries are much higher than in the Middle East. Of course, conditions vary from branch to branch; thus there seems little reason to doubt that in the Middle East, as elsewhere, fixed costs account for the bulk of total costs in pipelines and for a very high proportion in refining, and that the general average is brought down by the production branch. For instance, the operating costs of the Trans-Arabian Pipeline were only about 25 per cent of the total costs, and the fixed costs represented the bulk of the balance (see Section J of this Chapter).

E. Low Costs in Middle Eastern Production

Information on this subject has, until recently, been scanty. In 1947, a United States Senate Committee brought out the fact that, early in 1945, the cost of production of crude oil in Saudi Arabia, excluding a royalty of 22¢ a barrel, was 19¢, of which operating costs represented 8¢; in Bahrein, the total cost was 10¢, not including a royalty of about 15¢.[24] In Kuwait, "very approximate data" supplied to Standard Oil Company of New Jersey by the Anglo-Iranian Oil Company in 1946 indicated that, on the basis of 4 billion barrels of reserve and a production of 300,000 barrels a day, producing costs, including gathering costs, would be about 14¢ a barrel; this excluded a royalty payment of about 13¢ a barrel.[25] Actual costs appear to have been higher than this figure but to have declined sharply with the rise in output. In the 1952 agreement between the government of Iraq and the three companies operating in that country, it was estimated (Article 9) that "actual costs"

TABLE 26

BREAKDOWN OF COST OF OPERATIONS IN THE MIDDLE EASTERN OIL INDUSTRY, 1948-58
(Millions of Dollars)

Year	Wages and Salaries (1)	Payments to Local Contrac-tors (2)	Purchase of Local Supplies (3)	Other Local Expendi-tures (4)	Imports (5)	Total Expendi-tures (6)	Depre-ciation (7)	Gross Invest-ments (8)	Costs of Operations in Other Areas (9)	Total Costs of Operations (10)
1948	98.3	37.7	12.2	53.8	266.3	468.3	39.3	282.0	28.3	253.9
1949	111.9	38.5	8.4	63.9	272.4	495.1	52.1	328.0	55.9	275.1
1950	108.8	22.2	3.4	63.6	98.6	296.6	68.1	119.5	41.6	286.8
1951	99.3	20.0	4.0	36.8	117.0	277.1	61.6	140.4	66.8	265.1
1952	68.9	22.3	4.7	10.6	163.1	269.6	59.7	166.6	75.2	237.9
1953	76.0	19.9	3.9	11.2	125.2	236.2	72.8	130.6	82.4	260.8
1954	82.2	18.3	4.6	11.8	80.1	197.0	85.0	109.9	105.4	277.5
1955	123.6	18.0	9.2	25.3	103.7	279.8	113.9	120.0	114.4	388.1
1956	136.5	28.7	12.5	27.6	182.1	387.4	120.0	175.1	114.0	446.3
1957	144.4	35.9	18.1	35.7	223.2	457.3	134.2	212.8	116.6	495.3
1958	151.9	52.8	26.2	57.0	202.8	490.7	151.3	272.4	121.7	491.3
Total	1201.8	314.3	107.2	397.3	1834.5	3855.1	958.0	2057.3	922.3	3678.1

Sources: For figures in Columns (1) – (6), see Appendix Table 5. Figures in Column (7) were calculated on the basis of 8-per-cent average depreciation charges on the value of net fixed assets unless actual depreciation charges were available as in Iran. For figures in Column (8), see Table 12. For Column (9), which shows the costs of oil operations in Aden, Bahrein, and the pipeline transit countries the figures have been estimated on the basis of average unit costs of crude oil production, refined oil outputs, and transportation in other countries of the Middle East on the one hand, and the volume of oil produced, refined, and transported on the other. In certain cases, the actual published cost figures were used as a yardstick in making the estimates—for example, the cost of crude oil production in Bahrein and the cost of pipeline operations by Tapline. The figures in Column (10) are the total of Columns (6), (7), and (9) minus Column (8).

Note: For the coverage of Columns (1) – (8) see Appendix Table 5.

(which were defined in Article 1 as including "operating expenses and overheads" and "depreciation of all physical assets in Iraq at the rate of ten per centum per annum and amortization of all other capital expenditure in Iraq at the rate of five per centum per annum until such assets and expenditures are fully written off") were 23*s.* per ton for 1951, 17*s.* 6*d.* for 1952, and 13*s.* thereafter, or about 42¢, 33¢, and 24¢ a barrel, respectively. In Qatar, the Supplementary Agreement of 1955 between the Sheik and Qatar Petroleum Company (Article 3) put costs of production, excluding royalty, in 1953 at £4,594,463 and in 1954 at £5,182,099.[26] This works out at £1.2.9 and £1.1.7 a ton, respectively, or about 40¢ and 39¢ a barrel, respectively. And for Iran, costs of production, excluding royalty, in 1955 were estimated at 30¢ a barrel and were expected to decline to below 20¢ once output picked up.[27]

In addition to the foregoing published data, it is possible to make rough estimates of costs of production from the figures given in Appendix Table 5, p. 192, which shows actual data on expenditure including both operating and investment. In order to arrive at the cost of crude oil production, investment expenditures and refining costs should be deducted and depreciation charges added. Investment expenditures are given in Table 12, p. 45, and estimates on refining costs are given below; depreciation may be estimated on the basis of investments.

While the average cost of crude oil production in the Middle East in recent years has been under 20¢ a barrel, it has been about 80¢ in Venezuela and about $1.75 in the United States; it has also been reported that the cost of production and transport of the Soviet crude oil that was delivered at Black Sea ports in 1960 was about 80¢ a barrel; none of these figures include royalties.

There are three major reasons for the lowness of costs in the Middle East: the very large scale on which operations can be carried out, which has already been alluded to; unusually favorable geological formations; and the nature of the concessions. To these should be added a very minor one, low labor costs.

F. Geological Formations

Little need be said about the geological formations except to point out that most of the Middle Eastern oil fields now being operated are close to the coast (the northern fields of Iraq being the major exception);[28] that, in general, they have not necessitated very deep drilling; and, above all, that they contain what seem to be the world's largest pools, with great gas pressure and a porosity which make it possible to have a very high production per well. Few recent estimates of the size of the major Middle Eastern fields have been published and estimates made even a few years ago are misleading, since proved reserves have greatly increased as a result of further prospecting and development of known fields. In Iran, the reserves of Gach Saran field were recently estimated at 12 billion barrels and those of Agha Jari at 7 billion.[29] In Kuwait, at the end of 1960, the total reserves of 60 billion barrels were contained in five fields, of which Burgan is by far the largest; in Saudi Arabia, reserves of 51 billion barrels are distributed among fifteen fields, of which the largest are those of Ghawar and Abqaiq; and in Iraq, total reserves amount to 24 billion barrels, contained in eight fields, of which by far the largest is that of Kirkuk. Even in the smaller producing countries the fields are relatively large, viz., 225 million barrels in Bahrein and 2.3 billion in Qatar, while in the Neutral Zone, estimates for Wafra field have been raised from some 705 million barrels in 1956 to 2.9 billion in 1960.

By way of comparison, in the United States, "producing wells draw upon 4,000 or more pools, which range in size from less than one million barrels up to the mammoth East Texas pool, which had a content of approximately 5 billion barrels,"[30] averaging only 8 million barrels per pool. And in Venezuela, the number of fields in production in 1960 was 114, while proved reserves totaled 16.9 billion barrels.[31] As regards depth of drilling, conditions naturally vary, but on the whole the Middle East does not compare too unfavorably with its main competitors. Table 27 shows that the bulk of production comes from wells not over five or six thousand feet deep.[32] In the United States, where conditions also vary greatly, the average depth of productive wells in 1956 was 4,070 feet;[33] in Venezuela, depths in the two main producing areas, Zulia and Eastern Venezuela, ranged in 1960 from 3,000 to 8,000 feet and from 5,000 to 10,000 feet, respectively.[34]

G. System of Concessions

The prevailing system of concessions in the Middle East also helps greatly in reducing costs of production. Until very recently, only one concessionary company operated in most of the countries. The areas leased to such companies are huge—about 360,000 square miles in Saudi Arabia (which was later increased by the "additional area" of 80,000 square miles, part of which was subsequently relinquished); the whole of Iraq (about 170,000 square miles, covered by Iraq Petroleum

TABLE 27

DATA ON MIDDLE EASTERN OIL FIELDS, 1960

Country, Name of Field, Discovery Date	Depth (Feet)	No. of Wells[a]	Production, Barrels Daily Average	Production, Barrels Cumulative (Thousands)	Gravity, °API
Bahrein					
Bahrein, 1932	2,200- 4,500	150	45,063	238,119	33-36
Iran					
Agha Jari, 1937	4,900-10,000	33	650,961	1,262,675	34.2
Ahwaz, 1958	8,419	1	5,442	1,009	32.0
Alborz (Qum), 1956	8,500	...	b	...	...
Gach Saran, 1928	2,800-10,000	13	61,865	196,339	32.0
Haft Kel, 1928	1,900- 4,900	20	166,125	1,201,860	37.8
Lali, 1938	4,900- 9,000	5	12,271	335,765	35.2
Masjid-i-Sulaiman, 1908	680- 5,300	31	63,910	959,435	37.8
Naft-i-Shah, 1935	2,100- 3,000	4	4,908	39,288	41.9
Naft Safid, 1935	3,000- 7,000	17	44,025	101,769	35.2
Sarajeh, 1958	8,000- 8,590	...	b	...	...
TOTAL		124	1,009,507	4,098,140	
Iraq					
Ain Zalah, 1939	5,800	4	18,425	55,245	31.8
Bai Hasan, 1953	4,800	5	33,387	1,498	34.5
Butmah, 1952	5,100	2	8,516	12,891	31.7
Jambur, 1954	5,700	2	11,033	5,115	34.5
Kirkuk, 1927	2,800	44	643,087	1,917,830	35.9
Naft Khaneh, 1923	3,000	2	3,300	60,116	42.0
Rumaila, 1953	10,800	11	172,648	225,377	34.9
Zubair, 1949	11,000	25	72,936	248,814	35.0
TOTAL		95	963,332	2,526,886	
Kuwait					
Burgan, 1938	3,500- 4,800	232	...	...	30-32
Magwa-Ahmadi, 1952	3,500- 4,800	80	...	...	
Minagish, 1959	9,000-10,000	2	c	...	
Raudhatain, 1955	7,800-10,000	28	...	...	
Sabriya, 1957	7,500- 8,200	d	...	...	
TOTAL		342	1,579,600	3,689,201	
Neutral Zone					
Wafra, 1953	1,200- 7,100	157	128,896	144,958	17-26
Qatar					
Dukhan, 1940	6,550	34	172,707	420,319	41.7
Saudi Arabia					
Abqaiq, 1941	6,800	59	266,755	1,568,353	38
Abu Hadria, 1940	10,115	c	...	10	35
Damman, 1936	4,850	28	35,983	400,845	35
Fadhili, 1949	9,850	...	...	...	37
Ghawar, 1948	7,125	86	727,001	1,852,091	35
Khurais, 1957	5,200	c	13	5	33
Khursania, 1956	6,900	c	138	25,098	31
Manifa, 1957	7,900	c	...	...	27
Qatif, 1945	7,350	5	14,722	106,770	35
Safania, 1951	5,560	23	174,422	93,926	27
TOTAL		201	1,219,034	4,047,098	

Source: The *Oil and Gas Journal* (Tulsa, Oklahoma, December 26, 1960).
[a]All wells are flowing except for forty in the Neutral Zone, and two in Butmah, Iraq.
[b]National Iran Oil Company discovery, not in production.
[c]Shut in.
[d]Not in production.

Company and its two affiliates, but in late 1961 the government of Iraq passed a law reducing drastically the areas under these concessions); about 100,000 square miles in Iran, covered by the consortium of oil companies; the whole of Kuwait (about 6,000 square miles); the Neutral Zone (about 2,000 square miles); Qatar (about 4,000 square miles); and Bahrein (about 200 square miles). By way of contrast, in Venezuela, exploration permits cover only 10,000 hectares (38 square miles); in the United States, leased areas are also generally small. This means that the Middle East is spared all the evils of excessive competitive drilling which, while it has accelerated production, has led to the sinking of thousands of unnecessary wells in the United States and of many in Venezuela; this has not only raised costs of production in those two countries, but has also resulted in the loss of much gas pressure and the reduction of the quantity of oil ultimately recoverable from their fields.[35] A striking contrast is presented in this respect by Abqaiq and East Texas fields. Although they are different in certain respects, both are approximately similar in surface area and magnitude, Abqaiq being about 30 miles long and 6 miles wide and having reserves estimated at 5.9 billion barrels and East Texas being 42 miles by 5 miles, with 5 billion barrels. But whereas in 1952 there were 62 producing wells in the former field, the latter had no less than 26,000.[36]

Two important consequences for Middle Eastern production follow from this. First, there has been a great saving in capital costs, due to the much smaller number of wells drilled; this is illustrated by the figures given in Table 15, p. 53. Second, the concessionary arrangements make it possible to exploit fully the favorable geological conditions, resulting in a very high output per well; the Middle Eastern average in 1960 was 4,510 barrels per day, compared with 271 in Venezuela, 172 in Indonesia, 12 in the United States, and 90 in the Soviet Union.[37]

Moreover, in the absence of any compulsion to maximize output for fear of losing oil to neighboring competitors—"the law of capture"—Middle Eastern companies can regulate the rate of production so as to obtain maximum technical efficiency. As a result, not only is output per well very high, but practically all the oil is obtained by "free flow"; the only Persian Gulf country in which there were pumping wells in 1959 was the Neutral Zone. In the Persian Gulf area, there were 30 pumping wells out of a total of 1,100 producing wells, whereas in Venezuela 71 per cent of the 9,400 producing wells and in the United States 87 per cent of the 600,000 producing wells were pumping wells.[38] In the Soviet Union, "free-flowing wells account for two-thirds of all crude oil output. Pumping accounts for 30 per cent and gaslift operations for 5 per cent, mostly in the older areas around Baku."[39] It should be added that the concession agreements do not impose on the companies any conservation obligations apart from having to "maintain in good working order all borings, so long as they are economically productive" (Article 7 of 1925 Convention in Iraq), or to carry out operations "in accordance with first-class oil field practice" (Article 8 of December, 1950 Agreement in Saudi Arabia), or to follow "good industry practices" (Article 4 of 1954 Agreement in Iran), or to apply "the most appropriate scientific methods" (Article 2 of 1934 Agreement with Kuwait). This, together with the absence of nearby markets, accounts for the fact that until recently practically all the natural gas produced in association with crude oil in the Middle East has been flared; only in the last few years have significant amounts been reinjected into the fields (see Chapter I, Section D and Chapter VII, Section F).

All this does not mean that the areas granted in concession in the Middle East are necessarily of optimum size. In the short run, the host government is interested in having as many concessionaires operating in its country as possible, since this would lead to greater competition, with a corresponding rise in the government's bargaining power; would increase the number of producers, thus augmenting the amounts it receives as bonuses and rents; and might stimulate production and thus still further augment government receipts, unless competition between producers should result in a more than proportionate fall in prices. The example of Venezuela illustrates these points, as does that of Iran more recently. On the other hand, competitive drilling carried to excess not only raises costs, and to that extent diminishes government revenue, but could jeopardize good conservation practice and might in the long run do considerable harm to the country either by reducing the amount of reserves ultimately recoverable or by increasing costs of production. The ideal would seem to be to have several competing firms, each exploiting separate fields as units, but this is a criterion that is very difficult to apply since the extent of the fields can be determined only after considerable drilling, which is normally carried out after the concession has been granted.

H. Labor Costs

Labor costs form a small fraction of total value added in the oil industry in the Middle East; as Table 31, p. 107, shows, wages and salaries declined from 13.1 per cent of total value added in 1948–49 to 6.5

in 1960. Labor costs are a function of wage rates and productivity of labor. As regards the former, the following may be said: First, wage rates in the oil industry are distinctly above the rates prevalent in other sectors of the economies of the respective Middle Eastern countries; second, they have been steadily rising; and third, they are only a small fraction of wages in the other major oil-producing countries, Venezuela and the United States.

With regard to the first point, comparison of wages paid in the oil industry and in other sectors is particularly favorable at the lowest levels; the minimum wages paid in the oil industry to unskilled laborers are well above rates prevailing in adjacent areas and also above the minimum legal rates, where such exist. For the more highly skilled workers the gap is much smaller, since there is a keen demand for such labor from the other sectors of the economy, a demand that has been partly stimulated by the impact of the oil industry on the local economy; thus a comparison of wages paid to carpenters, mechanics, blacksmiths, crane drivers, and truck drivers in Iran, Iraq, and Saudi Arabia in 1958 showed that the level in the oil industry was some 5 to 15 per cent higher than outside.[40] It should also be remembered that in the oil industry workers receive many benefits in addition to wages, such as subsidized food, clothing, housing, medical and educational services, and various amenities on a scale unknown in the surrounding areas.[41] In Saudi Arabia these are almost equal to the wages paid, but in other countries the proportion is lower.

Second, the rise in wage rates is reflected in the 85 per cent increase in wages and salaries in 1948–58, since, as is shown in Table 28, the total number employed rose by only some 10 per cent over the period. Between 1948 and 1959, minimum daily wages in the oil industry doubled in Iraq and rose by 140 per cent in Iran and 250 per cent in Saudi Arabia.[42] In the same period, the cost of living rose by 62 per cent in Iran and fell by 23 per cent in Iraq, the only two countries for which indices are available.[43] Further factors, in addition to the rise in real minimum wages, tending to swell payrolls are decreasing labor turnover and upgrading of workers. As regards the first, in the Iranian petroleum industry annual turnover (defined as the proportion of employees who left their work during the year to the average strength of the labor force in that year) fell from 21 per cent in 1950 to 10 per cent in 1956 and 4 per cent in 1958; in Iraq it fell from 28 per cent in 1954 to 10 per cent in 1956 and 4 per cent in 1958; and in Saudi Arabia it fell from 34 per cent in 1951 to 26 per cent in 1953, 11 per cent in 1957, and 6 per cent in 1959.[44] As for upgrading, it has been promoted both

TABLE 28

DIRECT EMPLOYMENT IN THE MIDDLE EASTERN PETROLEUM INDUSTRY, 1948-60[a]
(Numbers)

Country	1948	1950	1954	1956	1958	1960
Aden	—	—	2,272	2,525[b]	...	...
Bahrein	6,078	7,749[c]	8,532	8,785	8,455	7,684
Iran	50,393	55,970[d]	...	55,234	57,309	54,030
Iraq	14,241	11,374	12,770	15,832	15,981	16,702
Kuwait	10,223	10,164	8,014	7,814	9,364	7,161
Neutral Zone	—	—	270	...	...	...
Saudi Arabia	18,637	16,860	21,858	19,632	17,171	14,834
Qatar	...	...	...	4,500	...	...

Sources: Annual Reports of various companies; National Iranian Oil Company, *Petroleum Statistics 1958-60*; The Government of Iraq, *Statistical Abstract*; United Nations, *Economic Developments in the Middle East, 1959-61* (New York, 1962); David H. Finnie, *Desert Enterprise: The Middle East Oil Industry in its Local Environment* (Cambridge, Harvard University Press, 1958); Benjamin Shwadran, *The Middle East, Oil and the Great Powers 1959* (New York, Council for Middle Eastern Affairs Press, 1959); International Labour Office, *Labour Conditions in the Oil Industry in Iran* (Geneva, 1950); Aden Colony, *Annual Report of the Department of Labour and Welfare 1955* (Aden, n.d.); *Petroleum Press Service* (London, August, 1959).

[a]Figures exclude persons employed by contractors, numbering in Iran 13,603 in March, 1951, and 3,206 in 1960; in Kuwait, numbering 6,409 in 1958; and in Saudi Arabia, numbering 6,900 in 1948 and 9,454 in 1958. Iranian figures include employees of the National Iranian Oil Company, numbering 9,310 in 1956, 11,282 in 1958, and 18,085 in 1960.

[b]1955.

[c]1951.

[d]1949.

by the increased stability of the labor force and by the large-scale training supplied by most oil companies in the region. As an illustration, whereas in 1951, some 77 per cent of the employees of Aramco were in the lowest grades, 1–3, by 1958 no less than 67 per cent were in grades 4–6.[45]

Third, as regards the relative level of wages in the Middle Eastern oil industry compared to that in other major producing areas, the following figures are illustrative. The minimum daily wage in Saudi Arabia was 1.5 Saudi riyal in 1945, 3 in 1950, 6 in 1955, and 8 in 1958, or 40¢, 81¢, $1.62, and $2.13, respectively.[46] In Iran, the minimum daily wage was 40 rial in 1948, 82 in 1955–56, and 99 in 1957,[47] or, at the official rates of exchange, which in the earlier year greatly overvalued the rial, $1.50, $1.08, and $1.30, respectively. In Iraq, the minimum daily wage was equivalent to 90¢ in 1948, $1.10 in 1950, $1.60 in 1955, and $1.80 in 1959.[48] In Kuwait, in 1959, the minimum daily wage was 8.50 rupees, or $1.79, to which should be added a housing allowance of 1–2 rupees.[49] In Bahrein, at the beginning of 1954, the average (not minimum) daily wage in the lowest category was 4.25 rupees, or 90¢.[50] These do not include other employee benefits, which in some countries have a monetary value as great as the wages.

Other illustrative figures are the average earnings per Iraqi employee in the Iraq Petroleum Company, which rose from about 290 Iraqi dinar in 1951, or some $800, to about 420 dinar, or nearly $1,200, in 1954.[51] In Kuwait, average gross monthly earnings of payroll employees of the Kuwait Oil Company were 603 rupees (or the equivalent of $1,500 a year), in December, 1958, and 670 rupees (or about $1,700 a year), in December, 1959.[52] And in Saudi Arabia, the average annual income of Saudi Arab employees more than doubled between 1953 and 1959, reaching 7,082 riyal or $1,888 at the end of 1959.[53] It may be noted that average annual earnings in the United States oil industry were, in 1948, $3,470 in petroleum and natural gas production and $3,750 in refining and, in 1958, $5,700 and $5,970, respectively.[54] In Venezuela, the minimum daily wage was $2.00 in 1950 and $3.70 in 1959;[55] in 1950, the annual cost per employee of the Creole Petroleum Corporation was $5,400 and in 1960, $9,600.[56]

Against the relative lowness of the wages, compared to most major oil producing areas, must be set, as already mentioned, the lowness of the productivity of Middle Eastern workers, arising from many factors. First, there is the fact that labor, being cheap, is used more extensively in the Middle East than in other areas. Second, there is the unfamiliarity with machinery and modern industrial techniques of almost all recruits into the Middle Eastern oil industry; this can be only partially remedied by the intensive and widespread training courses given by practically all oil companies operating in the region. Third, most of the workmen entering the oil industry are illiterate, and large numbers remain so throughout their term of service. Fourth, newcomers to the industry are in poor health and inadequately fed; although the companies offer them excellent medical services and often subsidized meals, their level in this respect remains well below that of their counterparts in more advanced countries. The same is true of housing conditions, again in spite of noteworthy efforts by the companies to improve matters.

In addition to these factors there is, in some countries, evidence of overstaffing arising from the reluctance of companies to dismiss redundant personnel. This has certainly been true in Iran since the nationalization crisis of 1951, and has probably been true of Iraq since the revolution of 1958. The following example, contrasting Kuwait and

Iran, is illustrative, though it must of course be remembered that other factors than labor are involved and, indeed, that local labor is one of the cheaper factors of production in the region:

> Perhaps partly because of the tight labor market, Kuwait Oil Company's operations are well organized so as to conserve labor. Its crude loading port, Mina Al Ahmadi, is the largest in the world, yet only 132 men are employed at the terminal (exclusive of marine personnel). This figure may be compared with the 4400 people employed at Anglo-Iranian Oil Company's oil loading port of Bandar Mashur in 1950.[57]

There is, therefore, every reason to believe that labor productivity in the Persian Gulf oil industry is well below that in the United States oil industry, but in the present state of knowledge it is impossible to say how much below. However, the over-all production of oil per worker in the Persian Gulf is greatly raised by the abundance and very high quality of the cooperating factors—the highly productive natural oil resources, the high degree of mechanization, and the efficient technical and managerial organization. Perhaps the best estimate, in these circumstances, is that the lowness of labor productivity in the Middle East does not entirely offset the relative lowness of wages, and that effective Middle Eastern labor costs are therefore somewhat lower than those of the United States and probably still more below those of Venezuela. It should, however, be noted that the increasing level of wages in the Middle East has stimulated the oil companies to reduce the number of their employees to prevent their labor costs from rising. As a result the size of the labor force engaged in oil operation in Saudi Arabia, Kuwait, and Bahrein declined in recent years; There was also a sharp fall in Iran in 1961. This development has taken place despite a considerable rise in the output of petroleum and hence production per worker has appreciably increased.

I. Refining Costs

Very little information is available on refining costs in the Middle East, but what there is seems to indicate that they are not substantially different from, though slightly lower than, costs in other regions. Thus in 1947, the cost of refining in Saudi Arabia, including overhead, was put at 30¢ a barrel.[58] Since then this figure has risen appreciably because of higher costs of labor, materials, and capital equipment, to about 50¢ a barrel in 1955–56. Estimates based on available information indicate that in Iran, where the cost of refining per barrel was the highest in the

Middle East owing to unused capacity and redundant labor, it averaged 65¢ in 1956–58.[59] Costs in Bahrein appear to have been lower than in the above-mentioned countries. In the United States, in recent years, typical refining costs for fuel type refineries have ranged between 65¢ and $1.30.[60] In Western Europe, in 1960, refining cost per barrel of output was estimated to amount to 80¢ in a 10,000-barrel-a-day refinery, declining to 35¢ in a 100,000-barrel-a-day refinery; the corresponding cost figures for cracking refineries were $1.40 and 62¢, respectively.[61]

Four main factors, working in opposite directions, seem to be mainly responsible for the fact that costs in the Middle East are close to those in other regions. First, all refinery equipment in the Middle East is imported, which appreciably raises capital costs; chemicals, some other materials, and spare parts are also imported. Second, Middle Eastern refineries often have to carry greater costs for economic and social overheads. On the other hand, the fact that Middle Eastern refineries are much larger than the world average substantially reduces their unit capital and operating costs (see above). Last, Middle Eastern refineries are less complex than those in other regions; this reduces the value of their output but also that of their capital and operating costs.

In the discussion of refinery margins, i.e., the difference between the cost of a barrel of crude oil input and receipts from its refined products, two further factors are relevant; on the one hand, the product-mix in the Middle East, with its lower proportion of the more valuable products, due to the less complex types of refinery in the region and the lower proportion of catalytic or reforming plants (see Table 6, p. 15); and on the other the relatively low price of crude oil; this question is discussed more fully in Chapter V, Section G.

J. Transport Costs

During the earlier part of the period covered in this study, the lower production cost of Middle Eastern oil was partly offset by its higher cost of transportation to its main markets in Western Europe and its still higher costs to the Western Hemisphere. Even by 1949, when freight rates were some 30 per cent below United States Maritime Commission rates[62] (for the rates, see Table 29), it was estimated that the cost of transportation on a T-2 tanker (16,600 tons) from Venezuela (Puerto la Cruz) to Southampton was 55¢ a barrel and to New York 26¢ a barrel; on a 26,000-ton tanker costs fell to 50¢ and 23¢, respectively. The corresponding figures for transport from the Persian Gulf (Bahrein or Ras Tanura) were $1.08 and $1.28 on a T-2 tanker and

TABLE 29

UNITED STATES MARITIME COMMISSION TANKER RATES FOR THE TRANSPORTATION OF PETROLEUM AND PRODUCTS FROM LOADING PORTS TO VARIOUS DESTINATIONS
(Dollars Per Long Ton)

Destination	Origin: Persian Gulf Ras Tanura	Origin: Eastern Mediterranean	Origin: Caribbean Aruba and Curacao	Origin: U. S. Gulf
Western Hemisphere				
Montreal	12.85	8.55	4.05	4.50
U.S. East Coast	12.70	7.80	2.70	2.85
Rio de Janeiro	12.50	9.45	5.50	7.85
Buenos Aires	13.45	11.45	7.20	9.70
Valparaiso	16.40	...	6.25	7.30
Europe				
Stockholm	12.80	7.35	8.05	9.15
United Kingdom	10.90	5.45	6.55	7.65
Gibraltar	9.15	3.75	5.65	7.35
Naples	8.15	2.80	7.05	8.75
Africa				
Dakar	11.80	5.70[a]	5.15	...
Capetown	7.15	9.55	8.95	...
Durban	6.35	8.75	9.75	...
Asia				
Bombay	2.40	6.65	14.20	15.90
Singapore	5.75	9.85[a]	18.65[a,b]	20.28[a,b]
Yokahama	10.20	14.50[a]	14.20	15.40
Oceania				
Sydney	11.30	...	14.10	14.90

Sources: United States Maritime Commission; reproduced in: Walter J. Levy Associates, *Venezuelan Oil in the Framework of Western Hemisphere Supplies, An Economic Survey for the Government of the United States of Venezuela* (New York, March 26, 1951).
[a]U.S.M.C. rates not available. Rates given are calculated on the basis of distance.
[b]Via Suez.

\$1.04 and \$1.23 on a 26,000-ton tanker; from the Mediterranean (Haifa), they were 44¢ and 67¢ on a T-2 tanker and 42¢ and 63¢ on a 26,000-ton tanker; the latter figures do not include the cost of transport through the pipeline.[63]

In the last few years, however, the situation has changed. In the first place, the pipelines from Saudi Arabia and Iraq, which were built in the postwar years and the capacity of which has been successively increased, now carry over 45 million tons of Middle Eastern oil to the Mediterranean, as against 115 million tons passing through the Suez Canal (see Table 9, p. 21). This has eliminated not only the 3,600-mile haul around Arabia but also the Canal toll, at present about 10¢ a barrel.[64] In 1950, the tanker haul cost some 65¢. By 1960, however, the increase in tanker size had brought down the cost of the haul around Arabia drastically; for a 46,000-tonner it was put at 38¢.[65] On the other hand, the cost of transporting crude oil through the Trans-Arabian pipeline was 20–21¢ a barrel; 4¢ of this represented operating costs and the balance consisted of amortization, transit payments, and social services expenditure.[66] Hence there was a net saving of nearly 45¢ a barrel in 1950, which in recent years has declined to nearly 20¢.

Second, the increase in the size of tankers has appreciably reduced the unit cost of the transport of oil (see above). In 1945 the whole of the world's tanker fleet was composed of ships under 25,000 tons, but by 1959 over 37 per cent consisted of ships over 25,000 tons and 16 per cent consisted of ships over 35,000 tons.[67] It should, however, be added that since ships of over 38,000 tons cannot pass through the Suez Canal fully laden (see Chapter I, Section G), the advantages to the Middle East from this trend have been somewhat reduced.[68]

Third, with sharp but brief interruptions during the Korean War and the Suez crisis, tanker freight rates have steadily declined in the post-war period, owing to the great increase in tanker availabilities compared to the volume of oil transported by water. Freight rates for a single voyage, which fell as low as 45 per cent below United States Maritime Commission (USMC) rates in 1949 and rose to a peak of 180 per cent above those rates in November, 1951, fell back sharply to their 1949 level by 1954—and, after climbing back to USMC flat during the Suez crisis, dropped again as low as USMC minus 70 per cent in 1959. The effect of these reductions in freight rates may be judged from the fact that, on a spot cargo basis, "the advantage of Middle East crude [on the Eastern coast of the United States] increased by 7 cents per barrel for every 5-point drop in tanker rates below USMC minus 35 per cent. At a level of USMC minus 50 per cent, therefore, Middle East crude was about 20 cents per barrel cheaper at the U.S. East Coast than United States and Venezuelan crude before the 1953 price increase, and 23 cents after July 1953."[69]

By late 1958, the Middle Eastern differential over Venezuelan crude on the basis of posted prices and current spot rates was 16¢ to 21¢ a barrel on the U.S. East Coast, 28¢ to 33¢ in South America, and 45¢ to 68¢ in Europe, and this advantage widened still further during the following year.[70]

V. Returns on Investment

A. Definitions

There are several concepts that can be used for measuring returns in an industry. From the national point of view, the "value added" by an industry is of greatest significance.[1] From the industry's point of view, the "return to capital" is paramount. Such return, which is arrived at by deducting all intermediate, labor, and capital inputs (the latter includes depreciation and amortization) from gross receipts, indicates the income of an industry; depending on whether government taxes are included in the return to capital or not, the income may be considered as "gross" or "net." Net income, in turn, when divided by capital investment, indicates the profitability of an enterprise. Finally, from the investor's point of view, the "dividend" and the prospects of capital appreciation are of utmost importance, and determine his choice of investment. The dividend is arrived at by deducting from the net income that portion that is transferred to reserve funds for new investment—in other words, it refers to income actually paid to investors.

An attempt will be made here to apply these concepts of measurement of returns to investment to the petroleum industry of the Middle East. This has to be based partly on estimation, since the balance sheets of the petroleum companies operating in the region are not generally made public, either directly or through their parent companies. However, considerable information and statistics have been published on the Middle Eastern petroleum industry in the past fifteen years by the United States Congress, the governments of the region, the international organizations, the trade journals, and the oil companies themselves. These materials have provided the basis and bench marks for estimates, the results of which are presented here. Such results whenever possible have been checked against the actual data.

In the discussion of returns on investments, it must be stated at the outset that, taking the world oil industry as a whole, or the operation of the major international companies, such returns have not been significantly different from those of other leading industries. However, if the Middle Eastern oil industry, which forms part of the network of the international oil industry and which is almost wholly owned or operated by the major companies, is studied on its own, it will be found that, compared to other large-scale enterprises in the recent economic history of the world, its experience has been unique in its unusually high remuneration to both foreign investors and local economies. This exceptional outcome has resulted from the fact that the region is essentially a producer and exporter of crude petroleum and that its crude operations have benefited from a high economic rent. (See Table 30,

TABLE 30

DISTRIBUTION OF GROSS RECEIPTS OF THE PETROLEUM INDUSTRY IN THE MIDDLE EAST COMPARED WITH THAT OF VENEZUELA AND THE UNITED STATES, 1948 AND 1958
(Percentages of Total)

Item	Middle East 1948	Middle East 1958	Venezuela 1948	Venezuela 1958	United States[a] 1948	United States[a] 1958
Operating costs (excluding royalties and rents)	19.7	8.5	26.5	29.1	65.1	70.8
Depreciation and depletion	5.0	6.0	7.0	10.9	7.8	10.8
Royalties, rents, and bonuses	14.1[b]	8.5	19.0	17.8	6.0	4.6
Income and other taxes	0.7	27.9	17.5	21.1	7.2	5.4
Income paid to stockholders[c]	23.6	45.5	0.7	18.3	3.6[d]	4.8[d]
Investment of retained earnings	36.9	3.6	29.3	2.8	10.3	3.6
TOTAL GROSS RECEIPTS	100.0	100.0	100.0	100.0	100.0	100.0

Sources: Middle East: See Appendix Table 4 and its sources; data on royalties and rents have been estimated on the basis of terms of payments in the petroleum agreements. Venezuela: The Ministry of Mines and Hydrocarbons of Venezuela. United States: F. G. Coqueron and J. E. Pogue, *Capital Formation in the Petroleum Industry*, published by the Chase National Bank (New York, 1952); The Chase Manhattan Bank, *Petroleum Industry*, 1959 (New York, July, 1960).

[a]Data for the United States cover the domestic and foreign oil operations of thirty oil companies in 1948 and thirty-two oil companies in 1958; consequently, the figures include part of the petroleum activities carried out by American oil companies in the Middle East and other regions. Royalties and rents have been estimated at 15 per cent of the value of total crude oil (at posted prices) produced by the same companies.

[b]Includes Iran's share of profits and Saudi Arabia's receipts from settlement of the gold pound controversy.

[c]Stockholders of the oil companies operating in the Middle East and Venezuela are in general the international major oil companies.

[d]Including income applicable to minority interests.

which compares the distribution of gross receipts in the Middle East, Venezuela, and the United States.) In the analysis of the price structure of the petroleum industry (see Chapter III, Section C), it was shown that the prices of the low-cost Middle Eastern crude oil are linked to the Gulf of Mexico prices of petroleum, which in turn are determined by the costs of marginal producers of crude oil and coal. The relatively large margin between the cost of production and the sale prices of Middle Eastern crude petroleum comprises the following elements: royalty, economic rent, interest, and profit. This breakdown of the crude oil margin—or gross income—is of importance in considering the evaluation of the distribution of income between the oil companies and the oil-producing countries.

Royalty is paid to the owner of a mine in return for the taking away of minerals from exhaustible natural deposits; it is usually either a proportion of mineral output or a fixed sum based on the volume of production.[2] In the Middle Eastern oil industry, royalties were fixed in the past at four gold shillings (in Iran, Iraq, and Saudi Arabia) or three rupees (in Bahrein, Kuwait, and Qatar) per ton of crude oil produced and sold. In recent years, a percentage payment has been introduced in Iran, Iraq, and Kuwait, amounting to 12.5 per cent of petroleum exports (see Chapter VI, Section C).

Interest is the return on the use of capital invested in an industry, whether the capital is owned by a lender or by the entrepreneur. The rate of interest on capital is established in the capital and money markets and is influenced greatly by the monetary policies of governments through their central banks; it also varies from one type of transaction to another. In the postwar years, the interest rate has ranged, for large-scale and long-term investment with relatively little risk, between 3 and 6 per cent; in recent years, however, it has followed an upward trend.[3]

Profit is remuneration to the owners of an enterprise for their entrepreneurial skills and the risks of undertaking the business. Very often it is calculated as the margin between gross income, on the one hand, and all costs of operation and interest to capital, on the other. However, in the Middle Eastern oil industry, the margin thus computed is so unusually high that it cannot be attributed to "normal profits" alone—even allowing rates double or triple those of "normal profits" in the United States and Europe.

The difference between this margin and "normal profits" may be termed "economic rent." This rent results partly from the higher productivity of the Middle Eastern oil fields, which is largely responsible for the low cost of production, and partly from the fact that Middle Eastern prices have been in line with the high price of crude oil in the Gulf of Mexico. In the past, determination of prices was handled exclusively by the oil companies within the market framework, but following the two price declines in 1959 and 1960, the governments of several petroleum exporting countries decided to interfere in price determination and set up an organization to regulate, among other things, the price of their exports (see Chapter VIII, Section A).

The sharing of this high economic rent has been a source of conflict in the relations between the oil companies and the producing countries, though the rent has not been usually recognized as such but generally referred to as high profits. Until recently, the governments of the oil-producing countries in the Middle East had a relatively small share in this high economic rent. Gradually, however, they have secured an increasing share, which is presently manifested in the equal profit-sharing formulas customary in the Middle East since 1950. However, it must be stated that this 50 per cent share of the governments includes all forms of payments by the companies from their income, i.e., royalties, income tax, and other taxes and duties.

B. Net Value Added

We shall now return to the measurement of returns on investment from the national point of view. Table 31 has been constructed to show the net value added by the Middle Eastern petroleum industry during the period between 1948 and 1960.[4] The value added is broken down, first, by its origin to show returns to labor and to capital and resources, and second, by its destination to illustrate the contribution of petroleum to local economies (including income of labor, revenues of the governments, and net investment of the petroleum industry in the region) and the investment income of the oil companies transferred outside the region. Finally, the total assets of the companies are given to calculate the capital-output ratio in the petroleum industry of the region.

The following observations may be made on the basis of these figures. First, the total amount of value added has risen very rapidly during the period 1948–60, though the rate of growth slowed down during the latter half of the period. The trend has roughly followed the increase in output of crude petroleum; the small decrease in value added in 1949 and 1959, despite a considerable rise in petroleum production in both those years, was caused by a decline in petroleum prices.

Second, the value added has grown faster than the capital investment in the industry, and as a result the capital-output ratio has declined considerably; in other words, the productivity of capital has increased. This trend has been favorably affected by the structural changes in the pattern of investment in the region's oil industry. These changes have

TABLE 31

TOTAL NET VALUE ADDED, ITS ORIGIN AND DESTINATION, IN THE MIDDLE EASTERN PETROLEUM INDUSTRY, 1948-60
(Millions of Dollars and Per Cent)

Period	Value Added, Millions of Dollars						Capital-Output Ratio, Per Cent (7)
		Origin		Destination			
	Total Value Added (1)	Labor (2)	Capital and Resources (3)	Absorbed Locally (4)	Transferred Abroad (5)	Average Net Assets (6)	
1948	885	108	777	505	380	850	96
1949	865	122	743	555	310	1,150	133
1950	1,127	122	1,005	412	715	1,340	119
1951	1,298	121	1,177	484	814	1,420	109
1952	1,339	94	1,245	601	738	1,490	111
1953	1,661	105	1,556	749	912	1,560	94
1954	1,910	116	1,794	860	1,050	1,595	84
1955	2,218	163	2,055	1,072	1,146	1,610	73
1956	2,372	180	2,192	1,221	1,151	1,690	71
1957	2,480	187	2,293	1,301	1,179	1,830	74
1958	3,064	197	2,867	1,547	1,517	2,035	66
1959	2,998	205	2,793	1,647	1,351	2,265	76
1960	3,305	215	3,090	1,735	1,570	2,390	72
1948-60	25,522	1,935	23,587	12,689	12,833	21,225	83
Percentage of total, 1948-60	100	8	92	50	50	—	—

Sources: Column (1): The data have been derived by adding the income of labor to the income of petroleum companies before direct payments to local governments. Column (2): The data given in Table 26 on wages and salaries of five countries (Iran, Iraq, Kuwait, Qatar, and Saudi Arabia) have been adjusted to include those of Aden, Bahrein, the Neutral Zone, and pipelines extending to the Eastern Mediterranean. Oil company payments to contractors, which contain a wage element, are not included because they have been treated as costs of inputs. Column (3): See Appendix Table 4; the figures include payments to local governments and the net incomes of oil companies. Column (4): See Appendix Table 4; the data include wages and salaries, direct payments to local governments, and retained earnings (taken as equal to net investment). Column (5): See Appendix Table 4; the figures include net income minus retained earnings (net investment). Column (6): Figures have been calculated as the average of the value of net fixed assets in the whole petroleum industry of the Middle East at the beginning and end of the years stated (see Table 11). Since the coverage of the fixed assets exceeds that of the value added by approximately one-fifth, it has been assumed that this additional amount would be roughly equal to the liquid assets of the petroleum companies. Column (7): Column (6) divided by Column (1).

resulted in an increase in the investment share of crude petroleum producing and handling facilities, which bring in higher returns than do those of refining and transportation. On the other hand, the existence of increasing excess capacity in the Middle Eastern oil industry has prevented the capital-output ratio from declining further. Compared to petroleum industries in other areas or to manufacturing industries in general, the capital-output ratio of the Middle Eastern oil industry is extremely low. This is essentially due to the very high productivity of the oil resources of the region, which also accounts for its high economic rent. It should be noted that the capital-output ratio is low even though the capital-labor ratio is high (see Chapter VII, Section E).

Third, the share of labor in value added has been very low, continuing to decline from 12 per cent in 1948 to 6 per cent in 1960, while returns to capital and resources have increased from 88 per cent of value added to 94 per cent. The low level of returns to labor in the value added is only partly due to the relatively low wages in the region (see Chapter IV); it is mainly due to the high capital-labor ratio of the industry and to the high productivity of the oil resources.

Fourth, the share of value added that has accrued to the local economies, following a decline from 66 per cent in 1949 to 37 per cent in 1951, has continued to increase gradually to 53 per cent in 1960. The decline in the early part of the period was due mainly to a decrease in net investments by the petroleum industry in the region, while the increasing revenues of the governments in subsequent years were mainly responsible for the rise.

C. Gross and Net Income

For an analysis of returns on investment from the point of view of the major international oil companies and their stockholders, Table 32 has been compiled in an attempt to show the magnitude and development of the gross and net income of the oil industry in the Middle East and Venezuela. When we summarize the financial results of petroleum operations in the former area from their establishment at the turn of the century until 1960, it is estimated that gross receipts of the oil companies from exports and local sales of crude petroleum and refined products amounted, approximately, to $32.1 billion. After deducting, from these gross receipts, an estimated amount of $5.9 billion for costs of operations, the industry's gross income, before deducting payments to Middle Eastern governments, is estimated at $26.2 billion for the corresponding period. Of this gross income, a sum of $9.9 billion was paid to these governments as royalties, rents, taxes, and share in profits; the balance, consisting of $16.3 billion, accrued to the oil companies. In turn, the oil companies reinvested about $1.7 billion of their net income in the expansion of the region's oil industry, and transferred the remaining $14.6 billion abroad (see Appendix Table 4).[5]

TABLE 32

DISTRIBUTION OF INCOME OF PETROLEUM INDUSTRY IN THE MIDDLE EAST AND VENEZUELA, 1913-60
(Percentages of Total Gross Income, Unless Otherwise Specified)

	Middle East					Venezuela				
		Net Income					Net Income			
Period	Payments to Local Governments	Net Investment	Transfer of Income Abroad	Total Net Income	Total Gross Income (Millions of Dollars)	Payments to Local Government	Net Investment	Transfer of Income Abroad	Total Net Income	Total Gross Income (Millions of Dollars)
1913-47	19	16	65	81	2,660	26	33	41	74	3,611
1948	20	31	49	80	777	55	44	1	45	760
1949	21	37	42	79	743	60	51	-11	40	570
1950	24	5	71	76	1,005	51	9	40	49	644
1951	24	7	69	76	1,177	55	5	40	45	857
1952	32	9	59	68	1,245	55	16	29	45	908
1953	38	4	58	62	1,556	54	10	36	46	894
1954	40	1	59	60	1,794	53	5	42	47	967
1955	44	—	56	56	2,055	52	- 4	52	48	1,149
1956	45	3	52	55	2,192	52	25	23	48	1,423
1957	45	3	52	55	2,293	52	28	20	48	1,851
1958	43	4	53	57	2,867	65	5	30	35	1,487
1959	47	4	49	53	2,793	69	11	20	31	1,400
1960	46	3	51	54	3,090	69	-13	44	31	1,500
1948-60	40	6	54	60	23,587	58	13	29	42	14,410
1913-60	38	7	55	62	26,247	51	17	32	49	18,021

Source: See Appendix Table 4.

Note: Gross income is defined as gross receipts minus costs; net income, as gross income minus payments to governments. Net investment is assumed to equal retained earnings.

The greater part of this development took place during the postwar period as a consequence of the large-scale expansion of the Middle Eastern petroleum industry. For instance, the industry's gross income aggregated about $23.5 billion during 1948–60 as compared with $2.7 billion in 1910–47; its net income was $14.2 billion, compared with $2.1 billion. However, allowance should be made for the decline in purchasing power of currencies in postwar years, which would reduce somewhat, but not substantially, the gap between these figures.

The distribution of gross income has changed considerably in the past decades. The share of oil companies in the gross income of the industry has declined from 80 per cent in 1948 to 54 per cent in 1960 and averaged 55 per cent in the period 1955–60, as compared with 81 per cent for the period prior to 1948. This decline has been brought about by a corresponding increase in the share of local governments.[6] Despite this decreasing tendency, the share of oil companies in the gross income of their operations in the Middle East has remained substantially higher than in Venezuela, though the gap between the two areas has been reduced. The corresponding ratio in Venezuela was 45 per cent in 1948, declining to 31 per cent by 1960.

The transfer of income by the oil companies to their parent companies abroad, which is defined here as the difference between the net income of oil companies and their net investment (i.e., gross investment minus depreciation) in the region, has fluctuated with the amount of net investment. The latter represented 31.2 per cent of gross income in 1948, declining to 0.3 per cent in 1955 and increasing to 3.8 per cent in the period 1957–60. The transfer of income abroad amounted to 54 per cent of gross income in the period 1948–60, as compared with 65 per cent for the period prior to 1948, and declined to 50 per cent in 1959–60. There has been no limitation on the transfer of these net incomes abroad, according to the oil agreements concluded between the producing countries of the Middle East and the companies. This favorable treatment, which contrasts with conditions in certain other countries, such as Argentina and Indonesia, where oil companies are subject to restrictions in transfer of their foreign exchange earnings abroad, has encouraged investment in the region.

D. Ratio of Income to Capital

The income of oil companies may further be studied in relation to the total net assets and physical output of the petroleum industry. The first criterion, the ratio of income to net assets, measures the profitability of petroleum operations in terms of capital;[7] the second, the ratio of income to the volume of production, estimates income per physical unit of output. Both of these criteria are rather important, though not decisive, to the major international oil companies when they consider the allocation of output among their oil fields in different parts of the world.

The ratio of estimated gross income to capital assets in the oil industry of the Middle East, as compared with Venezuela and the United States, is given in Table 33. In interpreting the table, attention should be drawn to the fact that, as already mentioned, the Middle East and Venezuela are primarily producers and exporters of crude oil, the refining, transport, and marketing of which—with their lower rates of return—are carried out largely in other countries. This structure accounts for the high rate of returns in the petroleum industry in those two regions, especially in the Middle East with its low costs of production. The figures for the United States, however, cover all the activities carried out by oil companies in that country as well as those of U.S. integrated companies operating abroad. Hence, they reflect a much higher percentage of refining, transport, and marketing activities. Earnings by American companies operating abroad, including the Middle East and Venezuela, are included in total United States earnings. The table shows that the rate of returns in foreign operations is much higher than in domestic; it also shows, despite this fact, that returns on total operations of United States oil companies are not higher than those of other leading American industries. The same applies to other major international oil companies; thus in 1960 the returns on net assets of Royal Dutch–Shell were under 9 per cent.

In the Middle East, gross income, before deducting payments to local governments, has continued to increase from an average of 78 per cent of net assets in 1948–49 to an average of 130 per cent for the period 1958–60, and averaged 111 per cent for the period 1948–60.[8] The corresponding ratio for Venezuela was 45 per cent in 1948–49 and 47 per cent in 1958–60, with an average of 49 per cent for the period 1948–60. The increase in the profitability of Middle Eastern operations was due partly to economies associated with the expansion of the industry and partly to changes in the pattern of investment in favor of crude petroleum production as against refining; on the other hand, there was a slight increase in the share of refining in investments in Venezuela during that period.

The ratio of net income (i.e., gross income after deducting payments to local governments) of the oil companies to their net assets in the Middle East has also risen, despite the fact that an increasing share of

TABLE 33

RETURNS ON INVESTMENTS IN THE PETROLEUM INDUSTRY OF THE MIDDLE EAST, VENEZUELA, AND THE UNITED STATES COMPARED TO TOTAL MANUFACTURING INDUSTRY IN THE UNITED STATES, 1948-60

Period	Middle East			Venezuela			United States				
							Oil Industry[a]				Ratio of Net Income to Net Assets in Manufacturing Industry[b]
							Ratio of Net Income to Net Assets			Ratio of Cash Dividends to Net Assets	
	Ratio of Gross Income to Total Net Assets	Ratio of Net Income to Total Net Assets	Ratio of Transferred Income Abroad to Total Net Assets	Ratio of Gross Income to Total Net Assets	Ratio of Net Income to Total Net Assets	Ratio of Transferred Income to Total Net Assets	Domestic Operations	Foreign Operations	Total		
1948	91	73	45	56	25	1	...	...	20.0	4.3	18.9
1949	65	51	27	34	14	-4	...	...	12.9	4.8	13.8
1950	75	57	53	35	17	14	13.8	18.3	14.6	5.3	17.1
1951	83	63	57	45	21	18	14.1	24.7	15.9	5.8	14.4
1952	84	57	50	46	21	13	11.5	26.4	14.0	5.6	12.3
1953	100	62	58	42	19	15	11.9	25.6	14.2	5.9	12.5
1954	112	67	66	45	21	19	9.8	28.5	13.0	5.5	12.4
1955	128	72	71	53	25	27	10.2	30.1	13.5	5.7	15.0
1956	130	71	68	61	29	14	10.5	28.8	13.9	5.9	13.9
1957	125	69	64	67	32	13	10.1	23.8	13.0	5.7	12.8
1958	141	80	75	48	17	15	7.2	17.3	9.5	5.3	9.8
1959	123	65	60	44	13	9	8.5	13.8	9.7	5.2	11.6
1960	129	70	66	50	16	22	...	...	...	...	...
1948-60 (Average)	111	67	61	49	21	14	10.8[c]	23.7[c]	13.1	5.5	13.7[c]

Sources: For the figures on Middle East and Venezuela, see Table 31 and Appendix Table 4; for the data on United States see: Kenneth E. Hill, *This Changing Oil Industry*, Eastman Dillon, Union Securities and Company (New York, 1961); The Chase Manhattan Bank, annual survey, *Petroleum Industry* (New York); the National Industrial Board, Inc., *Economic Almanac*, 1960 (United States, 1960), p. 233.

[a]Data cover thirty to thirty-five petroleum companies.

[b]Data cover the leading manufacturing corporations.

[c]Unweighted averages.

Note: Gross income is defined as gross receipts minus costs of production; net income equals gross income minus payments to governments; income transferred abroad equals net income minus net local investment; net local investment equals gross investment minus depreciation; dividends paid in cash do not include common dividends in stock. Figures on net assets used for calculating returns on investments in the Middle East include all the assets in southern Iran transferred to the Iranian government by the British Petroleum Company.

their gross income has, as already mentioned, been absorbed by these governments. In other words, it was the rising rate of gross return to capital that absorbed the increased payments to local governments; in addition, this rise in profitability has brought about an increase in the rate of net income of the oil companies. As a result, the ratio of net income of oil companies to their net assets rose from 61 per cent in 1948–49 to 72 per cent in 1958–60, averaging 67 per cent for the entire period. The corresponding ratio for the Venezuelan oil industry, after rising from 20 per cent in 1948–49 to 30 per cent in 1956–57, declined to 15 per cent in 1958–60 and averaged 21 per cent for the whole period under study. In the United States, on the other hand, return on capital of 30 to 35 major oil companies declined from an average of 16 per cent in 1948–49 to 9.6 per cent in 1958–59.[9] The ratios for the United States would have been still lower if they had referred only to domestic operations and had not included the net income from foreign operations (see Table 33).

The difference in return to capital between these three areas becomes more distinct, and the economic rent more pronounced, if return to capital is taken as the ratio of net income, after net investment, to net assets. Such income, both in the Middle East and Venezuela, is assumed to be equal to the investment income transferred abroad. In the Middle East, it increased from 35 per cent of net assets in 1948–49 to 67 per cent in 1958–60, averaging 61 per cent for the period 1948–60. The corresponding ratio for Venezuela averaged 14 per cent during 1948–60, and the ratio of dividends paid in cash in the United States averaged 5.5 per cent in 1948–59.

E. Return per Unit of Output

The other criterion of profitability that was mentioned earlier, i.e., return per unit of volume of output, has been used in Table 34 for the entire operations of the oil industry of the Middle East and Venezuela. The table shows average gross receipts (from production and sales of crude oil and refined products, and transport by oil pipelines crossing national borders within the region) per barrel of crude petroleum produced. It also gives a breakdown by cost of operations, payments to the governments, and net income of the oil companies before net investment in the region. The average per barrel receipts of the Middle Eastern oil industry, after having declined from a high of $2.47 in 1948 to $1.99 in the following year, increased gradually to $2.16 in 1957 and declined again to $1.91 in 1960. These declines were due largely to

TABLE 34

DISTRIBUTION OF GROSS RECEIPTS PER BARREL OF OIL PRODUCED IN THE MIDDLE EAST AND VENEZUELA, 1913-60
(Dollars and Per Cent)

Period	Middle East				Venezuela			
	Cost of Operations	Payments to Government	Net Income of Oil Companies	Average Receipts	Cost of Operations	Payments to Government[a]	Net Income of Oil Companies	Average Receipts
1913-47 (Average)	0.44	0.21	0.88	1.53	0.52	0.23	0.66	1.41
1948	0.61	0.34	1.52	2.47	0.78	0.85	0.70	2.33
1949	0.54	0.31	1.14	1.99	0.91	0.71	0.47	2.09
1950	0.45	0.37	1.20	2.02	1.04	0.61	0.57	2.22
1951	0.38	0.41	1.27	2.06	0.91	0.75	0.63	2.29
1952	0.31	0.53	1.11	1.95	0.92	0.76	0.62	2.30
1953	0.30	0.66	1.09	2.05	1.07	0.75	0.63	2.45
1954	0.28	0.72	1.08	2.08	1.10	0.74	0.66	2.50
1955	0.33	0.76	0.97	2.06	0.96	0.76	0.70	2.42
1956	0.35	0.78	0.97	2.10	0.88	0.82	0.76	2.46
1957	0.38	0.80	0.98	2.16	0.88	0.94	0.88	2.70
1958	0.32	0.79	1.05	2.16	1.04	1.01	0.55	2.60
1959	0.33	0.79	0.88	2.00	1.00	0.96	0.42	2.38
1960	0.30	0.74	0.87	1.91	0.96	0.99	0.45	2.40
1948-60 (Average)	0.35	0.68	1.03	2.06	0.97	0.84	0.62	2.43
1913-47, Per Cent	29	14	58	100	37	16	47	100
1948-60, Per Cent	17	33	50	100	40	35	25	100

Sources: See Appendix Tables 1 and 4.
[a]Excluding bonuses.

price decreases in those years, while the decline in 1952 resulted mainly from the interruption of higher priced refined production in the Abadan Refinery. On the whole, a shift in the relative importance of exports from refined products to crude petroleum has affected unfavorably the per-barrel receipts of the region's oil industry.

In comparing the corresponding data for the Middle East and Venezuela, the following observations may be made. First, average receipts per barrel of oil were higher in the Middle East than in Venezuela in 1948, but the situation was reversed in the following years, and the gap between per-barrel receipts of the two areas continued to widen in favor of Venezuela. Second, this gap is not as wide as the difference between the posted prices of similar products in the Persian Gulf and Venezuelan ports. These developments have resulted from the following: first, a decline in the refined oil content of petroleum exports from the Middle East, and an increase of the same in Venezuelan exports; second, the export of a substantial volume of Middle Eastern crude oil from the Eastern Mediterranean ports, where posted prices are only a little below those of similar products in Venezuelan ports; third, exports of petroleum from the Middle East as refined products, which command more or less the same price as Venezuelan refined oil products; and finally, the fact that Middle Eastern oil, on the average, is of better quality, in terms of higher API gravity, than Venezuelan.

The breakdown of the gross receipts of the oil companies shows that the average per-barrel cost of petroleum (i.e., total cost of production of crude oil plus cost of refining that part that is delivered to the region's refineries plus charges of transportation within the region, divided by total output of crude oil) in the Middle East has declined gradually from 61¢ in 1948 to 30¢ in 1960. This decline was brought about partly by economies of large-scale production as the output of crude petroleum continued to climb, and partly by a decrease in the relative importance of refining. In 1958–1960, average costs in the Middle East represented nearly one-third of the corresponding figures for Venezuela, as compared to about 80 per cent in 1948. On the other hand, average payments to Middle Eastern governments increased from 34¢ per barrel of crude oil produced in 1948 to an average of 79¢ in the period 1957–59, but declined to 74¢ in 1960; the greater part of the increase between 1948 and recent years was met by the decline in the cost. The corresponding payments to Venezuela increased from 85¢ in 1948, after declining to 61¢ in 1950, to an average of 97¢ in 1957–59; and 99¢ in 1960; thus the gap between the per-barrel average income of governments in these two areas has been greatly reduced. Finally, the per-barrel income of the oil companies in the Middle East declined from an average of $1.23 in the period 1948–53 to an average of $0.97 between 1954 and 1960, and stood at 87¢ in 1960. In Venezuela, on the other hand, the profitability of the oil industry has been much lower than in the Middle East, and the per-barrel income of the oil industry averaged 62¢ in the period 1948–60 and by 1960 had declined to 45¢.

F. Income from Production of Crude Oil

The income of petroleum companies operating in the Middle East may be divided, for further analysis of income, into three major categories. First, there is income derived from the production of crude oil and its delivery either to local refineries or to offtakers of crude petroleum, in both cases calculated at posted prices (minus 2 per cent discount) for different qualities of crude in different ports. Second, there is income accruing from the refining of crude petroleum within the region and the disposal of refined products either for local consumption or for export, the latter also at the posted market prices for various refined products (minus 2 per cent discount). Third, there is income attributable to the transportation of crude petroleum within the region through the intercountry petroleum pipelines. Thus, the income of the Middle Eastern oil industry, the bulk of which is derived from the production of crude oil, has been calculated on the basis of petroleum activities within the region and has not been traced beyond that region to the final consumers; it does not, therefore, include income derived from transport, refining, and marketing outside the region.

The above classification is made with the aim of investigating the difference in income derived from the three types of operations per physical unit, and also to indicate their differences in various countries of the region, as far as possible. This investigation will show that the profitability of the Middle Eastern oil industry lies in its output of crude oil, which produces a very high income per barrel; the other two operations also contribute substantially to the profits of oil companies, though income per physical unit is much lower than in crude oil activity.[10]

Table 35 presents the prices, costs, income, and payments to local governments per barrel of crude petroleum in most of the oil-producing countries of the region, in selected years for which reliable data were available. There exist slight differences in these items between the countries of the region. On the whole, the income of oil companies per barrel of crude oil, after increasing between the early postwar years

TABLE 35

PRICES, COSTS OF PRODUCTION, PAYMENTS TO GOVERNMENTS, AND INCOME OF OIL COMPANIES PER BARREL OF CRUDE OIL PRODUCTION; 1946-59
(Dollars Per Barrel)

Country and Period	Cost of Production	Royalty and Other Payments to Government	Income of Oil Companies	Estimated Average Posted or Realized Price of Crude Oil
Bahrein				
1946	0.10	0.15	0.93	1.18
1951	(0.10)	0.28	1.30	1.68
1957-59	(0.15)	0.80	0.80	1.75
Iran				
1956-58	0.24	0.78	0.78	1.80
Iraq (on Syrian border)				
1949	0.45	0.22	1.43	2.10
1953	0.24	0.75	1.01	2.00
1955-56	0.20	0.90	0.90	2.00
Kuwait				
1950-51	0.10	0.08	1.29	1.47
1957-59	0.10	0.75	0.75	1.60
Qatar				
1950	0.35	0.08	1.34	1.77
1957-59	0.28	0.87	0.87	2.02
Saudi Arabia[a]				
1946	0.19	0.22	0.77	1.18
1951	0.20	0.56	0.92	1.68
1956	0.31	0.78	0.78	1.87

Sources: Cost of production: Data on Bahrein and Saudi Arabia for 1946 are taken from United States Senate, Eightieth Congress, *Hearings Before A Special Committee Investigating the National Defense Program* (Washington, 1948); data on Iran are calculated on the basis of figures given in the annual reports of the National Iranian Oil Company; figure for 1956 on Saudi Arabia is computed from the annual accounts of Aramco for the same year published in United States Senate, Eighty-Fifth Congress, *Emergency Oil Lift Program and Related Oil Problems, Joint Hearings Before Subcommittees of the Committee on the Judiciary and Committee on Interior and Insular Affairs* (Washington, 1957), pp. 2838-9; other data have been calculated on the basis of figures given in Table 12 and Appendix Tables 1, 5, and 6. Royalties and other payments to governments: Figures have been calculated on the basis of data given in Appendix Tables 1 and 6; adjustments have been made to exclude income from refining in Iran and Saudi Arabia; the figure for Iraq refers to the operations of the Iraq Petroleum Company only. Income of oil companies: For earlier years, posted prices minus cost of operation and payments (royalty and other payments) to government; for recent years, income is taken as equal to government receipts. Estimated Average posted and realized prices: For earlier years, see Table 21; 2 per cent has been deducted for discounts, brokerage, and other expenses; for recent years, prices are the sum of the other three columns.

[a]Cost of production in Saudi Arabia declined to 23 cents in 1960.

Note: The above data are approximations and indicate only orders of magnitude.

and the early 1950's, has declined in recent years, while payments to local governments have shown a substantial increase.

G. Income from Refining

The income derived from refining depends to a large extent on the yield pattern, i.e., the product-mix, of refineries. The higher are the yields of lighter and higher priced refined products such as gasoline and kerosene, the larger is the income from refining. This yield pattern in the Middle Eastern refineries is not very favorable, although some of them, especially Abadan and Bahrein, have reduced the share of output of heavier products (see Table 6, p. 15). Despite this disadvantage, Middle Eastern refineries enjoy a favorable price structure that results in a substantial refining margin. This arises from the fact, as previously stated (see Chapter III, Section C) that the prices of refined products f.o.b. the Persian Gulf refineries are almost the same as those prevailing in the Gulf of Mexico (i.e., equal to Platt's "low" prices for similar products), while crude oil prices are substantially lower in the Persian Gulf. Hence the crude oil input of the Middle Eastern refineries is priced much lower than that of other major refining centers. As a result, the refining margin, i.e., the difference between the value of crude oil input and that of refined products output, in the Middle East is much higher than in Venezuela and Western Europe, and comparable to that of the United States. In order to arrive at the income from refining, it is necessary to deduct the cost of refining from these margins (see Chapter IV, Section I). Refining margins are shown in Table 36.

H. Income from Transportation by Pipelines

The income accruing to the oil companies from transportation of crude petroleum by pipelines from Iraq and Saudi Arabia to the eastern Mediterranean ports has also been substantial in the past, though it has declined in recent years. This decline has resulted from a decrease in the margin of crude oil prices—the difference between the prices at the Iraqi border or Ras Tanura on the one hand and the price at eastern Mediterranean ports on the other—which in turn has followed the declining trend of tanker rates. Table 37 indicates the financial results of the operation of the Trans-Arabian Pipeline Company. The pipeline, which started working in late 1950, was constructed at a cost of about \$230 million,[11] and during the period 1950–60 brought into Tapline an estimated income of \$366 million, although the per-barrel income de-

TABLE 36

GROSS REFINING MARGIN IN MIDDLE EAST AND OTHER COUNTRIES, SELECTED YEARS
(Dollars)

Country and Year	Value of Major Refined Products Produced from Each Barrel of Crude Oil Input						Per-Barrel Cost of Crude Oil Input	Gross Refinery Margin per Barrel of Crude Oil Input
	Gasoline	Kerosene	Distillate Fuel Oils	Residual Fuel Oils	Other Products	Total		
Aden[a]								
1955	0.70	0.33	0.42	1.14	...	2.59	1.91	0.68
1959	0.51	0.42	0.73	0.87	...	2.53	1.88	0.65
Bahrein								
1950	1.17	0.33	0.51	0.72	0.04	2.77	1.70	1.07
1955	0.99	0.41	0.69	0.71	0.04	2.84	1.91	0.93
1959	0.97	0.34	0.86	0.69	0.04	2.90	1.87	1.03
Iran								
1950	0.87	0.31	0.51	0.76	0.06	2.51	1.65	0.86
1955	0.80	0.65	0.47	0.86	0.06	2.84	1.86	0.98
1959	0.84	0.66	0.67	0.61	0.06	2.84	1.81	1.03
Kuwait								
1950	0.07	0.02	0.62	1.22	...	1.93	1.47	0.46
1955	0.17	0.05	0.61	1.46	...	2.29	1.68	0.61
1959	0.07	0.02	0.66	1.39	...	2.14	1.66	0.48
Saudi Arabia								
1950	0.92	0.26	0.80	0.60	0.02	2.60	1.68	0.92
1955	0.65	0.38	0.72	0.94	0.02	2.71	1.89	0.82
1959	0.51	0.49	0.63	0.90	0.02	2.55	1.86	0.69
TOTAL ABOVE COUNTRIES								
1950	0.91	0.30	0.55	0.74	0.04	2.54	1.67	0.87
1955	0.77	0.43	0.61	0.90	0.04	2.75	1.89	0.86
1959	0.66	0.45	0.70	0.82	0.04	2.67	1.81	0.86
United States								
July, 1955	2.44	0.26	0.83	0.26	0.16	3.95	2.87	1.08
July, 1959	2.46	0.26	0.84	0.25	0.16	3.97	3.09	0.88
Venezuela								
July, 1955	0.62	0.17	0.65	1.06	0.09	2.59	2.00	0.59
July, 1959	0.58	0.17	0.66	1.09	0.09	2.59	2.19	0.40
Italy								
July, 1955	0.89	0.22	0.84	1.17	0.23	3.35	2.65	0.70
July, 1959	0.77	0.22	0.84	1.08	0.23	3.14	2.58	0.56
N.W. Europe								
July, 1955	1.18	0.15	1.04	0.80	0.29	3.46	2.90	0.56
July, 1959	1.19	0.16	1.06	0.83	0.29	3.53	2.88	0.65

Sources: The data for the Middle Eastern countries have been calculated on the basis of output of refined oil products (Appendix Table 2), the prices of refined products (Table 22), and the prices of crude petroleum (Table 21). Prices have been reduced by 2 per cent in order to take into account brokerage and other charges. The figures for other countries have been obtained from Paul H. Frankel and Walter L. Newton, "Product-mix of Foreign Refineries and Profitability of International Oil Companies, *The Analysts Journal* (New York, November, 1959).

[a]No adjustments have been made for transport costs for either the cost of crude input or the price of refined products.

TABLE 37

ESTIMATED COST AND INCOME OF TRANS-ARABIAN PIPELINE COMPANY AND THROUGHPUT OF IRAQ PETROLEUM COMPANY PIPELINES, 1950-60

Period	Trans-Arabian Pipeline					IPC
	Throughput of Crude Oil (Thousands of Barrels) (1)	Crude Oil Price Differential Between Sidon and Ras Tanura (Cents per Barrel) (2)	Increase in Value of Crude Oil Transported by Tapline (Millions of Dollars) (3)	Estimated Total Cost of Crude Oil Transported by Tapline (Millions of Dollars) (4)	Net Income of Tapline (Millions of Dollars) (5)	Pipeline Throughput (Thousands of Barrels) (6)
1950	9,324	66	6.2	1.9	4.3	46,099
1951	107,830	66	71.3	21.6	49.7	58,397
1952	114,883	66	75.8	23.0	52.8	112,916
1953	112,542	56	63.0	22.5	40.5	179,505
1954	116,563	44	51.3	23.3	28.0	186,834
1955	117,989	44	51.9	24.4	27.5	187,106
1956	120,607	53	63.9	24.0	39.9	158,997
1957	127,645	64	81.7	25.5	56.2	83,313
1958	135,182	41	55.4	27.0	28.4	169,338
1959	124,139	39	48.4	24.8	23.6	201,571
1960	91,961	37	34.0	18.4	15.6	251,305
1950-60	1,178,665	51	602.9	236.4	366.5	1,635,381

Sources: For figures in Column (1), see Appendix Table 3. For figures in Column (2), see prices in Table 21. Column (3) is Column (1) multiplied by Column (2). Column (4) is calculated on the basis of Column (1) and an average cost of 20¢ per barrel of crude oil transported by the tapline from Saudi Arabia to the Mediterranean Coast. Figures for 1955 and 1956 are actual figures published in the accounts of the Arabian American Oil Company. See United States Senate, Eighty-Fifth Congress, *Emergency Oil Lift Program and Related Oil Problems, Joint Hearings Before Subcommittee of the Committee on the Judiciary and Committee on Interior and Insular Affairs* (Washington, 1957). Part 4, Appendix B, p. 2839. Column (5) is the difference between Columns (3) and (4). For figures in Column (6), see Appendix Table 3.

clined from over 45¢ a barrel of crude oil throughput in 1950 to under 20¢ in 1960. Similar results have been realized by the Iraqi pipelines, which carry a greater volume of crude oil from the northern oil fields of Iraq to the eastern Mediterranean than does the Trans-Arabian pipeline, but the price differential between the Iraqi border and the Mediterranean is smaller than that between Saudi Arabia and the Mediterranean.

I. Geographical Distribution of Net Income

The geographical distribution of net income in the petroleum industry of the Middle East, before the deduction of net investment, is given in Table 38. Out of a total net income of $16.3 billion accruing to the

TABLE 38

ESTIMATED NET INCOME OF PETROLEUM INDUSTRY COMPARED TO DIRECT PAYMENTS TO LOCAL GOVERNMENTS, BY COUNTRY, 1913-60
(Millions of Dollars)

Country	Estimated Net Income				Direct Payments, 1913-60
	1913-47	1948-53	1954-60	1913-60	
Aden	—	—	60	60	
Bahrein	129	245	254	628	110
Iran	1,567	816	1,451	3,834	1,884
Iraq	268	596	1,664	2,528	1,951
Kuwait	67	1,250	3,005	4,322	2,509[a]
Neutral Zone	—	-26	119	93	102
Qatar	—	91	340	431	345
Saudi Arabia	119	1,717	2,571	4,407	2,889[a]
TOTAL	2,150	4,689	9,464	16,303	9,790[b]

Sources: See Appendix Tables 4 and 6 for sources and method of estimation.
[a]Excluding its share in Neutral Zone.
[b]Excluding payments by petroleum companies to pipeline transit countries.

industry from the beginning of petroleum operations in the region until the end of 1960, Saudi Arabia contributed 27.0 per cent; Kuwait, 26.6 per cent; Iran, 23.5 per cent; Iraq, 15.5 per cent; Bahrein, 3.8 per cent; and the other areas, 3.6 per cent.

Iran, the oldest oil-producing country of the region, which contributed 74.2 per cent of the net income of the oil industry in the period 1913–47, suffered a setback after the nationalization of its oil industry and accounted for only 15.3 per cent of income during 1954–60, reaching 20.0 per cent in 1960. The gross income derived from the activities of the Anglo-Iranian Oil Company during the prenationalization period of 1913–51 is estimated to have reached 3.0 billion dollars, out of which the equivalent of $624 million accrued to the Iranian government and the remaining net income of $2.4 billion was transferred abroad.[12] For the period 1954–60, the net income of the consortium of oil companies operating in southern Iran is estimated to have amounted to about $1,450 million, including net income from refining and the bulk discount that is allowed in the agreement with the Iranian government. It is interesting to note that in Iran, as already mentioned, the government owns all petroleum installations utilized by the consortium of oil companies, while in other countries of the Middle East such assets are owned by the oil companies (see Chapter II, Section C). On the other hand, the terms of payment by the major oil companies to all the governments of the region are similar—they are all based on an equal profit-sharing formula—and there are no major differences in the terms prevailing in Iran and other countries. Hence, the Iranian government has allowed the use of its assets in the petroleum industry by these oil companies without provision for additional revenues as return on its capital investment; this fact makes the Iranian agreement with the consortium of oil companies one of the most attractive contracts to the oil industry in the Middle East, as far as terms of payment are concerned.[13]

The net income derived from Saudi Arabian petroleum operations is estimated to have exceeded $4.4 billion from the start of oil exports in 1936 until 1960. This estimate includes the net income of the Arabian American Oil Company and the net income accruing from the operations of the Trans-Arabian Pipeline Company and from refining and bulk discounts to the parent companies of Aramco. The net income of Aramco amounted to $3,232 million in the period under study (1936–60), of which $274 million represented declared income, before taxes to the United States goverment, prior to the application of the equal profit-sharing formula, i.e., in the period 1944–49;[14] and $2,593 million consisted of Aramco dividends to its parent companies in the period 1950–60.[15] There was also an earned surplus of $365 million at the end of 1956, which had been reinvested in Saudi Arabia.[16] The net income from the operations of Tapline, as already stated, amounted to about $366 million in the period 1950–60. Finally, the additional income of the parent companies from refining and from the bulk discount, as practiced until recently, has been estimated at nearly $810 million, since the beginning of operations in Saudi Arabia.

The net income of the Bahrain Petroleum Company, including income from both crude oil production and petroleum refining, has been estimated at $630 million in the period 1934–60. This figure does not include the income derived by the marketing of refined products by the California Texas Oil Company (Caltex). The Bahrain Petroleum Company was formed in 1929 and succeeded in discovering oil in its first drilling. By the end of 1946, the company had not paid any dividend to its parent companies, but had, according to its officials, surpluses amounting to $92.4 million.[17] In the following four years (1947–50), the income of the whole operation, including marketing, amounted to $240 million,[18] of which an estimated amount of $130 million was derived from petroleum mining and refining in Bahrein. No published data are available on the net income of the company for recent years; however, on the basis of value of output, cost of production, and payments to Bahrein, it has been estimated at $410 million for the period 1951–60.

The Iraq Petroleum Company and its associates have carried out their activities in Iraq, on behalf of their parent companies, as operating companies on a cost basis plus a fixed charge of 1*s.* per ton. Therefore, no profit and loss accounts of petroleum operations in Iraq have ever been published. However, on the basis of value of crude oil exports at the eastern Mediterranean ports, cost of production and transportation by pipelines, and payments to the Iraqi government and the transit countries, the net income of the group has been estimated at $2,530 million in the period 1934–60, of which $2,260 million was derived between 1948 and 1960.[19] Finally, Kuwait, the most important contributor to the income of the Middle Eastern petroleum industry in recent years, has accounted for an estimated amount of $4,330 million of net income in the period between 1946 and 1960.

VI. Government Receipts

A. Sources of Government Revenues

The revenues derived by the governments of oil-producing countries from the petroleum industry spring from different sources and vary from region to region, depending not only on the magnitude of the industry and its profitability but also on the legal and institutional framework within which production takes place (see Chapter I, Section I). The first two elements have already been discussed in Chapters I and V; as regards the latter, three different factors may be distinguished: ownership of resources, ownership of operating companies, and the tax system. Ownership of the subsoil resources may be vested in private individuals or in the state; in either case the owner receives payments in the form of bonuses, rents, and royalties. Similarly the operating company may be privately or state owned, or it may be a mixed enterprise; income here consists of profits, which may be either positive or negative. The tax system determines what exploration, exploitation, income, corporation, or other taxes are payable to the central and local government authorities by oil enterprises. In addition, various excise and sales taxes are usually levied on retail sales of oil products in both producing and consuming countries, but these taxes fall in a different category from the ones mentioned earlier since they are paid by consumers and not by producers of oil; they will therefore not be covered in the following discussion.

In the Soviet bloc, oil and other natural resources are owned by the state and the oil industry, like other industries, is owned and directly operated by the government, its profits and losses forming part of the general budget; the same applies to the oil industry of Mexico. In the United States, where ownership of land confers property rights over minerals lying below the surface, contracts are made between oil prospectors and individual owners of land. Usually the landowner is paid a bonus, ranging from one to several hundred dollars per acre, and in addition receives a rental for some five to ten years or until oil is discovered. Upon discovery of oil or gas, mineral rights become the property of the prospector, who ceases paying rental and instead pays the landowner a royalty, which may range from 5 to 50 per cent of the oil produced; it is usually one-eighth, since "experience shows that a one-eighth royalty takes about half of the profits in an average case."[1] Similarly, subsequent stages of operation, such as pipeline or other transport, refining, and marketing, are carried out by contracts between private individuals or corporations. Incomes generated at each stage, like other incomes, are subject to taxation on the part of municipal, state, and federal authorities, including the 52 per cent tax on corporation incomes, but a depletion allowance of 27½ per cent on gross receipts (not to exceed 50 per cent of net income) is allowed to producers of crude.

In Venezuela, ownership of the subsoil is vested in the state, and agreements to explore or exploit a given area must be concluded with the Ministry of Mines and Hydrocarbons. The conditions under which concessions have been granted have greatly changed since 1866, when the first lease was made, or 1904, when the first Mining Law was passed.[2] At present, the industry is subject to a variety of taxes, which took shape in the Law of Hydrocarbons of March 13, 1943, and the Income Tax Laws of 1943 and 1958.[3] Under the first, four taxes are levied: an Exploration Tax of 2 bolivares per hectare per year;[4] an Initial Exploration Tax of 8 or more bolivares per hectare, levied when a new concession is granted (in recent years large bonuses have been received from new concessionaires under this heading); a Surface Tax, rising progressively from 5 to 30 bolivares per hectare; and a royalty of 16⅔ per cent on the crude oil produced, payable in cash or kind. Moreover, under the Income Tax Laws, the oil industry pays three taxes on its earnings: a flat Basic Schedular Tax of 2½ per cent on net income; a Progressive Supplementary Tax ranging from 2 to 45 per cent of net income; and an Additional Tax, introduced in 1948 to ensure that the government shall receive at least 50 per cent of the net income of the oil industry and applicable where oil company income, after the above-mentioned taxes, is greater than the amount collected by the government. In 1958 a new income tax schedule raised the government's share to at least 65 per cent.

As a result of these changes, government receipts per barrel of oil produced rose from 18¢ in 1934–38 to 85¢ in 1948 and stood at 99¢ in 1960 (see Table 34, p. 114).

B. Middle East

In the Middle East, too, ownership of the subsoil is vested in the state, and concession agreements are negotiated with the government. Only one of the countries covered in this study, Iran, has enacted petroleum legislation—the Law of 1957—and all the major concession agreements in the region were negotiated in direct bargaining between companies and governments.[5] The main features of these agreements have been described in Chapter I, Section I. As regards their financial aspects, the following points should be noted. First, until 1950, the companies secured exemption from customs duties, income taxes, and other national or local taxes or dues; sometimes this was obtained in return for a small supplementary payment.[6]

Second, until 1948, the bonuses paid were relatively small, because the companies were exploring a region whose oil potentialities were largely unknown and were therefore reluctant to assume large financial burdens; also, there was little competition among companies of which the governments could take advantage. The D'Arcy concession of 1901 stipulated that the Iranian government was to receive £20,000 in cash and £20,000 in shares (Article 10). In Saudi Arabia, under the Standard Oil of California's Supplemental Agreement of 1939 (Article 4), bonuses totaling £140,000 were to be paid, £40,000 immediately and £100,000 upon discovery of oil in the "additional area" (Article 4).[7] In Bahrein, Article 6 of the Exploration Agreement of 1925 provided for a bonus of 20,000 rupees and Article 3 of the accompanying Concession Agreement for a further bonus of 10,000 rupees, or £2,250 in all. In Kuwait, Article 3 of the 1934 agreement provided for a bonus of 475,000 rupees, or £38,100; in Qatar, Article 4 of the 1935 agreement provided for a bonus of 400,000 rupees, or £30,000. Since 1948 there has been a large increase in bonuses paid to the governments (see Chapter VIII, Section B).

Third, there were small payments of annual dead rent that amounted to 10,000 rupees (£750), until production began, in the Bahrein Concession (Article 3); £5,000 gold in that of Saudi Arabia of 1933 (Article 5); 95,000 rupees in Kuwait in the 1934 agreement; and 150,000 rupees for five years rising thereafter to 300,000 in Qatar in the 1935 agreement. In Iraq, the Iraq Petroleum Company agreement of 1931 provided for payment of £400,000 gold per annum, of which half would be recovered from future royalties; the 1932 agreement with the British

Oil Development Company provided for a rental of £100,000 rising to £200,000 (guaranteed in gold); and the 1938 agreement with the Basrah Petroleum Company provided for an annual rental of £200,000 gold. The Supplemental Agreement of 1939 with Saudi Arabia (Article 4) provided for additional payment of an annual rental of £20,000 gold until oil was discovered in the "additional area" in commercial quantities or until the company relinquished the area.

Fourth, except for the D'Arcy concession in Iran, which stipulated a 16 per cent share in profits, all other agreements provided for payment of royalties to the governments, as the latter's main source of income from oil operations. This payment was made in the form of a flat royalty of 4*s*. gold or 3 rupees per long ton of oil produced and sold; the Iraqi agreement with the British Oil Development and the Basrah Petroleum Company, in addition, provided for a 20 per cent royalty in kind, salable to the producing company. After 1950, when profit-sharing agreements were concluded, royalty payments continued to exist in Saudi Arabia (Article 14 of the 1933 agreement and Article 14 of the 1957 agreement with the Japanese company), Qatar (Article 2 of the Supplementary Agreement of 1955), and Kuwait (Article 6 of the 1958 agreement with the Japanese company), supplemented by an income tax. In the Iraqi agreement of 1952 (Article 3) and the Iranian agreement of 1954 (Article 23), the government has the option of taking up to 12.5 per cent of the oil in kind, as a royalty, or its cash value; the same applies to Kuwait's 1951 agreement with the Kuwait Oil Company and its 1961 agreement with Shell (Article 9). In the agreements with the Japanese company, both the Saudi and Kuwait governments have the option of taking up to 20 per cent of the oil in kind (Articles 14 and 6, respectively).

Last, it may be pointed out that under the 1954 agreement, Iran receives a small payment for the natural gas utilized or sold by the Operating Companies (Article 11) and another for the products refined in the Abadan Refinery (Article 25).

The following part of this chapter will discuss in greater detail the major changes in financial obligations of petroleum companies to the producing countries, for carrying out the development, production, and marketing of crude petroleum. It will also present briefly the terms of payment with respect to refining of crude oil in the refineries of the region, as well as the financial arrangements concerning the transit of oil through pipelines with the transit countries, Jordan, Lebanon, and Syria.

C. Crude Oil Production[8]

The development of concession agreements in the producing countries may be divided into four stages: the earliest concessions granted, before or after the First World War, by Iran, the Ottoman Empire, and Saudi Arabia; the arrangements made in the 1920's or early 1930's; the postwar conflicts and negotiations which culminated in the 50–50 profit-sharing agreements of the early 1950's; and the new patterns which were ushered in by the Iranian-Italian and Saudi-Japanese concession agreements in 1957 (see Chapter I, Section I and Chapter VIII, Section B). Each of these stages marks an increase in the share of revenues accruing to the government, compared to the previous stage.

The effect of all these changes on rates of payment to governments is brought out clearly in Table 34, p. 114, and Table 35, p. 117, which cover the Persian Gulf countries and Venezuela. It will be seen that government receipts per barrel are still higher in Venezuela than in the Middle East, although in the latter they rose from an average of 21¢ before 1948 to 41¢ in 1951 and 74¢ in 1960. Table 32, p. 119, shows that the combined share of the Middle Eastern governments went up from 20 per cent of gross revenue in 1948 to 38 per cent in 1953 and 46 per cent in 1960. The huge absolute increase in revenues is shown in Table 39, which records a ninefold increase between 1948 and 1960.

Early Concessions. The first petroleum concession granted in the region, the Iranian agreement with Baron de Reuter of 1889, which was canceled ten years later, in many ways set the pattern for future concessions; under it, the Iranian government was to receive 16 per cent of net profits.[9] Under Article 10 of the D'Arcy concession of May 2, 1901, the share of the Iranian government was also fixed at 16 per cent of annual net profits. This arrangement might have eventually secured substantial revenues for the Iranian government, but for many years it did not, because of certain difficulties caused by the First World War, then by the question of the discount granted on oil sold to the British Navy, by conflicting interpretations as to whether or not the Iranian government was entitled to share in the profits of companies formed by the Anglo-Persian Oil Company but operating outside Iran, and by the shrinkage of profits after 1930. In 1926–29, payments averaged 12¢ per barrel. The concession was denounced by the government on November 27, 1932, and replaced by the agreement of April 29, 1933.[10]

In the Ottoman Empire, the negotiations between the Turkish Petroleum Company and the Ottoman government, which culminated in a

TABLE 39

DIRECT PAYMENTS OF THE PETROLEUM COMPANIES TO THE GOVERNMENTS OF THE MIDDLE EAST AND VENEZUELA, 1913-60
(Millions of Dollars)

Period	Bahrein	Iran	Iraq[a]	Kuwait[b]	Qatar	Saudi Arabia[b]	Payments to Crude Oil Producing Countries of Middle East	Payments to Pipeline Transit Countries of Middle East	Total Direct Payments to Governments of Middle East	Venezuela[c]
1913-47	14	326	115	1	1	43	500	(10)	510	946
1948	2	75	9	14	—	53	153	1	154	417
1949	2	82	11	11	--	50	156	1	157	342
1950	2	91	19	12	1	113	238	1	239	331
1951	3	50	42	18	4	165	282	2	284	469
1952	4	—	114	57	10	212	397	3	400	500
1953	5	—	163	169	18	226	581	5	586	486
1954	11	9	191	194	29	281	715	4	719	510
1955	9	91	206	282	34	275	897	6	903	596
1956	10	153	193	293	36	283	968	18	986	738
1957	10	213	144	308	45	303	1,023	12	1,035	954
1958	12	247	236	354	60	302	1,211	18	1,229	964
1959	13	262	242	414	53	306	1,293	32	1,322	972
1960	13	285	266	415	54	346	1,379	41	1,420	1,030
1948-60	96	1,558	1,836	2,541	344	2,915	9,290	144	9,434	8,307
1913-60	110	1,884	1,951	2,542	345	2,958	9,790	154	9,944	9,253

Sources: See Appendix Table 6 for sources and footnotes.
[a]Excluding payments by the Khanaqin Oil Company, Limited.
[b]Including its share in the Neutral Zone.
[c]Does not include bonuses.
Note: Figures do not add up because of rounding.

letter from the Grand Vizier of June 28, 1914, consenting to a concession, had not, at the outbreak of war, reached the point of specifying the conditions of the contract,[11] while the concession granted Admiral Chester on March 9, 1910, was never ratified by the Ottoman Parliament.

In Saudi Arabia, which at that time was bound by the Treaty of December 26, 1915, between Great Britain and Najd not to grant a petroleum concession without the approval of Britain, the first concession was given to Eastern General Syndicate, in August, 1923, "on terms which, in the light of recent oil developments in Arabia, can only be regarded as ludicrous"; these terms consisted of an advance of £2,000 a year "with a lien on concession to be negotiated in the event of the discovery of oil."[12] Owing to the nonpayment of rental, the concession was canceled in 1928.

Interwar Concessions. The pattern for this group was set by the concession granted by the Iraqi government to the Turkish Petroleum Company (later renamed the Iraq Petroleum Company) in 1925. Article 10 stipulated that, during the twenty years following the completion of a pipeline to transport Iraqi oil to a port for export, 4*s.* (gold) royalty would be paid per ton of crude "saved in field storage tanks or reservoirs";[13] after that period, the government's share would be raised or lowered in the same proportion as the profits made by the company during the previous five years had increased or decreased. In addition there were the small payments in lieu of tax, mentioned earlier. The royalty terms of the concessions of the British Oil Development Company of 1932 and the Basrah Petroleum Company of 1938 were almost identical with those of the Iraq Petroleum Company. In addition, they provided for payment of a dead rent of £200,000 (gold) per annum until production started and gave the government the right to take up to 20 per cent of the crude oil production free of charge; no royalty was to be paid on this oil, and the government could either use it for local consumption or sell it to the producing companies at world prices. The rate of royalty payment was equal in 1925 to 13¢ a barrel. When sterling was devalued in 1931, payment was made on the basis of the official London rate for gold, which, after the devaluation of the dollar in 1934, worked out at about 22¢ a barrel.

Similarly, when the Iranian government and the Anglo-Persian Oil Company signed a new agreement in 1933, Article 10 provided for an annual royalty of 4*s.* (gold) a ton on oil sold in Iran or exported, plus

20 per cent "of the distribution [of dividends and reserves] to the ordinary stockholders of the Anglo Persian Oil Company" above £671,000. In addition, small payments were to be made in lieu of tax, as mentioned above. Naturally, the rate of payment depended partly on the amount of profits distributed, and it was adversely affected by the rise in the rate of British taxation and by the policy of dividend limitation imposed during and after the war by the British government on all British companies, as well as by the company's policy of investing a substantial proportion of earnings in its world-wide activities.[14] In the late 1930's and in the early postwar years, the royalty was equivalent to about 20–22¢ per barrel.

The concession agreement between the Saudi Arabian government and the Standard Oil Company of California in 1933 provided for a royalty of 4*s.* (gold) per ton of crude produced (Article 11); this was not affected by the Supplemental Agreement of 1939. Here, too, as in Iraq, a controversy arose regarding the rate of conversion. Until 1948, the official rate for the sovereign was used, giving a royalty equivalent to $1.65 per ton or 22¢ per barrel, but in that year the free market rate was adopted, raising the payment to $2.50 per ton or about 32¢ a barrel; at the same time Aramco paid $20.3 million in settlement of this controversy. However, under the 1950 profit-sharing agreement, payment of royalty at the rate of 4*s.* was retained, and the parties agreed to adopt the International Monetary Fund gold rate, giving a royalty rate of 22¢ a barrel.

The terms of payment in the concession agreements granted by the three sheikdoms, Bahrein, Kuwait, and Qatar, did not differ substantially from those of Iraq and Saudi Arabia except in one respect: royalty payments were fixed in terms of rupees, not gold shillings.[15] In Bahrein, the 1925 agreement provided for a royalty payment of 3½ rupees per ton of crude oil (Article 8); this was equal to 17¢ a barrel in 1930, 12¢ after the devaluation of the rupee in 1931, 18¢ after the devaluation of the dollar in 1934, 14¢ after the devaluation of the rupee in 1939, and 10¢ after the last devaluation of the rupee, in 1949.

The course of events was similar in Kuwait. In the 1934 agreement, royalty payment was fixed at 3 rupees per ton of crude oil plus a quarter of a rupee in lieu of taxes; this was equivalent to 16¢ a barrel in 1934, 13¢ after the devaluation of the rupee in 1939, and 9¢ after the devaluation of the rupee in 1949. Similarly, in Qatar, the agreement of 1935 with the Anglo-Iranian Oil Company stipulated a royalty payment of 3 rupees per ton of crude oil.

Postwar Conflicts and Profit Sharing. During and immediately after the Second World War, new factors arose that led the three sovereign governments in the region to express dissatisfaction with existing agreements and to press for higher payments. In addition to various local grievances, such as the matter of evaluation of the price of gold discussed above, and to the general nationalist ferment which affected most parts of the region, two common problems stood out: the limitation of production and the rise in prices. During the war, production was reduced in all Persian Gulf countries. After 1945 there was a rapid expansion in Iran and Saudi Arabia. In Iraq, however, where pipelines constitute a bottleneck, the construction of new pipelines was started in 1946, but owing to political and material difficulties it was not until 1949 that the volume of oil flowing to the Mediterranean increased; in southern Iraq, where pipelines are not such an important factor due to the short distance between the fields and the Persian Gulf, oil was discovered only in 1949 and consequently production did not start until 1951. Moreover, the pipelines built in the early postwar years had small diameters, and the one to Haifa remained incomplete because of the Arab-Israeli War; the flow of oil through the previously existing pipeline to Haifa stopped in April, 1948.

As for the rise in prices, two aspects may be distinguished. First, there was the sharp inflation experienced by the Middle East during the war. In Iraq, the cost of living index rose from 100 in 1939 to 558 in 1948, and in Iran, where the rial was devalued by 50 per cent in 1941, to 639; import prices also increased considerably. This rise in prices, naturally, greatly reduced the real value of payments to the governments. Second, there was the rise in the price of petroleum, which had more than doubled between 1939 and 1948. Since payments to the governments continued to be made on a fixed royalty basis, this reduced the share of the governments in the value of the oil produced. Thus, in a memorandum presented by the Iranian government to the company in August, 1948, the following statement is made: "Royalty basis: the figure of four shillings a ton represented one-eighth of the price of Persian crude oil, whereas now, on the basis of gold, it is according to the company's accounts less than one-sixteenth. Thus the total of the Persian government's royalties in relation to the total price of the oil extracted represented 33 per cent in 1933 and only about 9 per cent in 1947."[16]

In the immediate postwar years, discontent had taken the form of disagreement with the companies on the interpretation of various clauses regarding payments, but three events occurred that sparked the demand for more radical changes. First, there was the introduction in

Venezuela of the Law of Hydrocarbons of 1943 and of the Additional Tax of 1948, which resulted in the increase of the government's share to at least 50 per cent of the net income of the oil companies and introduced a new and, to producing countries, far more attractive pattern in the oil industry. Second, there was the tentative agreement, in April, 1946, between the Soviet Union and the Iranian government for a Soviet-Iranian oil company in the northern provinces of Iran; this was part of the Irano-Soviet negotiations that resulted in the evacuation of Soviet troops from northern Iran.[17] Under this project, Iran would supply the oil resources and receive 49 per cent of the shares, and the Soviet Union would supply the capital and technical skills, receiving 51 per cent; after 25 years the shares would be changed to 50–50 for another 25 years; profits would be divided proportionately to shares. Although the agreement was vague regarding marketing and pricing, it had a certain attractiveness, especially when compared to other existing concessions. Nevertheless, in 1947, the Iranian Majlis (Parliament) almost unanimously rejected the Soviet offer, mainly on political grounds. At the same time it charged the government "in all cases where the rights of the Iranian people in respect to the sources of natural wealth, whether underground or otherwise, have been dissipated, especially with respect to Southern petroleum, to undertake negotiations and necessary steps in order to restore Iranian national rights and to inform the Majlis of the results."[18] This led to negotiations with the Anglo-Iranian Oil Company, at whom it had been leveled.

The third factor that encouraged the governments to ask for better terms was the concession agreements for the Saudi-Kuwaiti Neutral Zone concluded in 1948 and 1949. The agreement between Kuwait and the American Independent Oil Company of June 6, 1948 (Article 3), provided for a bonus of $7.5 million in cash, a royalty of $2.50 a ton or about 34¢ a barrel, and a 15 per cent "carried interest" or share of the net profits; the one of February 20, 1949, between Saudi Arabia and Pacific Western Oil Corporation (Articles 5–7) provided for a bonus of $9.5 million, a royalty of 55¢ a barrel, and a 25 per cent "carried interest" or share in the company's net profits.

The response of the companies to the demands of the various governments was not uniform. Iran was offered the Supplemental Agreement of July 17, 1949, which raised the royalty rate from 4*s*. to 6*s*. (gold) and provided for immediate payment of Iran's share in profits. This agreement was signed by the Iranian government although it had been pressing for a 50–50 profit-sharing agreement but, after long debate, the Majlis refused to ratify it. A further offer, made by the company in February, 1951, and embodying an arrangement for equal sharing of profits, came too late to prevent the passing of a law in March that nationalized the oil industry, and the crisis that followed.

In the meantime, the other companies had also offered better terms to the respective governments. As mentioned before, in Saudi Arabia the conversion rate of the sovereign was raised in 1948. In Iraq, the royalty rate was increased from 4*s.* to 6*s.* (gold) a ton, or about 33¢ a barrel, in August, 1950, and a payment of £5 million was made in settlement of Iraqi claims. In Bahrein, the royalty rate was raised in 1950 to 10 rupees a ton, or about 29¢ a barrel, and in 1951 payments were further increased. The royalty rate was similarly raised to 10 rupees in Qatar in May, 1951.[19] But the pattern for this period was set by the agreement between Saudi Arabia and Aramco of December 30, 1950, which followed the promulgation of income tax decrees on November 4, 1950, and December 27, 1950, providing, among other things, for the taxation of business profits.[20] The agreement accepted the principle of equal sharing of profits by stipulating, in Article 1:

> In no case shall the total of such taxes [i.e., Arabian income taxes] and all other taxes, royalties, rentals and exactions of the government for any year exceed fifty per cent (50%) of the gross income of Aramco, after such gross income has been reduced by Aramco's cost of operation, including losses and depreciation, and by income taxes, if any, payable to any foreign country but not reduced by any taxes, royalties, rentals or other exactions of the government for such year.

An important modification was introduced the following year, on October 2, 1951, when it was stipulated that the Saudi Arabian government's 50 per cent share was to be calculated *before* the deduction of foreign (i.e., United States) income taxes.[21] Similar profit-sharing agreements were adopted in Kuwait on December 3, 1951, in Iraq on February 3, 1952, in Qatar on September 1, 1952, in Bahrein in September 1952, and in Iran, after the settlement of the nationalization dispute, on September 19, 1954.[22] Several of these agreements stipulated that payments would not be below a specified sum, while a few established minimum production levels.

A major feature of these agreements was the acceptance, by both the governments and the oil companies, of posted prices of crude petroleum in the Middle East as the basis for calculation of the value of crude oil produced and marketed, or delivered, to refineries by oil companies. This could obviously differ from actual receipts. For example, if discounts were given to bulk buyers of oil beyond the rates agreed upon in oil concessions, the actual receipts of the oil companies would be lower; or conversely, if tankers could be chartered at very low rates and oil exported to a distant market with its own posted price (such as the United States), then the realized receipts of the oil companies would be higher because of the savings made from low tanker rates. The reduction in posted prices in the Middle East and Venezuela in 1959 and 1960 as a result of a weakened oil market and increased competition from independent oil companies and the Soviet Oil Trust, but without any accompanying decline in prices in the Gulf of Mexico, brought about strong criticisms from the governments of Venezuela and the Middle East, and led to the setting up of the Organization of Petroleum Exporting Countries (see Chapter VIII, Section A) to resist price decreases by oil companies without prior agreement with the governments.

A related point affecting all the above agreements was the question of volume discounts from posted prices allowed by the operating companies to their parent companies, which amounted to some 15 to 20 per cent of posted prices. The Iranian government, in the 1954 agreement, allowed only a 2.3 per cent discount for marketing expenses and brokerage fees on the 87.5 per cent of production accruing to the companies—averaging a discount of 2 per cent on total exports.[23] The question of discounts had not been dealt with in the agreements previously concluded by the other countries, but had subsequently been raised by them. The other governments now asked for terms similar to those obtained by Iran, and secured them in the succeeding years. They also obtained settlement for their back claims on this issue; thus Saudi Arabia received $145 million for the years 1952–55 and Iraq $41 million for the years 1951–58. Further small discounts were allowed on bulk purchases, but they have since been reduced or abolished.

In order to determine the share of governments from oil income under the equal profit-sharing agreements, it is necessary to deduct from the value of crude oil exported or delivered to local refineries the cost of crude oil production. Some of the agreements, like those with Saudi Arabia and Iran, provide for deduction of actual cost of production, while some others, like those with Iraq and Qatar, specify an agreed sum as the cost of crude output, subject to adjustment in case the actual cost differs from the agreed cost by a certain specified percentage. The governments have been given the right to check the accounts of the oil companies and verify costs. As to the coverage of costs, they usually include, in addition to the fixed and variable costs attributable to production of oil, certain exploration and drilling outlays. The difference between the value of crude oil and its cost of production, which is defined as the income of oil operations, is shared equally by oil companies and governments. Actually, irrespective of the amount of such income, the governments receive royalties, rentals, and other fixed taxes, but in determining their 50 per cent share from income, such payments are taken into account and the balance is paid in lieu of income tax.

New Patterns. The oil agreements concluded in the Middle East since 1957 have introduced a new pattern, much more favorable to the governments than the profit-sharing formulas of the early 1950's. These agreements may be expected to have repercussions on the entire oil industry of the region and to stimulate new adjustments in existing arrangements (see Chapter I, Section I and Chapter VIII, Section B).

D. Refining

The foregoing equal profit-sharing arrangements apply only to the production of crude petroleum. Until the early 1950's, the oil agreements included no provision for payments to governments from the income of refining operations, with the exception of the Anglo-Iranian Oil Company's agreement with Iran, which had provided a share for the government from all income of the company. The recent oil agreements include provisions for refining fees that are specified and shared equally between governments and companies. Article 25 of the 1954 agreement between Iran and the consortium provides for a refining fee equal to 5 per cent of the value of crude oil input into refineries; this percentage was raised to 10 per cent in 1959 and 12 per cent in 1960, then reduced to 10 per cent in 1961, i.e., it increased from the equivalent of about 9¢ a barrel in 1955 to 22¢ in 1960 and declined to 18¢ in 1961. The corresponding figure in 1959 for Aden was 6¢ a barrel, and for Kuwait, 8¢.

In Saudi Arabia, the 1948 agreement between Aramco and its parent companies had provided for a fixed fee of $2 million for the operations of Ras Tanura refinery. Upon the introduction of the profit-sharing agreement, the Saudi government became entitled to one-half of this fee as its share in profits. In June, 1956, Aramco agreed to submit to the application of equal profit-sharing on the operation of the refinery; value of oil products was to be calculated on the basis of the "low" of Platt's U.S. Gulf prices, on prices quoted at Ras Tanura, or on actual receipts of the company from clients other than parent companies. In Bahrein, the profit-sharing agreement did not cover refining operations, but later Bahrein imposed a duty of 5.25¢ a barrel on imports of crude oil for local refining. Bahrein imports about three-quarters of its crude oil input. The agreement with Saudi Arabia, which was made retroactive to 1953, led the Iranian government to demand from the Oil Consortium the application of similar terms to the operation of the Abadan refinery and to enter claims for about $30 million with respect to the 1956–58 operations. An agreement was reached early in 1962 settling the dispute for an amount of $10 million.

In addition, all the agreements concluded with the oil companies concerning oil operations in the Neutral Zone provide for payment to the governments of Kuwait and Saudi Arabia of a share in profits which cover, *inter alia*, refining activities.

E. Transit

The first major Middle Eastern pipeline, from Kirkuk to the Mediterranean, with one terminal in Tripoli and another at Haifa, necessitated agreements "in almost identical terms" between the Iraq Petroleum Company and the four transit countries of Lebanon, Palestine, Syria, and Transjordan. The joint agreement with Lebanon and Syria of March 25, 1931, which was for a duration of 70 years, exempted the company from all taxes, fees, and customs duties; however, the company was to pay dues of 2*d*. per ton for sea-line loading in Tripoli and 5*d*. for oil dock loading in Haifa.

In 1947, the company volunteered to pay £45,000 a year to each of Lebanon and Palestine, £60,000 to Jordan, and £75,000 to Syria; in 1950 the payment to Syria was raised to £108,000 in order to compensate for the devaluation of sterling, and in 1951 that to Lebanon was raised to £65,000. In 1952 the loading fee in Lebanon was raised to 2.88*d*.[24]

In the meantime, negotiations were being carried on with the transit countries by the Trans-Arabian Pipeline Company. On August 8, 1946, Tapline signed its first agreement with Transjordan, under which the government was to receive an annual payment of about $250,000,[25] and in August, 1947, with Lebanon, under which the government was to receive a transit fee of 30*s*. per thousand tons of oil and a loading fee of 2*d*. per ton, raised in 1952 to 2.88*d*., for a total of about £Leb. 1.5 million (nearly $500,000).[26] Preliminary agreement with Syria was reached in September, 1947, but unsettled political conditions in that country delayed ratification until May 16, 1949.[27] As a result, Syria obtained slightly better terms, namely, £40,000 a year for security, a transit fee of 30*s*. per thousand tons, and the sale of 200,000 tons of crude oil a year to the government at world prices; total annual payments were about $500,000. The duration of the concession in all three agreements was fixed at 70 years, and in all three the company secured exemption from taxes, fees, or customs duties.

The signing of profit-sharing agreements with the oil-producing countries led to the demand by the Lebanese and Syrian governments for the acceptance of a similar principle by the pipeline companies. Negotiations were therefore started in 1951 with Tapline and the Iraq Petroleum Company, both of which agreed to raise their payments to the governments. Thus Tapline offered Jordan $600,000 a year, plus 100,000 tons of crude at Mediterranean posted prices; Syria about $1.2 million, plus increased quantities of crude; and Lebanon about $1.4 million. The Iraq Petroleum Company also offered to increase its payments in Lebanon, for example, to £450,000 per annum.[28] However, following the change in regime in 1952, the Lebanese Parliament refused to ratify the agreements and demanded that the government continue negotiations, and the Syrian government likewise decided against ratification. Negotiations were therefore resumed, and in the meantime Iraq Petroleum Company continued to make its payments at the 1950 rates and Tapline at the higher rates proposed in 1952. In July, 1955, by an exchange of letters, a provisional agreement was reached between Iraq Petroleum Company and Lebanon, raising the latter's annual receipts from about £Leb. 1 million (about $300,000) to £Leb. 4 million and giving it a lump sum of £Leb. 6.5 million in settlement of back payments at the rates suggested in 1952. An agreement between Iraq Petroleum Company and Syria was also reached in November, 1955; it provided for payment of 1*s.* 4*d.* per 100 ton-miles for the distance traveled by petroleum in Syrian territory plus 13*d.* per ton in respect of terminal dues, 3*d.* per ton in respect of loading dues, and £750,000 in respect of protection services. This was expected to raise Syria's annual receipts to $18 million, compared to the $4.4 million it had been receiving until then, while settlement of claims for the previous years brought in an additional lump sum of £8.5 million.[29]

However, agreement could not be reached between Iraq Petroleum Company and Lebanon regarding the projected pipeline, which was to have its terminal at Tripoli, since the length of the pipeline in Lebanese territory was only 30 kilometers, as against 420 in Syrian, and since the company was proposing the same basis of payments as in Syria, whereas the government was insisting on a 50–50 split of profits on pipeline operations. On June 29, 1956, the Lebanese Parliament passed a law subjecting to income tax the profits of the oil companies.[30] The Iraq

Petroleum Company claimed that this law violated its concession agreement, and further negotiations were interrupted by the Suez crisis. By June 4, 1959, a new agreement had been reached that provided for the following payments: £200,000 a year for security payments; £207,500 a year in lieu of supply of crude oil; £250,000 a year for maintenance and repair of roads; 1*s*. 4*d*. per ton of oil passing through Lebanon and loaded onto ships; 6*d*. per ton of oil passing through Lebanon and supplied to the Tripoli refinery; and 3*d*. per ton of oil loaded onto ships in commutation of port dues.[31] Under this agreement, Lebanon's receipts were estimated to rise to about £1,235,000 with £5,818,000 in back payments.

As for Tapline, it had in 1956 announced that it accepted the principle of equal sharing of profits made on pipeline operations (see Table 37, p. 120) with the four transit countries, Saudi Arabia, Jordan, Syria, and Lebanon, leaving the apportionment of shares to be determined by them. The governments failed to reach agreement on the basis of division. Countries with small pipeline mileage, such as Lebanon, favored equal sharing—contending that payment is made for the right of transit, which any country could deny—while those with larger mileage preferred division according to the distance traveled by the oil in their respective territories; moreover, doubts were expressed by the three other countries as to whether Saudi Arabia should share in transit profits, since it already received half the profits made on the production of oil. In December, 1961, a supplemental agreement was signed between Syria and Tapline, providing for a transit fee of 1.423¢ per barrel for each hundred miles the oil is transported in Syria and for a $10 million cash settlement to cover all past claims. A similar agreement was signed with Jordan in February, 1962, with the main exception being that it raised the transit fee to 1.80¢ per barrel for each hundred miles. In view of a most-favored-agreement clause in both these agreements, this increase was automatically applicable to Syria too. Under the agreements, Syria's annual receipts are expected to be about $3.5 million and those of Jordan $4 million for an average throughput of 400,000 barrels per day. That with Lebanon in 1962 provides for similar transit fees of 2¢ per barrel, amounting to some $5 million a year.

The general effect of these changes may be judged from the fact that payments by the pipeline companies to the governments rose, between 1950 and 1961, from $0.3 million to $4.0 million in Jordan, from $0.1 million to $4.1 million in Lebanon, and from $0.4 million to $25.6 million in Syria. At the same time Egypt's receipts from Suez Canal tolls, largely derived from tankers, were rising rapidly; payments by the Canal Company to the government increased from $9.5 million in 1950 to $17.6 million in 1955. After the nationalization of the Canal Company, in 1956, all tolls were collected by the government, and receipts from tanker traffic alone were estimated to have risen to $102 million by 1961; however, since nationalization, the government has to meet from these earnings, in addition to local costs, certain foreign exchange expenditures for the operation and development of the Canal.[32]

As regards the Middle Eastern oil industry as a whole, including both producing and transit countries, the general effect of the changes discussed in this chapter may be summarized as follows. While in 1948 the Middle Eastern governments received 20 per cent of the gross income of the oil industry (of which only 1 per cent was in the form of taxes), by 1958 the figure was 43 per cent (of which 33 points were in taxes), and by 1960 the total rose to 46 per cent. In Venezuela, the corresponding figure in 1948 was 55 per cent (of which 26 points were in taxes), and in 1958, 65 per cent (of which 35 points were in taxes). The total had risen to 69 per cent in 1960. In the United States, government taxes absorbed 27 per cent of the gross income of the industry in 1948 and 29 per cent in 1958; in addition, further payments equal to 27 per cent in 1948 and 29 per cent in 1958 were made to landowners in the form of royalties, rents, and bonuses.

VII. Contribution to Local Economy

The development of the oil industry is, in many ways, the most important event that has occurred during the last fifty years in the countries bordering on the Persian Gulf, and its impact on the region has been tremendous. An account of its influence on the social, cultural, and political life of these countries would be a huge undertaking, and even an analysis of its ramifications in the economic field is beyond the scope of this book. Since, however, this study would be both incomplete and misleading without at least a short discussion of the effect of the oil industry on the economy of the Middle Eastern countries, an attempt is made in this chapter to indicate the extent of this impact by relating the contribution of the oil industry to gross national product, foreign exchange receipts, government budgets, capital formation, employment and training of labor, and the supply of fuel and raw materials to the local economy.

A. Gross National Product

The contribution of the oil industry to the gross national product of the various Middle Eastern countries consists of that part of the "value added" by the industry that remains in the given country. Value added comprises returns to labor, capital, and resources, in the form of wages, salaries, social charges, interest, profits, and rent; it can be gross or net, depending on whether the depreciation and amortization of capital is included in it or not. Value added indicates the contribution of an industry to the total economy (see Chapter V, Section A).

In the producing countries, that part of the value added that remains in the country is equal to the sum of the various payments made by the industry to the government; the wages, salaries, and other benefits of local employees for operating costs and that part of the wages and salaries of foreign employees that is spent in the country; and net investments (i.e., gross investment minus depreciation). This figure should equal the difference between gross receipts (i.e., the value of the crude oil and products exported or sold domestically), on the one hand,

and the value of intermediate products imported or purchased domestically plus factor payments sent abroad (by employees of the industry or as company profits remitted abroad), on the other. Similar considerations apply to the transit countries.

In addition to this direct contribution to the local economy, the oil industry also makes an indirect contribution and exercises a certain "multiplier effect" through its local purchases of goods and services. This often makes it possible for other industries and services to develop and benefit from economies of scale and external economies because of increased demand for local products either by the oil industry or by the recipients of the income generated by the oil industry. Other indirect contributions, such as the supply of oil for local consumption at prices below those prevailing in world markets (see Chapter III), the provision of various forms of assistance to governments, and the developing of labor skills and entrepreneurial talents (see below), should also be noted.

Needless to say, for most of the countries covered in this study, figures regarding gross national product are either nonexistent or fragmentary or, at best, very rough. Fairly reliable estimates are available for Iraq in 1956–60, more approximate ones for Iran in 1955–59, and very rough figures for Kuwait in 1952 and Saudi Arabia in 1958.[1] For the transit countries, Jordan, Lebanon, Syria, and the United Arab Republic (Egypt), estimates are somewhat more accurate.[2] Similarly, population statistics are incomplete. Census data are available for Bahrein (1950 and 1959), Iran (1956), Iraq (1947 and 1957), and Kuwait (1957 and 1961) among the producing countries, and Jordan (1952), Syria (1960), and Egypt (1947 and 1960) among the transit countries. The population of Qatar is reliably estimated at 40,000 while that of Saudi Arabia is usually put at 5–6 million.[3]

In view of all this, many of the figures shown in Table 40 must be regarded as mere indicators of orders of magnitude, while some of those in the last column are only informed guesses. Nevertheless, they do bring out certain significant trends, such as the sharp rise in value added per head of population and as a proportion of gross national product. They also show that, whereas until quite recently oil accounted for not more than some 10 per cent of gross national product in Iran and Iraq, and perhaps some 20 per cent in Saudi Arabia, these figures are now very much higher in the two latter and somewhat higher in Iran. Similar ratios for Bahrein, Kuwait and Qatar range between 55 to 90 per cent. Even in the transit countries, the contribution of the petroleum industry is now no longer negligible.

TABLE 40

VALUE ADDED BY THE OIL INDUSTRY REMAINING IN THE COUNTRY AND RELATION TO GROSS NATIONAL PRODUCT
(Various Units)

Country and Year	Population (Thousands)	GNP (Millions) of Dollars)	Value Added by Oil Industry		
			Total (Millions of Dollars)	Per Capita (Dollars)	Proportion of GNP (Per Cent)
Bahrein					
1948	100	...	5[a]	50	...
1958	140	...	23[b]	165	55
Iran					
1948	18,092	...	200	11	10
1958	19,677	2,610	390	20	15
Iraq					
1948	4,965	...	36	7	10
1958	6,590	920	260	40	28
Kuwait[c]					
1948	150	...	24	160	70
1958	210	...	398	1,900	90
Qatar					
1948	30	...	6	200	90
1958	40	...	68	1,700	90
Saudi Arabia					
1948	5,000	...	60	12	20
1958	5,000	800	425	85	50
Jordan					
1954	1,395	140	4[d]	3	3
Lebanon					
1952	1,321	350	8[d]	6	2
Syria					
1958	4,283	600	23[d]	6	4
U.A.R. (Egypt)					
1959	25,365	3,500	87[e]	3	3

Sources: Figures on value added by the oil industry in the producing countries have been derived from Appendix Tables 4, 5, and 6 except for the following: The 1958 figure for Bahrein was obtained from *Petroleum Press Service* (London, August, 1959), and that for the transit countries from International Bank for Reconstruction and Development, *The Economic Development of Jordan* (Baltimore: Johns Hopkins Press, 1957), pp. 64 and 461; Edward Fei and Paul J. Klat, *The Balance of Payments of Lebanon, 1951 and 1952* (Beirut: American University, 1954), p. 44; International Monetary Fund, *Balance of Payments Yearbook 1957-1958* (Washington, 1959); Syria, *Statistical Abstract 1959* (Damascus, 1960); and United Nations, Department of Economic and Social Affairs, *Economic Developments in the Middle East 1958-1959* (New York, 1960), p. 78; Plan Organization of Iran, *Outline of the Third Plan* (Tehran, 1961), p. 189.

[a] Rough estimate.

[b] Includes wages, royalties, local purchases and contracts.

[c] The Kuwait census of 1961 put the total population at 322,000, of whom nearly on half were foreigners.

[d] Value added by pipeline operations.

[e] Suez Canal dues paid by oil tankers.

The sharp rise in the contribution of the industry in both producing and transit countries has been mainly due to the rapid growth of direct payments to governments by the oil companies. Only in Bahrein, where the presence of the refinery has resulted in relatively high employment and where the small volume of crude production has kept payments to the government low, are expenditures on wages and investment of the same order of magnitude as direct payments to governments. A minor factor, but one that has considerable indirect effect, has been the increase in local expenditures by the oil companies, which in recent years have made strenuous efforts to expand their purchases of local goods—sometimes initiating or encouraging new lines of production for this purpose—to buy more foreign goods through local importers instead of importing them on their own account, and to make the fullest use of local contractors, often providing training for this purpose. Since excellent accounts of these activities are available,[4] this subject will not be pursued beyond noting that purchases of local goods and services in the producing countries, after declining from $12 million in 1948 to $4 million in 1953, rose to $29 million in 1959 (see Table 26, p. 90).

Attention should also be drawn to the considerable, if not easily measurable, impact which the oil industry has exerted on the local economy by developing entrepreneurial talents among its employees and contractors, many of whom have developed new lines of production in other branches of the economy, and by greatly enlarging, both directly and indirectly, the market for various goods and services (including transport and power). Some of the companies have also provided valuable technical assistance and other services to the governments of the producing countries; particularly noteworthy is the help given by Aramco to the Saudi government in its port, railway, and irrigation projects.

B. Foreign Exchange Receipts

The relative contribution of the oil industry to the foreign exchange receipts of the producing and transit countries, in the form of foreign exchange paid directly to the government or surrendered in return for local currency required for wages and local purchase of goods and services, naturally looms even larger than its contribution to gross national product.[5] Indeed it is no exaggeration to say that in the Arabian Peninsula countries, for which no figures on foreign transactions are available, oil accounts for practically all foreign exchange receipts. Throughout history these countries have had very few goods for export, the most important exception being the pearls of Bahrein and the other sheikdoms, and have covered their foreign exchange deficit by receipts from pilgrimage, transit trade, and shipbuilding. Until the early nineteenth century privateering and piracy also made their contribution to the balance of payments.

Table 41 shows the position in other countries of the area. In Iran the figures for 1957/58 and 1960/61 are comparable to those prevailing in the period between the end of the Second World War and the nationalization of the oil industry, but they are far above those for the period before the war, when oil contributed well below one-fifth of foreign exchange receipts. The contribution of the oil sector is still greater in Iraq and has shown a continual rise since 1950, interrupted only during the Suez crisis; until 1952, however, the foreign exchange contribution of the oil sector was lower than that of other exports alone. In Saudi Arabia, where oil activities provide nearly nine-tenths of foreign exchange receipts, expenditures by pilgrims, formerly the main source of foreign exchange receipts, still play a significant part in the balance of payments. In the transit countries, the contribution of the oil sector has sharply risen in the last few years owing to greater payments by the pipeline companies to the governments of Jordan, Lebanon, and Syria (see Chapter VI, Section E), to the increased flow of tanker traffic through the Suez Canal (see Table 9, p. 21), and to the Canal's nationalization in 1956.

C. Government Budgets

Since the beginnings of oil operations in the Middle East, royalty and tax payments by the companies have occupied a prominent place in government budgets, and in recent years their importance has grown considerably. In Kuwait, petroleum revenues came to account for the bulk of government budgets from the very start of production, and by 1953/54 their percentage share in total receipts was 97, but with the growth in other revenues, it declined to 87 by 1957/58.[6] The same is true of Qatar, where the first budget, for 1950, showed that oil revenues were over 90 per cent of receipts. In Bahrein, direct payments by oil companies began to play a leading part in the budget in the mid-thirties, and by 1946 represented 55 per cent of total government revenues, which amounted to 7 million rupees; by 1957 total government revenues had risen to 72.4 million rupees, of which petroleum payments accounted for 66 per cent; the corresponding figures for 1959 were 74.4 million and 83 per cent.[7] In Saudi Arabia, oil revenues began to assume

TABLE 41

FOREIGN EXCHANGE DERIVED FROM OIL INDUSTRY AND RELATION TO TOTAL FOREIGN EXCHANGE EARNINGS
(Millions of Dollars and Per Cent)

Country and Year	Millions of Dollars				Per Cent
	Foreign Exchange Derived from Oil Industry[a]	Exports of Goods	Other Current Earnings	Total Current Foreign Exchange Earnings	Share Oil as Proportion of Total Foreign Exchange Earnings
Iran					
1948/49	110	57	3	170	65
1957/58	256	132	64	452	57
1960/61	356	147	99	602	59
Iraq					
1948	38	41	32	111	34
1957	174	39	84	297	59
1960	319	30	59	408	78
Saudi Arabia					
1948	46	1	25[b]	72	64
1957	333	1	59[b]	393	84
1958	337	1	49[b]	387	87
Jordan					
1953	2	8	8	18	11
1954	4	9	9	22	18
Lebanon					
1951	11	57	130	198	6
1952	11	56	132	199	6
U.A.R. (Egypt)					
1958	82[c]	457	171	710	12
1959	87[c]	465	197	749	12
Syria					
1957	16	163	27	206	8
1958	23	128	20	171	13

Sources: International Monetary Fund, *Balance of Payments Yearbook, 1947-1960* (Washington); International Bank for Reconstruction and Development, *The Economic Development of Jordan* (Baltimore, 1957); Edward Fei and Paul J. Klat, *The Balance of Payments of Lebanon 1951 and 1952* (Beirut, 1954); National Bank of Egypt, *Economic Bulletin* (Cairo); United Nations, *Economic Developments in the Middle East 1958-1959* (New York, 1960); official estimates of Saudi Arabian Government.

[a] The data refer to the disbursements of foreign exchange by the oil companies in direct payments to governments and for other local expenditures. Therefore they do not include foreign exchange spent by the companies on their imports to these countries, or sums retained abroad either by the companies as profits or by their employees as savings from salaries.

[b] Pilgrims' expenditure.

[c] Tolls on tankers passing through the Suez Canal.

significance in the late 1930's. By 1947/48 they accounted for 65 per cent of total government revenues, which amounted to 215 million riyal; by 1952/53 the figure was 75 per cent out of a total of 758 million riyal; and by 1959/60 it stood at 81 per cent out of a total of 1,410 million.[8]

In Iran in 1937/38, direct oil payments represented 13 per cent of total government revenues, which amounted to 1,644 million rial, and there was little change during the war and early postwar years, the 1948/49 figure being 11 per cent out of a total of 7,154 million. Following the settlement of the nationalization crisis, during which oil revenues had ceased, the percentage rose rapidly; in 1959/60 it was 41 out of a total government revenue of 48,257 million rial.[9] In Iraq, oil revenues constituted a larger share of the total before the war, the percentage share in 1937/38 being 26 out of a total of ID 7,480,000. Thereafter, however, the percentage fell sharply, to 11 per cent in 1944/45 and a low of 7.5 in 1948/49, owing to the fact that petroleum revenues showed little increase, or actually declined, while total government receipts rose rapidly. The large increase in revenue after 1951 once more pushed the percentage share up, to 61 per cent in 1953/54 and in 1959/60 out of a total government revenue of ID 81.2 million and 143 million, respectively.[10]

In Jordan in 1955/56, direct payments by oil companies represented 5 per cent of government revenues, which equaled JD 6,655,000,[11] rising to about 15 per cent in 1962. In Lebanon, payments by oil companies in 1950 represented only 0.4 per cent of government revenue, which was LL 83.3 million, but rose to 10 per cent by 1960, when revenue was LL 295 million, and is now somewhat higher. In Syria, payments by oil companies accounted for less than 1 per cent of a total of £S 152.4 million of government revenues in 1949, but rose to 25 per cent out of a total of £S 493 million in 1960/61. In Egypt, the £E 37 million of gross receipts contributed by Suez Canal dues on tankers in 1961 represented 10 per cent of total government revenue, which was estimated at £E 371 million in 1960/61.

D. Capital Formation

This subject, in spite of its great importance, must be treated summarily for lack of data. Briefly put, the petroleum industry finances the greater part of capital formation in the producing countries, both directly through investments undertaken by the oil companies and indirectly in the form of development projects paid for by the revenues received by the governments from the companies. To this should be added a secondary form of investment, carried out by merchants and contractors from income earned from activities connected with the oil industry, but the magnitude of such investment must be relatively small.

As Table 12, p. 45, shows, direct gross fixed investment by the oil industry in Iran, Iraq, Kuwait, the Neutral Zone, and Saudi Arabia averaged \$220 million in 1956–58, a decline from the 1948–50 average, and the addition of Bahrein and Qatar may raise the total to some \$250 million per annum. The combined annual gross national product of these countries may have been some \$4.5 to \$5 billion in those years, which would mean that direct gross fixed investment represented an average of 5 to 6 per cent.

As regards investment carried out by the governments, the following broad statements may be made. In Iran and Iraq, the principle that oil is a wasting asset and that therefore revenues accruing from it should be used to build up the country's capital equipment, and thus create alternative sources of income, has been recognized since the 1930's and embodied in legislation since 1949. Consequently, part of the oil revenues were usually allocated to an extraordinary or development budget and spent on capital works or social overheads, although budgetary exigencies often led the governments to use part of these revenues for financing ordinary expenditure. More recently, with the large growth in oil revenues, the greater part has been used for development.[12]

In the Arabian Peninsula countries, the greater part of oil revenues has been used to finance current budgetary expenditures. The most important exception has been Kuwait, where the bulk of these revenues has either been allocated for economic and social development or invested abroad; the same is true, on a smaller scale, of Bahrein and Qatar. In Saudi Arabia, a Development Board was established in 1959 as part of the general administrative and economic reforms carried out in that year, and its activities are financed by oil revenues.

As regards the individual countries, in Iran the gross fixed investment by the operating companies in 1957 was \$35.3 million, or about 1.5 per cent of the gross national product, but by 1958 the figure had risen to \$83.7 million, or over 3 per cent; the latter figure was about equal to the 1948–49 average but represented a smaller percentage of gross national product. To this should be added investments by the Italian and United States companies, which concluded oil agreements in 1957 and 1958. As for government investment, in 1956/57 to 1958/59, government development expenditure through the Plan Organization averaged 10.3 billion rials (\$137 million), or some 6 per cent of gross national product. In recent years, the Plan Organization has been receiving about 50 per cent of the oil revenues accruing to the government, or a little less than the average yearly expenditure of $137 million just mentioned. Of the remaining revenue a part has been allocated to the National Iranian Oil Company whose expenditures and investment are not included in the Plan Organization's budget, but the bulk has been used for ordinary budgetary expenditure. Between them, direct investments by the petroleum industry and government investment financed by petroleum revenues (i.e., excluding government investment financed from other sources) accounted for about half of the total gross domestic investment, which was estimated at some $450 million in 1957/58 and $550 million in 1958/59.[13]

In Iraq, annual gross investment by the oil companies in 1956–58 averaged $25.8 million, or somewhat over 3 per cent of gross national product; in 1948–50, investments had been almost twice as high and may have represented nearly 10 per cent of gross national product. As for government investment, between 1956/57 and 1958/59 the expenditure of the Development Board averaged ID 58.4 million ($164 million) or some 19 to 20 per cent of gross national product.[14] It seems probable that between them these two categories must have accounted for at least three-quarters of total gross domestic investment in Iraq. It should be added that during the period 1950–56 the Development Board's revenues from oil, which accounted for 70 per cent of total oil revenues, considerably exceeded its expenditure; the balance was invested abroad, raising Iraq's foreign exchange reserves from $117 million in 1950 to $353 million in 1956, after which there was a decline to $254 million by 1960.

Investment by the oil companies accounts for a larger proportion of gross national product in Kuwait. In 1956–58 it averaged $52.7 million per annum, or perhaps 10 per cent of gross national product; to this should be added investment in the Neutral Zone by the independent oil companies and, since 1958, also by the Japanese Company. In absolute terms, these figures set a record, though percentagewise they mark a decline from the 1948–49 period. As for development expenditures by the Kuwaiti government, they averaged 420 million rupees ($88 million) in 1956–58, or perhaps 17 per cent of gross national product.[15] In addition, oil revenues not only financed ordinary government expenditure but made it possible for Kuwait to have a huge foreign exchange surplus, which was largely used for investment abroad. The value of these investments, according to official sources, was £240 million at the end of 1961; most of them were in Great Britain. In order to finance development projects in other Arab countries, the government of Kuwait set up a fund with an initial capital of £50 million, from which loans have already been granted to the Sudan and Jordan. In addition, petroleum finances, directly or indirectly, almost the whole of capital formation. The same must be true of Qatar; it must also hold, to a lesser extent, for Bahrein, for which no recent figures are available, but where it has been customary to allocate a third of oil revenues to the Sheik, use another third for current expenses and general development, and invest the remaining third abroad.[16]

As for Saudi Arabia, investment by Aramco averaged $82.1 million in 1956–58, or perhaps a little over 10 per cent of gross national product; to this should be added investment by Tapline and, as in Kuwait, investment in the Neutral Zone. As for government expenditure in development, it amounted to 379 million riyals in 1955/56 and 234 million in 1957/58, and fell to 182 million in 1959;[17] this is an average of $70 million per annum, or perhaps a little under 10 per cent of gross national product. The greater part of oil revenues was used to finance ordinary government expenditure. Clearly, here too, petroleum finances, directly or indirectly, an overwhelming proportion of capital formation.

E. Employment

One of the most striking characteristics of the petroleum industry, which has been repeatedly referred to above, is its very high capital-labor ratio (see Chapter IV, Section C). Consequently, the number of persons employed in it is relatively small and the ratio of both capital investment per worker and value added per worker is much higher than in most other industries. This holds particularly true of the Middle Eastern oil industry, which represents a very highly capitalized and technically progressive enclave in a region where, owing to the abundance of labor and scarcity of capital and skills, industry is backward in its methods and equipment, employs much labor per unit of capital, and has a very low productivity, and where handicrafts continue to play a role that is by no means negligible. The fact that the Middle Eastern petroleum industry refines only a small proportion of its total output limits its capacity to provide additional employment, since, as has been pointed out (Chapter III, Section H), it takes roughly 3.5 times as many man days to produce a ton of refined products as a ton of crude oil. A striking contrast is provided by the petroleum industry in the Persian Gulf area and the textile industry in such a relatively advanced Middle Eastern country as the United Arab Republic (Egypt). In the mid-1950's, total employment in the petroleum industry in the producing countries was about 140,000 compared with textile factory employment in Egypt of 114,000, but net capital per worker was about $14,000 compared with $760, and value added $16,000 compared with $883.[18] Nevertheless, the petroleum industry is the largest private employer in the oil-producing countries, and in most it is by far the largest (see Tables 28 and 42, pp. 97 and 152).

In the transit countries, employment in the oil industry is naturally much smaller, but it is worth noting that in 1956 the Iraq Petroleum Company employed 3,786 persons in Syria,[19] or nearly 4 per cent of the industrial labor force of that country, and employment by Tapline in 1956 amounted to 1,150.

But the importance of the oil industry in the labor market is even greater than these figures would indicate. In the first place, the wages paid by the petroleum companies are higher than those earned in other branches of the economy, and working conditions are much better (see Chapter IV, Section H); it may therefore be presumed that the industry has attracted and retained a higher proportion of able industrial workers. Second, the training given by the industry to its employees is unique in the region. There is an abundant literature on this subject, to which the reader is referred for full details.[20] To take only one example, in 1959 an average of 6,086 Saudi Arabs, or over half the total employed, were enrolled in one or more of the following training programs provided by Aramco: Job-Skill Training, Industrial Training Centers, Campaign Against Illiteracy, and Management and Special Training.[21] In addition, most of the companies, at their own expense, send students for advanced training overseas. For example, the Iraq Petroleum Company group is required to send 50 Iraqi students abroad each year, and in recent years Aramco has been providing scholarships for 60 Saudi Arabs, many of whom are not company employees, to study abroad. Similarly, starting in the early 1930's, the Anglo-Iranian Oil Company sent many Iranian students abroad; this, coupled with the training provided by the company locally, has made it possible, in the last few years, to fill most of the technical posts in the oil industry with Iranians. Moreover, the companies in the larger countries have made important contributions to technical and general education; most noteworthy in this respect are the Abadan Technical Institute, opened in 1939 and financed and administered by the Anglo-Iranian Oil Company; the Iraq Petroleum Company's Technical School in Kirkuk, opened in 1951; and the ten elementary schools that were built, equipped, and staffed by Aramco and transferred by it to the Saudi government. In these circumstances, it is not surprising that oil workers have been the first group in the

TABLE 42

EMPLOYMENT IN PETROLEUM INDUSTRY AND RELATION TO TOTAL EMPLOYMENT
(Thousands and Per Cent)

Country	Year	Thousands				Per Cent: Employment in Oil Industry as Ratio of:	
		Total Population	Active Population[a]	Employment in Industry[b]	Employment in Petroleum Industry[c]	Active Population	Employment in Industry
Iran	1956	18,955	5,908	858	63	1	7
Iraq	1956	6,343	2,046	128	18	1	14
Saudi Arabia	1958	5,000[d]	(1,650)	...	27	2	...
Kuwait	1958	210	(85)	...	16	19	...
Aden	1955	139	(46)	...	3	6	...
Bahrein	1956	132	(44)	30	9	20	30
Qatar	1953	20	(8)	...	4	50	...

Sources: United Nations, *Monthly Bulletin of Statistics* (New York, May, 1961); United Nations, *Statistical Yearbook, 1954-1960* (New York); Statistical Office of the United Nations; K. G. Fenelon, *Iraq, National Income and Expenditure, 1950-1956* (Baghdad, 1958); National Iranian Oil Company, Teheran; *Statistical Abstract of Iraq, 1958* (Baghdad); Arabian American Oil Company, *Report of Operations to the Saudi Arab Government, 1958; United States Senate, Eighty-Fifth Congress, Emergency Oil Lift Program and Related Oil Programs, Joint Hearings Before Subcommittees of the Committee on the Judiciary and Committee on Interior and Insular Affairs*, (Washington, 1957), p. 2245; R. S. Porter, *Report on the Census of Employment in Bahrein, 1956* Beirut, 1957).

[a]Data in parentheses are assumed to be one-third of the total population for Saudi Arabia, Aden and Bahrein, and 40 per cent of the total population for Kuwait and Qatar.

[b]Including mining, manufacturing and public utilities; the figure for Bahrein, in addition, comprises transportation and construction. The figure for Iraq appears to be underestimated.

[c]Data cover the number of workers employed in all phases of petroleum operations (production, refining, transportation, and marketing); they also include workers employed by contractors except for Aden and Qatar.

[d]Rough estimate.

Persian Gulf countries to become aware of their new industrial environment and to form trade unions, affiliated with one or another of the main international federations.[22]

The oil industry also exercises an important indirect effect on the labor market through those of its employees who leave it for other occupations. Turnover rates were formerly very high, although they have now sharply declined (see Chapter IV), and the number of persons who have spent some time in the oil industry is very great; for example, Aramco estimates that it has employed in the course of its operations over 100,000 Saudi Arabs.[23] As mentioned earlier, many of these have moved on to other industrial employment and some have established their own firms, while contractors and merchants supplying the company have often branched out into other lines of business. The pattern is similar in the other countries.

Against these factors must be set the fact that foreigners have accounted for a significant, though declining, proportion of the labor force of most of the oil-producing countries. These foreigners fall into three groups, Europeans and Americans occupying the top administrative and technical posts, Arabs from the Levant and Indians and Pakistanis providing clerical and skilled labor, and immigrants from other parts of the Persian Gulf providing semiskilled and unskilled labor where such was not available locally in sufficient quantities (this is particularly true in Kuwait, Bahrein, and Qatar, where foreigners play a leading part in most branches of the economy).[24] It is difficult to see how the oil industry could have started and developed without these foreigners, but it is easy to understand why their presence, especially at the higher levels, led to local resentment. Hence, in the last ten years, the companies have accelerated the training of nationals for higher posts and substituted them for foreigners. In this they were spurred by the governments which, in some of the renegotiated concession agreements with the older companies and in the agreements granted to new companies, have imposed stricter limitations on the employment of foreigners. The most striking example of the change is Iran, where the number of foreigners, 80 per cent of whom were in the "staff" category, fell from 4,503 (of whom 2,725 were British) in 1950 to 572 in 1959; 89.8 per cent of the "staff" category was Iranian, compared to 60.4 per cent in March, 1951.[25] In Iraq, where foreign employment is almost wholly restricted to the top level, the percentage of foreign "staff" members fell from over 90 per cent in the early 1950's to 51 per cent in 1960.[26] In the other countries management is still predominantly foreign, but long steps have been taken in the direction of promoting nationals to responsible positions, reducing the number of foreign managers, and replacing foreign clerks and skilled workers by nationals. Thus in 1959, 72 per cent of Aramco's employees were Saudi Arabs, compared with 66 per cent in 1948 and 60 per cent in 1952; of the rest, 15 per cent were Americans and 10 per cent Indians or Pakistanis.[27] The percentage of Saudis in the category of "skilled and supervisory" employees rose from 2 per cent in 1948 to 37 per cent in 1958. And in Kuwait, the number of Arabs employed as "senior staff" by Kuwait Oil Company increased from 5 in 1955 to 140 in 1959.[28]

F. Supply of Fuels and Raw Materials

Until the Second World War, coal was the principal fuel used in the Middle East, but petroleum had already supplanted it in the Persian Gulf area. During the war, there was a large-scale shift from coal to oil and since then consumption of coal has been negligible, except in Turkey, while that of oil has rapidly expanded, owing to increased mechanization and economic development, as well as to the reduction in relative prices of oil products discussed in Chapter III, Section F. In the producing countries, consumption of oil products has increased severalfold (see Table 43). A similar increase was registered in the transit countries, in Jordan from 55,000 tons in 1950 to 220,000 tons in 1960, in Lebanon from 225,000 to 680,000 tons, and in Syria from 230,000 to 880,000 tons.[29] However, per capita energy consumption is still low, except in the smaller oil-producing countries. In 1960 it averaged 264 kilograms of coal equivalent for the Middle East as a whole, compared to a world average of 1,405 and a West European average of 2,565. For Iran the figure was 366 kilograms, for Iraq, 430; and for Saudi Arabia, 229. The corresponding figures were 355 for Aden, 6,730 for Bahrein, 9,200 for Kuwait, and 2,250 for Qatar; all these figures include refinery consumption. As for the transit countries, consumption in Jordan was 190; in Lebanon, 596; and in Syria, 289.

In the more developed countries, petroleum and its by-products, natural gas and refinery gases, constitute a rich source of raw materials; in fact petroleum has in recent years replaced coal as the main basis of the chemical industry. In the Persian Gulf region, however, because of the general economic and social underdevelopment of the oil-producing areas, very little use has been made of these materials. Nevertheless, in Iran, Iraq, and Saudi Arabia a few industries based on petroleum or gas are being developed, such as fertilizers, liquefied petroleum gas, poly-

TABLE 43

DOMESTIC CONSUMPTION OF MAJOR REFINED PETROLEUM PRODUCTS IN LEADING OIL-PRODUCING COUNTRIES OF THE MIDDLE EAST[a]
(Thousand Barrels)

Country and Year	Gasoline	Kerosene	Distillate Fuel Oil	Residual Fuel Oil	Total Major Products
Iran					
1948	1,142	1,279	373	2,411	5,205
1959	4,643	5,526	4,551	6,400	21,120
1960	3,935	6,137	5,393	6,925	22,390
Iraq					
1948	791	709	160	2,223	3,883
1959	1,885	2,154	1,224	3,878	9,141
1960	2,144	2,526	1,510	4,370	10,550
Kuwait					
1955	429	124	72	–	625
1959	1,092	227	296	–	1,615
1960	1,400	306	(400)	–	(2,106)
Qatar					
1955	17	3	1	–	21
1958	70	29	19	–	118
1960	143	43	157	–	343
Saudi Arabia					
1950	386	24	132	–	542
1959	1,625	484	811	–	2,920
1960	1,779	533	872	–	3,184

Sources: National Iranian Oil Company; *Statistical Abstract of Iraq, 1950 and 1960; The Petroleum Times* (December 9, 1960), p. 619; Department of Economic and Social Affairs of the United Nations; Arabian American Oil Company, *Report of Operations to the Saudi Arab Government, 1955 and 1960;* United States Bureau of Mines, *World Petroleum Statistics, 1960* (Washington, 1961).

[a]Data do not include consumption of petroleum products by oil companies, including their refineries.

vinyl, matches, oxygen, carbon black, caustic soda, and hydrochloric acid.

Until quite recently, owing to the absence of nearby markets, most of the natural gas released in the course of oil production (see Chapter I, Section D) was flared, but now conservation measures, involving reinjection of gas into the oil fields to maintain pressure, have been introduced. Apart from reinjection, the main use of natural and refinery gases has been as fuel for the petroleum industry, and in Kuwait for water distillation and domestic use.[31] In Iran, a gas pipeline from the southern oil fields to Shiraz has been completed and another project is under way for building a pipeline from Sarajah gas field to Tehran. In Iraq work will soon start on a pipeline to provide gas for domestic purposes in Baghdad.

Projects for large-scale petro-chemical industries have also been studied, and in Iran construction has been completed on a 90,000-ton ammonium nitrate fertilizer plant, in the city of Shiraz, using natural gas. In Kuwait two contracts were signed in 1961. Kuwaiti interests, government and private, together with an Italian firm, will set up a $45 million petro-chemical plant capable of producing 200,000 tons per annum of caustic soda and chlorine, urea, and polyvinyl chloride from natural gas and petroleum by-products. Kuwaiti interests, government and private, together with an American firm, will set up a $42-million plant to produce 50,000 tons per annum of aluminum from imported alumina.[32] In Iraq, a consulting firm drew up, in 1956, plans for a set of petro-chemical projects based on natural gas and producing sulfur, ammonium sulfate fertilizers, and plastics, but so far these plans have not been implemented.[33] The same applies to the suggestions made in Saudi Arabia.[34] As for the transit countries, Syria is planning to use the gas produced in its newly built refinery for the production of nitrate fertilizers, and in Israel the petro-chemical industry makes much use of the gases of the Haifa refinery, which was originally built to treat Iraqi crude. The refinery gases in Suez are also used for the production of nitrate fertilizers.[35]

VIII. Recent Changes and Trends

The account of Middle Eastern oil operations given in the previous chapters has drawn attention to two outstanding features in the postwar period: the remarkable expansion in the volume of production and exports and the very large margin between receipts and outlays. The expansion in output has been made possible, on the one hand, by the discovery of huge oil reserves in the last thirty years and, on the other, by the continually rising demand for Middle Eastern oil from Europe and other consuming areas. The large margin between receipts and outlays may be attributed to several factors. First, there is the fact that Middle Eastern oil prices were sustained by a high level of world demand and by the pricing system (see Chapter III, Section C). Second, there are the various technical, institutional, and economic factors that make for exceedingly low costs in the Middle East (see Chapter IV, Section E). Last, the share taken by the companies out of this very large margin increased in the early postwar years, while that accruing to the governments declined. This was because, until 1950, payments to the governments continued to be made mainly on the fixed royalty basis established in the 1920's or 1930's;[1] hence, although in most countries the absolute amount received by the governments increased, the sharp rise in oil prices greatly reduced the governments' share from oil income, even where royalties were on a gold basis (see Chapter VI, Section C). It was only after the conclusion of the 1950–54 profit-sharing agreements, and the subsequent amendments, that the governments' share of gross revenues rose appreciably (see Chapter V, Section C).

The pattern described above has, however, begun to change. New forces are operating on both the demand and the supply side, and their impact may be considerable. This concluding chapter will first examine the forces at work outside the region, and then those within it.

A. Factors Outside the Region

Forces outside of the Middle Eastern region are influencing and changing the former patterns of production and distribution of oil and the revenues and profits from it. These forces can be seen at work in the areas of both demand and supply, and are discussed in the following paragraphs.

Demand. The first important variable on the demand side is the trend in growth of world consumption of petroleum, which must be studied in the context of world consumption of all forms of energy. Naturally, estimates of future movements are tentative and show significant divergences, but they all have two features in common: a large anticipated rise in total consumption, and a distinct slowing down in the high rate of growth that had characterized the 1950–60 period.

Three studies on this subject were presented to the Petroleum Congress in 1959.[2] Levy expected world consumption of energy, excluding that by the Soviet bloc, almost to double between 1956 and 1975, rising from 42.22 million barrels a day of crude oil equivalent to 81.65 million, while consumption of oil would almost triple, from 13.11 to 37.11 million barrels; this, however, would represent a decline in the annual rate of growth of total energy from 4.6 per cent in 1950–56 to 3.5 per cent, and in oil from 7.8 to 5.6 per cent. Guyol's estimates, which include consumption by the Soviet bloc, show a more than doubling of total energy consumption, from 51.7 million barrels a day of crude oil equivalent in 1955 to 117.7 million in 1975, and almost a tripling in that of oil, from 16.1 to 46.2 million; here, too, the rate of growth is expected to decline to 4.2 and 5.4 per cent, respectively. Two earlier studies published by the Chase Manhattan Bank[3] estimated that, during the decade 1957–67, demand for liquid petroleum in the whole world, excluding that of the Soviet bloc, would grow at an average rate of 6.3 per cent per annum, compared with 7.9 per cent in 1946–56. A more recent estimate put the anticipated rise in world consumption of energy between 1960 and 1965 at 3 per cent per annum and in consumption of oil at 5 per cent per annum, which would imply a still sharper decline in the rate of growth.[4]

The most thorough study of past and anticipated future uses of various energy sources in the United States showed a total anticipated increase of 88 per cent, or 3.2 per cent per annum, in all forms of energy between 1955 and 1975, compared with 2.8 per cent in the postwar period; the projection for crude oil showed a total rise in consumption of 85.8 per cent in 1955–75, or also about 3.2 per cent per annum.[5] As for Europe, the most recent study of energy requirements showed an anticipated decline in the rate of growth; thus the projected increase in total energy consumption in the O.E.E.C. area in 1955–65 was put at

25–35 per cent and in 1965–75 at 26–36 per cent, or, taking the mean figures, an annual rate of growth of 2.65 per cent compared with 3.4 per cent in 1948–58.[6] For oil, the increase in consumption in 1955–65 was put at 90–123 per cent and for 1965–75 at 48–62 per cent, compared with over 250 per cent in 1948–58; putting it slightly differently, it is anticipated that imports of oil into Europe "will grow in the period 1955 to 1965 by an average of 10 million tons each year, equivalent to 7 per cent yearly over the period. Since World War II we have got used to a rate of growth of oil demand in Europe of the order of 11 to 15 per cent."[7]

The over-all picture that emerges from these estimates is of a continuing rise but a slowing down in the rate of increase in the demand for petroleum in the two major consuming areas, the United States and Western Europe; this, of course, does not mean that the absolute average annual increments will be smaller than in the past. It is unlikely that this decline in the rate of growth can be compensated by the acceleration in oil consumption that is expected to take place in the underdeveloped countries, since their intake still forms only a small fraction of the world total.[8] As an authority put it:

> In all these areas oil demand is likely to grow at a considerably faster rate than in Europe, but their indigenous sources of oil are also growing rapidly. It is extremely difficult to gauge how fast their imports may grow since there are so many unknown factors involved, but an average rate of 5 to 7% per year would seem a probable maximum and, in any event, their imports would remain small in comparison with Europe's in the foreseeable future.[9]

This is substantially confirmed by another authoritative estimate, shown in Table 44, which anticipates an acceleration in over-all consumption of energy coupled with a deceleration in consumption of petroleum in 1959–65.[10]

As for the Soviet bloc, it too will probably show an increase in the rate of growth of oil consumption, but it seems probable that its production will rise more than proportionately and that the bloc will increase its export surplus (see below).

The absolute increase in energy consumption expected in all the above estimates is based on the anticipation of continued population growth, industrialization, mechanization, and rise in real incomes; thus it has been estimated that, in the O.E.E.C. area, a 1 per cent increase in gross national product is accompanied by a rise of 0.8 per cent in energy consumption.[11] But this ratio seems to be declining in the more

TABLE 44

ENERGY AND PETROLEUM CONSUMPTION BY MAJOR AREAS,[a] 1938-65
(Thousands of Barrels Per Day and Index)

Area and Year	Energy Consumption: Thousands of Barrels Per Day	Energy Consumption: Index, 1938 = 100	Petroleum Consumption: Thousands of Barrels Per Day	Petroleum Consumption: Index, 1938 = 100
United States				
1938	9,015	100	3,115	100
1950	15,664	174	6,507	209
1959	19,865	220	9,451	303
1965	26,260	291	11,450	368
Canada and Latin America				
1938	1,080	100	521	100
1950	2,031	188	1,181	227
1959	3,345	310	2,423	465
1965	4,688	434	3,450	662
Western Europe				
1938	7,597	100	733	100
1950	8,071	106	1,235	168
1959	10,826	142	3,500	477
1965	14,740	194	6,200	846
Africa, Asia, and Oceania				
1938	2,365	100	598	100
1950	2,759	117	974	163
1959	4,716	199	2,120	355
1965	6,428	272	3,336	558
TOTAL ABOVE AREAS				
1938	20,057	100	4,967	100
1950	28,525	142	9,897	199
1959	38,752	193	17,494	352
1965	52,116	260	24,436	492

Source: G. T. Ballou, *Current Challenges in the International Petroleum Industry* (Second Arab Petroleum Congress, Beirut, October, 1960), p. 19.
[a]Excluding Soviet bloc countries.
Note: 1965 figures are forecasts.

advanced countries. This is due not only to an increase in "thermal efficiency," caused by technological progress, such as greater use of diesel engines and electricity, and the elimination of waste, but also to greater "economic efficiency," i.e., to the fact that a greater proportion of energy consumption is going to such uses as commercial space heating, where its efficiency is high, and a smaller proportion to mechanical work, where its efficiency is low. The latter trend is connected with the relative decline in the contribution of manufacturing and mining to gross national product and the rapid growth of services characteristic of mature economies, the first group being relatively more energy consuming than the second.[12]

The anticipated deceleration in consumption of petroleum is largely due to these factors, but it also reflects the fact that petroleum products, and in particular fuel oil, are meeting with increasingly stiff competition from other fuels and that petroleum's rate of advance into their market is being slowed down. In both the United States and Europe, productivity in coal mining has sharply risen. Thus, in the United States, where wages constitute at least half of total costs, average output per man-day rose from 6.43 tons in 1949 to 12.12 tons in 1959. Further improvement is expected owing to the spread of strip-mining and auger-mining techniques and, in underground mining, of continuous mining; the last-mentioned method has, in certain mines, reduced manpower requirements by as much as 70 to 85 per cent. In addition, transport costs—another important element in the delivered price of coal—are being drastically cut by such devices as pipelines for "slurry," and electricity is being generated near coal mines and transmitted to consuming centers.[13] Similarly, in Europe much progress has been made: In the United Kingdom, over-all output per man-shift rose from 1.042 tons in 1946 to 1.245 tons in 1955 and 1.352 tons in 1959; for France the corresponding figures were 0.601, 1.042, and 1.161 tons, respectively; for Western Germany, 0.863, 1.163, and 1.433 tons, respectively.[14] These increases in productivity seem to have more than offset increased capital costs due to mechanization and the rise in wages. After 1956, stocks of coal piled up and the price of coal weakened. Thus the wholesale price of coal in the United States, which had climbed, first steadily and then rapidly, from $4.76 per short ton in 1951 to $5.56 in 1957, fell to $5.15 by the end of 1960; in the United Kingdom the rise, and still more the drop, were sharper, from 95*s*. per long ton to 154*s*. and 90*s*., respectively.[15]

All of this implies that the competitive position of coal has greatly improved. In addition, there are continuing strong social pressures on the governments of coal-producing countries, at least in Europe, to encourage consumption of coal, on which the livelihood of millions depends. Moreover, coal is produced domestically, whereas oil has to be imported; increasing oil consumption at the expense of coal therefore implies both dependence on outside sources and considerable outlay of foreign exchange. It is significant that, whereas the consumption of bituminous coal in the United States fell by 17 per cent between 1920 and 1955, it is expected to rise by 75 per cent between 1955 and 1975,[16] while in the world as a whole it is expected to increase by 67 per cent.[17]

At the same time, output and consumption of natural gas have greatly increased and are expected to rise still more rapidly. Thus, in the United States, natural gas consumption increased in 1945–55 by 132.6 per cent, a rate about double that of oil, and is expected to rise by another 106.6 per cent in 1955–75, a rate of growth appreciably above that of oil.[18] In Western Europe, output rose from 4 billion cubic meters in 1954 to about 11 billion cubic meters in 1960, and is expected to reach 16 to 20 billion cubic meters by 1965; further large supplies, about 10–12 billion cubic meters per annum, may be imported from Algeria through a proposed 3,000-kilometer pipeline costing about $1,000 million; additional amounts are also to be shipped, by tankers, to Great Britain.[19] In both these regions, part of this increase may be at the expense of imported oil, including that from the Middle East.

Last, mention should be made of two other potential competitors, shale oil and atomic energy. Experiments in pilot plants in the western United States have significantly brought down the costs of producing shale oil, to a level where it could just about compete with crude oil at its present price on the United States Pacific Coast.[20] As for atomic energy, its output is likely to increase quite rapidly, but since (apart from propelling submarines and other warships) it is being used mainly for the generation of electricity, its initial impact will probably be felt more by coal than by oil, though the effects on the latter are not negligible.[21]

Supply. The picture on the supply side is clearer: new sources of production have been developed and there exists considerable excess capacity, though it should be remembered that a certain amount of excess capacity is necessary to provide flexibility in the industry and to give consumers the possibility of drawing on alternative supplies, if some of their habitual sources of oil should suddenly be cut off. Output is rising in several areas which are, or shortly will be, large producers, and their exports may be expected soon to weigh on the international market. What is more significant, some of the new sources of production have been developed by government-owned enterprises or independent oil companies. In the last twenty years or so, the discovery of huge reserves and the development of new productive capacity has not depressed oil prices because almost all of this was carried out by the major international companies, which also were dominant in most markets and consequently adjusted output to demand.[22] The independent oil companies, however, whose share in total output has increased, are under great pressure to start producing and marketing soon after discovery, in order to recover part of their heavy initial outlays; the

Soviet and other governments engaged in oil production and export are, of course, guided by still other considerations.

Moreover, it should be remembered that the discovery of new reserves and the development of capacity by the major international companies in other parts of the world increase potential competition with the Middle East, since these new sources can be put to use should operations in the Middle East become very difficult or much less profitable. The outstanding example is Venezuela, where the concessions granted in 1956 and 1957, many of them to Independents, have brought in new productive capacity of over 15 million tons per annum.[23] Another competitor, though on a much smaller scale, is the East Indies, whose output rose from 7 million tons in 1948 to 16 million tons in 1954 and 25 million tons in 1960; moreover, unlike Venezuela, the East Indies are close to the most important markets for Middle Eastern oil lying east of Suez. Still more serious is potential competition from North Africa, which has the advantage of proximity to the European market; appears to be free from some of the grave political risks posed by the Suez Canal and Syrian pipelines; and, at least as regards Algeria, enjoys a preferential position in France. Moreover, several of the North African concessions have been granted to independent oil companies, which are under great pressure to produce and sell. In Libya, two pipelines with an initial throughput capacity of about 15 million tons per annum each are under construction, and in Algeria two additional pipelines with a combined throughput capacity of 13 million tons per annum are being built;[24] Algerian production is expected to rise to 27 million tons in 1964, and Libyan production to 20 million tons.[25]

The potential pressure of rising supply in the major producing countries may be gauged by Table 45, which shows the high level of excess capacity existing in some areas in 1959 as well as a projection for 1964.

As for exports from the Soviet bloc to the rest of the world, these have risen rapidly from a negligible amount in the early 1950's to 7.7 million tons of crude and products in 1957, 22.7 million in 1960, and 27.5 million in 1961.[26] According to information given by the Soviet delegate to the Arab League's Oil Congress held in Beirut in October, 1960, Soviet exports of petroleum are expected, for some years to come, to rise by 15–20 per cent annually;[27] the announced objective of the Soviets is to regain their former share of the European market, namely 14 per cent. In 1960, the Soviet Union provided almost all of Iceland's requirements of foreign oil, 95 per cent of those of Finland, and an appreciable proportion of Norway's.[28] A Western study of the Soviet petroleum industry, presented to the same Congress, judged that the Soviet Union's goal

TABLE 45

ESTIMATED WORLD PETROLEUM PRODUCING CAPACITY AND OUTPUT,[a] 1959 AND 1964
(Thousands of Barrels Per Day and Per Cent)

Area	1959			1964		
	Thousands of Barrels Daily		Per Cent	Thousands of Barrels Daily		Per Cent
	Production	Capacity	Production as Percentage of Capacity	Production	Capacity	Production as Percentage of Capacity
Western Hemisphere						
United States	7,920	10,400	76	9,450	10,900	87
Canada	520	1,000	52	850	1,400	61
Venezuela	2,770	3,500	79	3,400	4,000	85
Other Western Hemisphere	810	850	95	1,150	1,200	96
TOTAL WESTERN HEMISPHERE	12,020	15,750	76	14,850	17,500	85
Eastern Hemisphere[a]						
Middle East	4,590	6,000	76	6,300	8,000	79
Africa	100	300	33	1,100	1,350	82
Far East	570	680	84	700	800	87
Europe	270	270	100	350	350	100
TOTAL EASTERN HEMISPHERE[a]	5,530	7,250	76	8,450	10,500	81
TOTAL	17,550	23,000	76	23,300	28,000	83
From Soviet bloc	250	–	–	500	...	...
TOTAL SUPPLY	17,800	–	–	23,800	...	...

Source: Kenneth E. Hill, *Outlook for Oil Stocks*, Eastman Dillon, Union Securities and Co. (New York).
[a]Excluding Soviet bloc countries.
Note: 1964 figures are forecasts.

of doubling oil production in the current Seven Year Plan, to reach 4.8 million barrels a day, or 240 million tons a year, by 1965 "may be reached, or at least closely approached." If, as is planned, consumption of petroleum can be held down by greater domestic use of natural gas and by maintaining coal output, exports of oil from the Soviet bloc to the rest of the world are expected to reach 50 million tons a year by 1965, of which 45 million will come from the Soviet Union.[29] An earlier estimate, placing Russian oil exports for 1965 at 30 million tons and for 1970 at 45 million, appears to have been too low.[30]

It should be added that output is also expanding significantly in some of the minor producing countries. Thus, production of crude oil in Colombia rose from 5.5 million tons in 1955 to 7.7 million tons in 1960, and by 1964 it is expected to be about or over 11.5 million tons;[31] in Argentina it rose from 4.4 million to 9.2 million tons and is expected to be around 17 million by 1964;[32] and in Nigeria, where large-scale production has just started, output is expected to grow to possibly 10 million tons by 1970.[33] This means that exports from these countries may soon be sizable. Mention should also be made of the growth of oil production in Western Europe, from 2 million tons in 1948 to 14 million in 1960; forecasts for 1965 put the total at 20 million tons and for 1975 at 35 million.[34]

Last, there is a factor which, strictly speaking, belongs to the demand side of the equation but can be more conveniently treated here: the increasing restrictions on petroleum imports into the United States. The quotas imposed in March, 1959, will undoubtedly affect Middle Eastern oil exports, partly directly, since the United States absorbed nearly 10 per cent of Middle Eastern oil exports in the 1950's, and partly through their impact on exports from Venezuela, the chief competitor of the Middle East. "It has been reckoned that oil imports [into the United States] may rise by only perhaps 3 per cent a year in future compared with more like 10 per cent in the past."[35] Indeed, forecasts for 1961 show an actual decline in imports from the 1960 level, which in turn was only 2 per cent above that of 1959, and import quotas for the first half of 1961 were slightly below those set for the corresponding period in 1960.[36]

Effect of Above Factors. In assessing the effect of the above-mentioned demand and supply factors, it is essential to specify the time period under discussion. There is little reason to doubt that in the long run—and one that is perhaps not so very long—the demand for oil will rise appreciably, perhaps up to a point where supply will once more be tight. Nor is there any good reason to doubt that, in all probability, the absolute demand for Middle Eastern oil will go on rising uninterruptedly. Indeed, an estimate made in 1958 forecast an increase in Middle Eastern supply from 175 million tons in 1957 to 420 million in 1967, a rise of 145 per cent,[37] although this projection may have to be revised downward in the light of some of the factors discussed above, particularly the anticipated expansion of oil exports from other areas.

In the shorter run, however, prospects are not so encouraging. Indeed, it would seem that the slackening in the rate of increase of demand and growing competition have already begun to make themselves felt. Twice in recent years, posted prices of Middle Eastern oil have been reduced, by about 8 per cent in February, 1959, and by some 5 per cent in August, 1960. Moreover, in some markets, Soviet and other oils have either displaced Middle Eastern oil or forced the companies selling the latter to make significant price concessions, as in Ceylon, India, and Pakistan. A particularly interesting example is the reported barter deal between the state-owned Ente Nazionale Idrocarburi in Italy and the Soviet Oil Trust.[38] Under this agreement, which covers the years 1961–65, Italy will reportedly take 25 million tons of crude oil, supplying in return synthetic rubber, tankers, oil pipes, and other equipment; some of this oil may be re-exported by Italy after refining.[39] It may be added that the export price policy of the Soviet oil industry is far from clear, or perhaps it would be more accurate to say that it is extremely flexible. For, on the one hand, the Director of Soyuznefteexport "has expressed his belief in Platt's Oilgram prices as a generally good yardstick for Soviet oil exports," but on the other hand, Soviet oil has been sold at varying prices in different markets.

> In 1957, as reported, the average price of crude oil sold on the international market by the U.S.S.R. was $2.06 a barrel as compared with $2.79 a barrel for Middle East oil and $2.92 for Venezuelan oil. In 1958 the Soviet Union is said to have sold oil to Argentina at an average price of $1.60 a barrel at a time when Poland was paying $2.87 a barrel. By the Soviet arrangement with Italy in November 1960, crude oil was to be supplied at Black Sea ports at $1 a barrel, which indicated a cost at Italian refineries at about 62.5 per cent of the delivered cost of oil from Persian Gulf ports.[40]

Moreover, the Soviets have used and can continue to use a whole battery of devices, like barter deals in surplus raw materials and other products, acceptance of various local currencies, extension of credits, or assistance for building local refineries to capture a particular market.

The most uncertain factor would seem to be the future energy policy of Western Europe, which is, and for a long time to come is likely to remain, the leading market for Middle Eastern crude oil. Here, various trends may be discerned. First, there has been an increasing tendency to use the cheapest source of energy available, irrespective of its origin: thus Italy has been drawing on both Soviet oil and American coal, as well as on Middle Eastern oil. This may stimulate imports of Middle Eastern oil, by lessening the degree of protection given to high cost domestic coal in Europe, but at the same time it may expose it to greater competition from Soviet oil offered on specially favorable terms. Second, there has been, since the Suez crisis, an attempt to decrease Europe's dependence on the Middle East by diversifying its sources of supply of oil, and especially by developing the North African oil fields. Moreover, a greater effort has been made to utilize new sources of power, notably nuclear energy, or those hitherto used on a very small scale, e.g., reserves of natural gas in Italy, France, and other countries. To this category also belong the schemes to import natural gas from North Africa by submarine pipelines. Last, there is the question of the membership and future tariff policy of the European Economic Community. Under the Rome Treaty, crude oil is to be allowed to enter free of duty, but so far France has granted North African oil a preferential quota and Germany has protected its domestic producers of crude oil. In principle, such protection is to end by 1963, but it may well continue beyond that date, in which case the Middle East might be adversely affected. As against this, the Common Market members are also considering a unified energy policy and are expected to limit imports of oil from the Soviet Union.

Finally, it may be mentioned that, owing to increased competition from Middle Eastern and other crudes (including the loss of the Cuban market to Soviet oil), which has been intensified by the decline in freight rates, "the bulk of Venezuelan oil is not being sold at posted prices but at discounts which have occasionally been as high as $1 a barrel."[41]

It would seem, therefore, that during the next few years pressure on prices may continue, although it may well ease after that as consumption begins to catch up with supply. It is very difficult, however, to foresee what form this continued pressure will take. In the first place, a distinction must be made between different products. Thus fuel oil and gas oil, which can be replaced by coal and natural gas in many uses, may experience a decline in price, whereas gasoline and kerosene may be able to maintain their prices (see Chapter III). Second, the policy of the major international companies must be contrasted with that of independents and others; the former may prefer to maintain prices, even at the risk of losing marginal markets, while the latter may try to force their way into new markets at least partly by slashing prices. Last, all sorts of unforeseeable economic, financial, and political considerations may lead the major international companies to develop more rapidly one or another of the oil-producing regions, where they have concessions, and within this group of companies rival pressures may also be at work.

In the meantime, the price cuts of 1959 and 1960 and the fear of further reductions have led the main exporting countries to attempt to bolster prices by forming a producers' association. In September, 1960, representatives of Iran, Iraq, Kuwait, Saudi Arabia, and Venezuela met in Baghdad and agreed to set up the Organization of Petroleum Exporting Countries (OPEC); later, Qatar, Indonesia, and Libya joined the organization; these countries supply 90 per cent of world exports. The general objectives of the organization were stated to be agreement on common policies toward the companies, the restoration of the recent cuts in the price of crude oil, and assurance of notification by the companies before future price changes.[42] Two meetings were also held in Caracas, and Tehran, respectively, in January, 1961, and October, 1961. Two schools of thought have appeared among the governments. One of them would insist on prices being maintained, even at the risk of losing a few markets to outside competitors.[43] The other goes further, and recommends some form of "international prorationing" to restrict supply and maintain world prices; this idea seems to have been abandoned, however, perhaps owing to a realization of the difficulties involved.[44] The fourth meeting was convened at the Headquarters of the Organization in Geneva in June, 1962. A number of resolutions were adopted, one of which called for the immediate opening of negotiations by member countries with oil companies to rescind the 1960 price cuts. If negotiations are not successful, member countries will consult each other and take appropriate measures. The same resolution asks members to formulate a rational long-term policy for petroleum prices. It has been stated that an important element in devising a basis for oil prices would be the linking of crude oil prices to an index of goods imported by member countries.

B. Factors Within the Region

All the important factors under this heading fall on the supply side. It is true that the demand for oil within the Middle East is growing rapidly and that in recent years oil consumption has been rising at about

7 to 8 per cent per annum, the rate in the oil-producing countries being somewhat higher (see Chapter VII, Section F). It is likely to continue growing at the same, or even a slightly higher rate, in view of the developments that are taking place in industry, transport, and agriculture within the region. However, the total petroleum consumption of the Middle East (even including the United Arab Republic, Turkey, Israel, Syria, Lebanon, Cyprus, Jordan, and Aden, in addition to the Persian Gulf countries, and taking into account consumption in petroleum refineries as well) absorbs only 7 per cent of crude oil production.[45] Moreover, even this market may occasionally be invaded by outside competitors, as witness sales of Soviet bloc oil to the United Arab Republic and Israel and occasional offers to other countries.

The first factor to be considered on the supply side is cost of production of crude oil. There is no reason to believe that these costs will either rise or fall significantly in the near future. On the one hand, the abundance and easy accessibility of reserves make it unlikely that marginal costs will rise in the foreseeable future. Indeed, with the utilization of the existing large excess capacity, an increase in production may make it possible to spread fixed costs over a larger output and so reduce average total cost, but this too would probably not be very significant.

A much more important factor is the entry of independent firms into the region. In the last few years, independent companies have secured concessions in several Persian Gulf countries and such companies, unlike the international majors, are under great pressure to expand their output to possible limits and to produce and sell even costly and low-quality oil in order to recover their outlays. This has been true of the American independent companies operating in the Neutral Zone; it is probably not a coincidence that practically the only pumping wells to be found in the Persian Gulf region are located in the concession area of these independents, while all majors produce from flowing wells; that the field with the lowest quality oil exploited in the Persian Gulf area is operated by them; and that their output per well is the lowest in the region. It will soon apply to the Japanese-owned Arabian Oil Company, which struck what seems to be a very large field at Khafji, off the shore of the Neutral Zone, in January, 1960. "A production in the near future of several million tons a year is already envisaged," and although Japan's rising consumption may absorb this output, that will naturally imply the displacing of other, primarily Middle Eastern, oil.[46] Again, the discovery of an offshore field, south of Kharg Island, by Iran Pan American Company (a partnership between the National

Iran Oil Company and a subsidiary of Standard Oil of Indiana) in 1960–61 is likely to raise problems, since Standard Oil of Indiana has no Eastern Hemisphere marketing outlets and its importing quota into the United States for crude oil was only about 1.5 million tons a year in 1960.[47] The mixed company of Société Irano-Italienne des Pétroles, formed by National Iranian Oil Company with the Italian firm of AGIP Mineraria Company, also struck, off the shore of Bahrgan at the end of 1960, what seems to be a large field, and it too may enter into production in the not too distant future and weigh on prices.[48] In addition, the intensive prospection carried out in the other Persian Gulf sheikdoms and their offshore areas, notably Abu Dhabi and Qatar, has resulted in new discoveries; however, since this prospection has been carried out by members of the Iraq Petroleum Company group, British Petroleum Company and Compagnie Française des Pétroles, any new production capacity which may be developed will prove less disruptive to petroleum prices. The same applies to the concession acquired by Shell off the shore of Kuwait in November, 1960 (see below).

Third, there is the increased pressure by the Middle Eastern governments on the companies to refine a greater proportion of crude oil in the producing country. Some of the newer concessions stipulate minimum refining requirements. For example, the 1948 Kuwaiti concession covering the Neutral Zone provided for the erection of a refinery with a capacity of not less than 10 per cent of production as soon as output reached 15,000 barrels a day (Article 3) and the Saudi concession of 1949 covering the same zone provided that when output reached a level of 75,000 barrels a day, a 12,000-barrel-a-day refinery would be built (Article 10). Similarly, the 1957 concession given to the Japanese Company by Saudi Arabia (Article 27) provided that, within two years of the initiation of production, a refinery with capacity of not less than 30 per cent of production must be built. If such a pattern should spread, it may become more difficult to adjust the flow of oil to the demand of the various markets, in view of the ever greater pressure being put on the companies by the governments of consuming countries to refine more crude locally.

A fourth factor is increased competition from local government oil corporations. Thus the National Iranian Oil Company, in addition to its participation with foreign firms in oil developments, has directly carried out exploration and drilling, which have resulted in the discovery of appreciable quantities of oil, and is also engaged, with other companies, in transporting and marketing oil. The Kuwait National Petroleum Company, recently set up by the Government of Kuwait to take over the local marketing of oil products, is aiming at expanding into a fully integrated oil company with world-wide activities. The Iraqi government has also recently set up its own oil company for development of its oil resources. However, the impact of this trend is not likely to be great, at least in the near future.

Much more important is the increased pressure from the governments, which have committed themselves to rising outlays on development, welfare, and defense, on the companies for a greater share of the profits made in production and pipeline transport. Indeed, some government spokesmen have, at various times, claimed a share of the profits made at the later stages, such as refining, tanker transport, and marketing.[49] All the concessions granted in the region in the last few years contain provisions more favorable to the governments than the prevailing 50–50 profit-sharing agreements, thus opening a fourth stage in the evolution of petroleum agreements in the region (see Chapter VI, Section C). In Iran, under the Petroleum Law of July 31, 1957 (Article 1) the government-owned National Iranian Oil Company was authorized to enter into agreements with other companies, as a partner. In pursuance of this policy, three mixed companies were formed: Société Irano-Italienne des Pétroles (SIRIP) with AGIP Mineraria (a company formed by the Italian state-owned ENI corporation for oil and natural gas operations) in 1957; Iranian Pan American Company (IPAC) with Pan American Petroleum Corporation (a subsidiary of Standard Oil of Indiana) in 1958; and Iran-Canada Corporation with Canadian Sapphire, also in 1958.[50] In all of these agreements, the Iranian partner is given the right of providing half the capital required for development after oil is discovered and receiving 50 per cent of the profits made by the operating company; in addition the Iranian government is entitled to 50 per cent of the other half of the profits accruing to the foreign partner, thus raising Iran's total share to 75 per cent. Under the IPAC concession, the Iranian government also received a bonus of $25 million. In the Neutral Zone, under the offshore agreement of December 10, 1957, with the Arabian Oil Company, the Saudi Arabian government is to receive 56 per cent of the profits made by the company at all stages of operation. The corresponding agreement with the Kuwaiti government provides for the latter to receive 57 per cent of profits. Both agreements also stipulate payment of a dead rent and other obligations (see Chapter I). And in Kuwait, the offshore agreement of November 30, 1960, with Shell International Petroleum Company, gives the government the option of purchasing a 20 per cent interest in the newly formed Kuwait Shell Petroleum Development Company; in addition the government is to receive large bonuses and a dead rent (see Chapter I, Section I).[51] It should be added that, in 1958, the Venezuelan government amended the income tax law raising its share of oil profits to 65 per cent; a similar law was also passed in Indonesia in 1961 that increased the government's share to 60 per cent. These moves, like similar ones in the past, will probably have powerful repercussions on the Middle Eastern oil-producing countries, as witnessed by the recent negotiations between the government of Iraq and the Iraq Petroleum Company group. Indeed, one of the resolutions adopted at the fourth meeting of the OPEC in June, 1962, instructed member countries to demand higher payments from the oil companies. It was stated that royalties are to be considered payments to the owners of resources in return for removing the oil and that royalties should be included as part of the cost of production. Thus, governments should receive royalties plus 50 per cent of gross income. Negotiations have already begun on this issue between the governments and oil companies.

It will thus be seen that the conditions under which bilateral monopoly bargaining is being carried out between companies and governments are changing in favor of the latter.[52]

C. Conclusion

The argument of this chapter may therefore be summarized as follows. In the early postwar years, the profitability of oil operations in the Persian Gulf area was exceedingly high. This was due to four main factors: a rapidly rising level of demand, a relatively high level of prices, exceptionally low costs, and the small share of the governments of the producing countries in the profit margin. Now, however, the situation seems to be changing radically. On the one hand, the rate of growth in demand may be declining, and increasing competition from other oil producers, who have developed a large surplus capacity, is exerting pressure on the price of crude oil and may keep it from rising during the next few years; at the same time greater competition from other fuels is being felt by fuel oil and some other products. On the other hand, the governments of the producing countries, in the Middle East, in Venezuela, and in Indonesia, are exacting an ever-rising share of the profits made by the concessionary companies. The latter are therefore increasingly caught in a squeeze between the pressure on prices and the pressure for surrendering a higher proportion of profits to the governments. It may therefore be expected that an increasingly large share of the economic rent derived from the lowness of Middle Eastern production costs and from the price structure will be absorbed by the governments, and that, in the years to come, the rate of return on investments made in the Middle Eastern oil industry will tend to be distinctly lower than they have been in the last fifteen years.

Appendix: Summary of Concession Agreements*

MIDDLE EAST OIL CONCESSIONS
As of January 1, 1960

PETROLEUM CONCESSIONS, LTD.

ADEN

Exploration Permit.

Area: Aden, including Hadhramaut and island of Socotra. Permit in process of being dropped.

Ownership: Same as Iraq Petroleum Co., Ltd.

THE BAHRAIN PETROLEUM CO., LTD.

BAHREIN

Concession: Expires 2024.

Area: All of Bahrein, including islands, waters, and submerged lands over which the Sheik has or may acquire dominion.

Ownership:

Standard Oil Co. of California	50%
Texaco, Inc.	50%

DHOFAR-CITIES SERVICE PETROLEUM CORP.

DHOFAR

Concession: 25 years from date of commercial production, renewable for an additional 25 years. Granted January 17, 1953.

Area: Province of Dhofar.

Ownership: Cities Service Co. 100%
(Richfield Oil Corp. has a 50 per cent working interest).

IRANIAN OIL PARTICIPANTS, LTD.

(Under Agreement with Government of Iran and National Iranian Oil Co.)
(Iranian Oil Exploration and Producing Co., Operator)

IRAN

Agreement: 25 years from 1954, expires 1979; plus 15 years optional.

Area: Approximately 100,000 square miles.

* The information contained in this Appendix was obtained mainly from the Arabian American Oil Company.

Ownership:

British Petroleum Co., Ltd.		40%
Royal Dutch–Shell group		14%
Compagnie Française des Pétroles		6%
Gulf Oil Corp.		7%
Socony Mobil Oil Co.		7%
Standard Oil Co. of California		7%
Standard Oil Co. of New Jersey		7%
Texaco, Inc.		7%
Iricon Agency, Ltd.		5%
Richfield Oil Corp.	1.250%	
Signal Oil and Gas Co.	0.833%	
American Independent Oil Co.	0.833%	
Getty Oil Co.	0.417%	
San Jacinto Petroleum Corp.	0.417%	
Standard Oil Co. of Ohio	0.417%	
The Atlantic Refining Co.	0.417%	
Tidewater Oil Co.	0.417%	

IRAN PAN AMERICAN OIL COMPANY (IPAC)

IRAN–OFFSHORE

Concession: Agreement reached in June, 1958, for a duration of 25 years after date when the first 629,000 barrels of oil have been produced, sold, and delivered, with three 5-year extensions.

Area: Approximately 6,176 square miles in Persian Gulf, including about 386 square miles north and 5,790 square miles south of SIRIP's area.

Ownership:

Pan American International Oil Co. (Standard Oil Co. of Indiana)	50%
National Iranian Oil Co. (Iranian Government)	50%

SOCIÉTÉ IRANO-ITALIENNE DES PÉTROLES (SIRIP)

IRAN

Concession: Agreement reached in August, 1957, for a period of 25 years from start of petroleum sales, with three 5-year extensions.

Area: Approximately 8,839 square miles along part of northern continental shelf of Persian Gulf, on eastern slope of central Zagros Mountains, and on coast of Gulf of Oman.

Ownership:

AGIP Mineraria Co. (ENI–Italian state corporation for oil and natural gas)	50%

National Iranian Oil Co. (Iranian Government)	50%

BASRAH PETROLEUM CO., LTD.

IRAQ

Concession: 75 years from November 30, 1938; expires 2013.

Area: All of Iraq not covered by IPC, Mosul, and former Khanaqin concessions. Plus Iraq's undivided half-interest in Iraqi–Saudi Arabian Neutral Zone.

Ownership: Same as Iraq Petroleum Co., Ltd.

IRAQ PETROLEUM CO., LTD.

IRAQ

Concession: 75 years from March 14, 1925; expires 2000.

Area: Provinces of Baghdad and Mosul east of Tigris River (approximately 32,000 square miles) except for area covered by former Khanaqin concession, now owned by Iraq Government.

Ownership:

British Petroleum Co., Ltd.	23.75%
Royal Dutch–Shell group	23.75%
Compagnie Française des Pétroles	23.75%
Near East Development Corp. (Standard Oil Co. of New Jersey: 50%; Socony Mobil Oil Co.: 50%)	23.75%
Participations and Explorations Corp. (C. S. Gulbenkian Estate)	5.00%

MOSUL PETROLEUM CO., LTD.

IRAQ

Concession: 75 years from May 25, 1932; expires 2007.
Area: All of Iraq west of Tigris River and north of Latitude 33°N.
Ownership: Same as Iraq Petroleum Co., Ltd.

PHILLIPS PETROLEUM CO.

JORDAN

Concession: 55 years from February, 1956.

Area: Extending over one-third of the territory of Jordan. An exploration concession covering an additional one-third of Jordan was granted in 1959.

Ownership: Phillips Petroleum Co. 100%
(Phillips acquired this concession from Edwin Pauley during 1957–58. Pauley Petroleum, Inc., reserved a 9.6% net profits royalty interest.)

BP EXPLORATION CO., LTD.

KAMARAN

Exploration Permit (Work suspended by agreement with Aden Government).

Area: Kamaran and other British-controlled islands off coast of Yemen, including territorial waters. Islands are administered by government of Aden.

Ownership: British Petroleum Co., Ltd.	100%

BP (KUWAIT) LTD. AND GULF KUWAIT CO.
(Kuwait Oil Co., Ltd., Operator)

KUWAIT

Concession: 75 years from December 23, 1934; extended on December 1, 1951; expires 2026.

Area: All of Kuwait, including territorial waters to a 6-mile limit.

Ownership:

BP (Kuwait) Ltd.	50%
(British Petroleum Co., Ltd.)	
Gulf Kuwait Co.	50%
(Gulf Oil Corp.)	

COMPAGNIE LIBANAISE DES PÉTROLES

LEBANON

Concession: 75 years from August 24, 1955; expires 2030.

Area: Selected areas in Lebanon.

Ownership:

Lebanese and French nationals	50%
Gewerkschaft Elwerath	50%

PETROLEUM DEVELOPMENT (OMAN), LTD.

MUSCAT AND OMAN

Concession: 75 years from 1937; expires 2012.

Area: Muscat and Oman except Province of Dhofar.

Ownership:

Royal Dutch–Shell group	82.61%
Participation and Exploration Co.	17.39%

AMERICAN INDEPENDENT OIL CO.

NEUTRAL ZONE

Concession: 60 years from June 28, 1948; expires 2008.

Area: All of Kuwait's undivided half-interest in Saudi Arabian–Kuwait Neutral Zone, including islands and territorial waters.

Ownership:

Phillips Petroleum Co.	33.54%

Signal Oil and Gas Co.	30.16%
Ashland Oil and Refining Co.	12.70%
Ralph K. Davies	6.98%
J. S. Abercrombie	6.35%
Crescent Corp.	3.17%
Sunray Mid-Continent Oil Co.	2.65%
Globe Oil and Refining Co.	1.59%
Lario Oil and Gas Co.	1.59%
Pauley Petroleum, Inc.	1.27%

GETTY OIL CO

NEUTRAL ZONE

Concession: 60 years from February 20, 1949; expires 2009.

Area: All of Saudi Arabia's undivided half-interest in Saudi Arabian–Kuwait Neutral Zone, including islands and territorial waters.

Ownership:

J. Paul Getty interests	79%
Other shareholders	21%

ARABIAN OIL COMPANY, LTD.

NEUTRAL ZONE–OFFSHORE

Concession: 44½ years from July 5, 1958.

Area: Kuwait's undivided half-interest in offshore area of Saudi Arabian–Kuwait Neutral Zone, extending from 6 miles off coast into Persian Gulf. Precise boundaries to be determined.

Ownership: Arabian Oil Company, Ltd. 100%
(Japan Petroleum Trading Co., Ltd.)

ARABIAN OIL COMPANY, LTD.

NEUTRAL ZONE–OFFSHORE

Concession: 2-year exploration license from 1958 with 2-year renewal option and 40-year exploitation lease from date of discovery of commercial production.

Area: Saudi Arabia's undivided half-interest in offshore area of Saudi Arabian–Kuwait Neutral Zone, extending from 6 miles beyond territorial waters off coast into Persian Gulf to median line between Iran and Neutral Zone, including islands and adjacent waters.

Ownership: Arabian Oil Company, Ltd. 100%
(Japan Petroleum Trading Co., Ltd.)

QATAR PETROLEUM CO., LTD.

QATAR

Concession: 75 years from May 17, 1935; expires 2010.

Area: All of Qatar over which the Sheik rules, including territorial waters to a 3-mile limit.

Ownership: Same as Iraq Petroleum Co., Ltd.

SHELL COMPANY OF QATAR, LTD.

QATAR–OFFSHORE

Concession: 75 years from August, 1952; expires 2027.

Area: Continental shelf offshore from Qatar beyond a 3-mile limit.

Ownership: Royal Dutch–Shell group	100%

ARABIAN AMERICAN OIL CO.

SAUDI ARABIA

Concession: Original area, 66 years from July 14, 1933, expires 1999; additional area, 66 years from July 14, 1939.

Area: Some 340,000 square miles of Saudi Arabia, including offshore areas. Includes Saudi Arabia's undivided half-interest in Iraqi–Saudi Arabian Neutral Zone.

Ownership:

Standard Oil Co. of California	30%
Texaco Inc.	30%
Standard Oil Co. of New Jersey	30%
Socony Mobil Oil Co.	10%

SOCIÉTÉ DES PÉTROLES CONCORDIA S.A.R.L.

SYRIA

Exploration Permit.

Area: 49 rectangles with an area of 538.5 square miles in Syria.

Ownership:

Deutsche Erdoel Aktiengesellschaft	80%
Geberhardt & Koening–Deutsche Schachtbau G.M.B.H.	10%
Dea-Schliemann Mineraloelgesellschaft G.M.B.H.	10%

ABU DHABI MARINE AREAS, LTD.

TRUCIAL COAST–OFFSHORE

Concession: 65 years from March, 1953; expires 2018.

Area: Continental shelf area offshore from Abu Dhabi beyond a 3-mile limit.

Ownership:

British Petroleum Co., Ltd.	66⅔%
Compagnie Française des Pétroles	33⅓%

DUBAI MARINE AREAS, LTD.

TRUCIAL COAST–OFFSHORE

Concession: 60 years from August, 1952; expires 2012.

Area: Continental shelf area offshore from Dubai beyond a 3-mile limit.

Ownership:

British Petroleum Co., Ltd.	66⅔%
Compagnie Française des Pétroles	33⅓%

PETROLEUM DEVELOPMENT (TRUCIAL COAST), LTD.

TRUCIAL COAST

Concession: Various concessions for 75 years from 1937 and subsequent years.

Area: Land and selected offshore areas of a group of small sheikdoms.

Ownership: Same as Iraq Petroleum Co., Ltd.

YEMEN

Concession: 5-year exploration and 30-year development concession granted to John W. Mecom in February, 1961.

Area: 10,000 square miles on northwest coastal plains and offshore.

Ownership: American syndicate 100%

Statistical Appendix

APPENDIX TABLE 1

PRODUCTION OF CRUDE PETROLEUM IN THE MIDDLE EAST[a] BY COUNTRIES, 1913-60
(Thousands of Barrels)

Period	Bahrein	Iran	Iraq	Kuwait	Neutral Zone	Qatar	Saudí Arabia	Total
1913-33	34	536,768	5,411	—	—	—	—	542,213
1934	285	57,851	7,689	—	—	—	—	65,825
1935	1,265	57,273	27,408	—	—	—	—	85,946
1936	4,645	62,718	30,406	—	—	—	20	97,789
1937	7,762	77,804	31,836	—	—	—	65	117,467
1938	8,298	78,372	32,643	—	—	—	495	119,808
1939	7,589	78,151	30,791	—	—	—	3,934	120,465
1940	7,074	66,317	24,225	—	—	—	5,075	102,691
1941	6,794	50,777	12,650	—	—	—	4,310	74,531
1942	6,241	72,256	19,726	—	—	—	4,530	102,753
1943	6,572	74,612	24,848	—	—	—	4,868	110,900
1944	6,714	102,045	30,943	—	—	—	7,794	147,496
1945	7,309	130,526	35,112	—	—	—	21,311	194,258
1946	8,010	146,819	35,665	5,931	—	—	59,944	256,369
1947	9,411	154,998	35,834	16,225	—	—	89,852	306,320
1948	10,915	190,384	26,115	46,500	—	—	142,853	416,767
1949	10,985	204,712	30,957	90,000	—	750	174,008	511,412
1950	11,016	242,475	49,726	125,722	—	12,268	199,547	640,754
1951	10,994	123,512	65,122	204,910	—	18,009	277,963	700,510
1952	11,004	7,800	141,100	273,433	—	25,255	301,861	760,453
1953	10,978	9,400	210,268	314,592	—	31,025	308,294	884,557
1954	10,992	21,500	228,432	347,319	5,995	36,450	347,845	998,533
1955	10,982	120,562	251,206	398,493	8,848	41,983	352,240	1,184,314
1956	11,015	197,148	232,307	399,874	11,684	45,300	360,923	1,258,251
1957	11,691	263,134	163,498	416,045	23,259	50,798	362,121	1,290,546
1958	14,873	301,526	266,102	509,382	29,310	63,910	370,486	1,555,589
1959	16,473	338,810	311,311	504,855	42,438	62,197	399,821	1,675,905
1960	16,500	390,755	354,592	594,278	49,830	63,908	456,453	1,926,316
1913-47	88,003	1,747,287	385,187	22,156	—	—	202,198	2,444,831
1948-60	158,418	2,411,718	2,330,736	4,225,403	171,364	451,853	4,054,415	13,803,907
1913-60	246,421	4,159,005	2,715,923	4,247,559	171,364	451,853	4,256,613	16,248,738

Sources: American Petroleum Institute, *Petroleum Facts and Figures, 1959* (New York, November, 1959); United States Bureau of Mines, *World Petroleum Statistics, 1959* and *1960* (Washington); *World Oil* (Houston, Texas, August 15, 1960).

[a]Exclude Israel, Turkey, and the United Arab Republic.

APPENDIX TABLE 2

PRODUCTION OF MAJOR REFINED PRODUCTS IN THE MIDDLE EAST, 1948-60

(Thousands of Barrels)

Country and Item	1948	1949	1950	1951	1952	1953	1954	1955	1956	1957	1958	1959	1960
Aden													
Gasoline	—	—	—	—	—	—	1,075	5,161	5,627	5,089	4,599	3,926	3,315
Kerosene	—	—	—	—	—	—	333	2,842	2,665	2,100	2,707	3,311	2,502
Distillate fuel oils	—	—	—	—	—	—	1,273	3,763	5,104	6,504	5,674	5,937	6,133
Residual fuel oils	—	—	—	—	—	—	5,528	18,315	19,190	15,653	12,913	14,679	15,169
TOTAL	—	—	—	—	—	—	8,209	30,081	32,586	29,346	25,893	27,853	27,119
Bahrein													
Gasoline	12,597	13,807	15,432	17,646	19,171	18,008	19,626	17,079	15,367	13,902	17,249	16,704	14,329
Kerosene	5,234	4,793	5,648	6,619	8,868	8,543	8,371	8,242	7,256	4,559	5,307	6,019	9,321
Distillate fuel oils	9,498	8,861	10,021	9,733	9,730	11,777	13,839	14,615	13,780	14,447	15,257	15,777	16,870
Residual fuel oils	22,571	22,720	24,958	29,565	27,271	32,514	32,634	26,924	30,011	29,687	27,862	26,082	29,620
TOTAL	49,900	50,181	56,059	63,563	65,040	70,842	74,470	66,860	66,414	62,595	65,675	64,582	70,140
Iran													
Gasoline	33,850	37,101	38,738	21,400	2,300	2,210	4,160	10,460	18,549	24,041	23,724	28,240	26,250
Kerosene	14,570	17,226	17,833	10,000	1,550	1,390	2,570	9,910	14,236	16,896	18,857	22,816	21,941
Distillate fuel oils	29,000	30,676	33,478	16,900	1,310	1,160	2,350	7,490	13,594	18,948	20,249	24,058	20,850
Residual fuel oils	74,400	79,385	87,826	44,400	4,420	4,210	8,380	24,700	35,803	48,962	50,033	45,278	55,915
TOTAL	151,820	164,388	177,875	92,700	9,580	8,970	17,460	52,560	82,182	108,847	112,863	120,392	124,956
Iraq													
Gasoline	554	542	572	800	780	1,020	1,030	1,252	1,646	1,840	1,519	2,179	2,431
Kerosene	545	535	600	570	830	970	940	1,314	1,836	1,730	2,618	1,893	2,385
Distillate fuel oils	127	120	141	530	430	440	470	1,020	2,038	2,290	2,751	2,549	3,039
Residual fuel oils	1,517	1,475	1,571	1,820	2,790	3,690	3,750	4,703	4,822	5,280	5,739	4,842	5,693
TOTAL	2,743	2,672	2,884	3,720	4,830	6,120	6,190	8,289	10,342	11,140	12,627	11,463	13,548

Kuwait													
Gasoline	—	120	124	143	178	305	383	422	430	493	625	904	1,444
Kerosene	—	25	41	51	67	84	101	136	155	170	2,300	301	306
Distillate fuel oils	—	210	1,654	1,698	1,907	2,144	1,983	1,867	1,904	1,671	12,508	9,159	10,776
Residual fuel oils	—	460	5,780	6,404	7,002	7,774	7,784	7,980	7,797	7,375	26,979	39,734	49,693
TOTAL	—	815	7,599	8,296	9,154	10,307	10,251	10,405	10,286	9,709	42,412	50,098	62,219
Saudi Arabia													
Gasoline	10,813	10,872	8,193	12,146	12,265	13,278	12,697	11,092	10,873	8,906	7,491	8,149	10,066
Kerosene	2,811	2,519	2,947	4,675	4,996	7,584	8,490	7,679	6,051	7,060	8,475	8,003	8,500
Distillate fuel oils	10,718	12,018	10,542	13,924	16,030	17,167	17,636	15,177	15,059	10,965	14,664	10,546	10,637
Residual fuel oils	19,001	18,367	13,934	24,392	25,766	33,021	36,188	35,402	35,404	38,015	25,564	31,642	45,638
TOTAL	43,343	43,776	35,616	55,137	59,057	71,050	75,011	69,350	67,387	64,946	56,194	58,340	74,841
TOTAL MIDDLE EAST													
Gasoline	57,814	62,442	63,059	52,135	34,694	34,821	38,971	45,466	52,492	54,271	55,207	60,102	57,835
Kerosene	23,160	25,098	27,069	21,915	16,311	18,571	20,805	30,123	32,199	32,515	40,264	42,343	44,955
Distillate fuel oils	49,343	51,885	55,836	42,785	29,407	32,688	37,551	43,932	51,479	54,825	71,103	68,026	68,305
Residual fuel oils	117,489	122,407	134,069	106,581	67,249	81,209	94,264	118,024	133,027	144,972	149,090	162,257	201,728
GRAND TOTAL	247,806	261,832	280,033	223,416	147,661	167,289	191,591	237,545	269,197	286,583	315,664	332,728	372,823

Sources: American Petroleum Institute, *Petroleum Facts and Figures* (New York, 1959); Arabian American Oil Company, *Reports of Operations to the Saudi Arabian Government by the Arabian American Oil Company* (New York-Dhahran, 1948-60); United States Bureau of Mines, *World Petroleum Statistics, 1959* and *1960* (Washington); Statistical Office of the United Nations.

APPENDIX TABLE 3

EXPORTS OF CRUDE PETROLEUM FROM THE MIDDLE EAST, 1948-60
(Thousands of Barrels)

	1948[a]	1949[a]	1950	1951	1952	1953	1954	1955	1956	1957	1958	1959	1960
Exports													
Iran	26,400	25,352	49,640	26,800	–	370	3,600	61,768	105,819	141,830	178,585	212,657	246,286
Iraq													
Persian Gulf	–	–	–	680	16,156	21,644	33,657	52,527	61,750	67,208	81,950	(88,800)	(86,400)
Mediterranean	26,000	27,833	46,099	58,397	112,916	179,505	186,834	187,106	158,997	83,313	169,338	(201,571)	(251,305)
Total, Iraq	26,000	27,833	46,099	59,077	129,072	201,149	220,491	239,633	220,747	150,521	251,288	290,371	337,705
Kuwait	46,000	88,000	116,696	196,335	264,027	302,998	336,315	386,398	390,795	405,230	465,393	452,064	527,299
Neutral Zone	–	–	–	–	–	–	5,706	8,364	11,491	22,695	25,250	32,500	39,241
Qatar	–	115	11,700	17,919	24,837	30,355	35,816	40,801	44,248	50,346	63,152	61,237	62,424
Saudi Arabia													
Persian Gulf	96,754	126,127	148,167	113,091	124,129	119,454	151,725	159,797	166,895	162,350	172,731	211,182	279,548
Mediterranean	–	–	9,324	107,830	114,883	112,542	116,563	117,989	120,607	127,645	135,182	124,139	91,961
Total, Saudi Arabia	96,754	126,127	157,491	220,921	239,012	231,996	268,288	277,786	287,502	289,995	307,913	335,321	371,509
TOTAL EXPORTS	195,154	267,427	381,626	521,052	656,948	766,868	870,216	1,014,750	1,060,602	1,060,617	1,291,581	1,384,150	1,584,464
Imports													
Bahrein	42,939	45,330	45,891	46,027	47,643	61,478	67,215	63,153	58,026	44,718	48,739	50,786	59,599
Aden	–	–	–	–	–	–	10,694	30,762	33,936	32,995	27,546	30,761	31,332
TOTAL IMPORTS	42,939	45,330	45,891	46,027	47,643	61,478	77,909	93,915	91,962	77,713	76,285	81,547	90,931
NET EXPORTS	152,215	222,097	335,735	475,025	609,305	705,390	792,307	920,835	968,640	982,904	1,215,296	1,302,603	1,493,533

Sources: United States Bureau of Mines, *World Petroleum Statistics, 1950* to *1960* (Washington); Arabian American Oil Company, *Reports of Operations to the Saudi Arab Government by the Arabian American Oil Company* (New York-Dhahran, 1948-60); Ministry of Economics of Iraq, *Statistical Abstracts* (Baghdad).

[a] 1948 and 1949 export data are partly estimated on the basis of crude petroleum production and crude oil input to refineries.

GROSS RECEIPTS, EXPENDITURES, AND DISTRIBUTION OF
(Millions

Item	1913-47	1948	1949	1950	1951	1952
I. Middle East						
A. Gross Receipts						
Local sales of crude and refined products	...	34.4	46.7	50.9	28.2	9.0
Exports of refined products	...	682.5	578.2	674.2	561.4	376.9
Exports of crude	...	313.9	392.9	566.6	852.5	1,097.2
TOTAL	3,730	1,031	1,018	1,292	1,442	1,483
B. Expenditures						
Cost of petroleum operations	1,070	254	275	287	265	238
Payments to local governments	510	154	157	239	284	400
Net Income of oil companies	2,150	623	586	766	893	845
TOTAL	3,730	1,031	1,018	1,292	1,442	1,483
C. Distribution of Net Income						
Net Investment in fixed assets	425	243	276	51	79	107
Transfers of investment income abroad	1,725	380	310	715	814	738
TOTAL	2,150	623	586	766	893	845
II. Venezuela						
A. Gross Receipts						
Sales of refined products	...	113	107	200	275	303
Sales of crude	...	1,004	887	990	1,121	1,180
Other receipts	...	27	17	23	30	30
TOTAL	5,699	1,144	1,011	1,213	1,426	1,514
B. Expenditures						
Cost of petroleum operations	2,088	383	441	568	568	605
Payments to local governments	946	417	342	331	469	500
Net income of oil companies	2,665	343	228	314	389	409
TOTAL	5,699	1,144	1,011	1,213	1,426	1,514
C. Distribution of Net Income						
Net investment in fixed and liquid assets (increase in net assets)	1,180	335	293	60	48	143
Transfer of investment income abroad	1,485	8	-65	254	340	266
TOTAL	2,665	343	228	314	389	409
D. AVERAGE NET ASSETS	...	1,348	1,662	1,838	1,892	1,988

TABLE 4

NET INCOME IN THE MIDDLE EAST AND VENEZUELA, 1913-60
of Dollars)

1953	1954	1955	1956	1957	1958	1959	1960	1948-60
12.3	13.9	30.0	35.7	39.8	48.3	53.8	58.9	461.9
425.4	488.0	614.1	719.3	801.9	845.9	840.8	865.7	8,474.3
1,379.4	1,570.4	1,798.9	1,883.3	1,946.7	2,463.6	2,450.5	2,740.8	19,456.7
1,817	2,072	2,443	2,638	2,788	3,358	3,345	3,665	28,393
261	278	388	446	495	491	552	575	4,805
586	719	903	986	1,035	1,229	1,322	1,420	9,434
970	1,075	1,152	1,206	1,258	1,638	1,471	1,670	14,153
1,817	2,072	2,443	2,638	2,788	3,358	3,345	3,665	28,392
58	25	6	55	79	121	(120)	(100)	1,320
912	1,050	1,146	1,151	1,179	1,517	1,351	1,570	12,833
970	1,075	1,152	1,206	1,258	1,638	1,471	1,670	14,153
365	397	489	587	712	713	(714)	(750)	5,725
1,181	1,291	1,374	1,573	1,968	1,709	(1,650)	(1,700)	17,628
37	39	38	50	59	57	(50)	(50)	507
1,583	1,727	1,901	2,210	2,739	2,479	2,414	(2,500)	23,859
689	760	752	787	887	992	1,014	1,000	9,448
486	510	596	738	954	964	972	1,030	8,307
408	457	553	684	898	523	428	470	6,103
1,583	1,727	1,901	2,210	2,739	2,479	2,414	2,500	23,859
90	47	−43	361	523	70	148	−190	1,886
318	410	596	323	374	453	280	660	4,217
408	457	553	684	898	523	428	470	6,103
2,105	2,173	2,175	2,334	2,776	3,073	3,181	2,990	29,535

Sources:

I. Middle East:

A. Gross Receipts:

Local sales of crude and refined products: Actual data were obtained from the Department of Economic and Social Affairs of the United Nations. Exports of crude and refined products: Data have been estimated on the basis of the figures given in Tables 21 and 22 and Appendix Tables 1 and 2. An allowance of 2 per cent has been made for brokerage and other charges and discounts.

B. Expenditures:

Cost of operations: See Table 26. Payments to local governments: See Table 39 and Appendix Table 6. Net income of oil companies: The figures are the difference between total gross receipts, on the one hand, and costs of operations plus payments to governments, on the other.

C. Distribution of Net Income:

Net investment in fixed assets: The figures are the difference between gross investments and depreciation; see Table 26. The data do not include the investments made in Aden, Bahrein, and pipeline transit countries. Transfers of investment income abroad: The data are the difference between net income of oil companies and net investment.

II. Venezuela: Data are compiled by the Ministry of Mines and Hydrocarbons of Venezuela.

Note 1:

I. Middle East:

The data given for the Middle East in the above table cover the activities of the international oil companies in Aden, Bahrein, Iran, Iraq, Kuwait, the Neutral Zone, Qatar, and Saudi Arabia.

In the estimates of gross receipts there are two sets of omissions which partly offset each other.

(a) Gross receipts do not include the following: receipts from sales of products other than the four major ones; receipts from sales to oil company employees of consumption goods imported by the oil companies and the value of which is included in company expenditure.

(b) On the other hand, no attempt has been made to adjust gross receipts for either freight absorption on phantom freight on refined products exported in the early part of the period 1948-59—this problem does not arise for most of this period. No adjustment has been made for the discounts from posted prices that developed at the end of the period; these discounts applied to a small part of exports that were sold to third parties. Their magnitude is indicated by the fact that in 1960 they applied to about 18 per cent of Aramco's total sales and averaged 15 per cent, i.e., 2.7 per cent of the value of sales. This is to a certain extent compensated for by a part of the 2-per-cent allowance made above and also by recent declines in tanker freights, which have raised the realized price on certain exports, especially to distant markets.

II. Venezuela:

Payments to the government include, in addition to direct payments (taxes, royalties, and rents but not bonuses), import duties and other taxes; therefore, the original data have been adjusted to exclude the latter payments from costs and add them to government receipts. An exchange rate of 3.09 bolivars to the dollar has been used.

Note 2: Figures do not add up to totals because of rounding.

BREAKDOWN OF EXPENDITURES (OPERATING AND INVESTMENT)
COUNTRIES OF THE
(Millions

	1948	1949	1950	1951
Iran[a]				
Wages and salaries	56.0	65.9	66.2	48.4
Payments to local contractors	18.8	22.0	14.9	9.1
Purchase of local supplies	3.5	2.1	1.0	0.6
Imports	85.2	106.0	55.7	22.1
Other expenditures	46.7	57.2	58.6	30.9
TOTAL	210.2	253.2	196.4	111.1
Iraq[b]				
Wages and salaries	12.8	12.1	8.1	7.8
Payments to local contractors	5.6	3.9	1.7	3.4
Purchase of local supplies	4.4	2.1	0.8	1.7
Imports	25.2	26.1	10.1	17.9
Other expenditures	4.8	4.6	2.8	3.4
TOTAL	52.8	48.8	23.5	34.2
Kuwait[c]				
Wages and salaries	4.8	7.4	4.8	4.3
Payments to local contractors	7.6	7.6	1.7	1.9
Purchase of local supplies	2.3	2.4	0.7	0.8
Imports	67.5	38.9	7.2	7.2
Other expenditures	1.0	0.4	0.8	0.9
TOTAL	83.2	56.7	15.2	15.1
Qatar[d]				
Wages and salaries	1.2	1.8	1.1	1.4
Payments to local contractors	1.6	0.7	0.6	0.3
Purchase of local supplies	2.0	1.8	0.8	0.6
Imports	8.4	11.4	3.1	2.8
Other expenditures	0.4	0.7	0.3	0.3
TOTAL	13.6	16.4	5.9	5.4
Saudi Arabia[e]				
Wages and salaries	23.5	24.7	28.6	37.4
Payments to local contractors	4.1	4.3	3.3	5.3
Purchase of local supplies	—	—	0.1	0.3
Imports	(80.0)	(90.0)	22.5	67.0
Other expenditures	0.9	1.0	1.1	1.3
TOTAL	108.5	120.0	55.6	111.3
TOTAL FOR ABOVE COUNTRIES				
Wages and salaries	98.3	111.9	108.8	99.3
Payments of local contractors	37.7	38.5	22.2	20.0
Purchase of local supplies	12.2	8.4	3.4	4.0
Imports	266.3	272.4	98.6	117.0
Other expenditures	53.8	63.9	63.6	36.8
GRAND TOTAL	468.3	495.1	296.6	277.1

Sources: Data have been provided by the oil companies; see also United Nations, *Economic Developments in the Middle East, 1959-61* (New York, 1962), p. 132.

[a]Anglo-Iranian Oil Company, Limited, for the period 1948-51, and the consortium of oil companies for the period 1955-58.

TABLE 5

BY THE PETROLEUM INDUSTRY IN THE MAJOR OIL-PRODUCING
MIDDLE EAST, 1948-58
of Dollars)

1952	1953	1954	1955	1956	1957	1958
–	–	–	37.7	43.6	47.2	47.1
–	–	–	–	2.9	5.3	16.0
–	–	–	3.3	4.2	5.3	6.6
–	–	–	12.8	61.1	76.4	53.8
–	–	–	9.6	13.9	19.0	35.6
–	–	–	63.4	125.7	153.2	159.1
10.1	10.9	10.9	11.5	12.9	12.9	13.7
5.6	3.6	3.4	3.9	5.3	4.2	5.0
2.5	2.0	2.2	2.5	3.4	3.4	5.6
28.6	24.1	10.9	13.2	15.1	18.5	33.6
7.3	7.0	7.3	9.5	6.7	7.0	7.8
54.1	47.6	34.7	40.6	43.4	46.0	65.7
5.8	6.8	7.6	8.0	10.2	12.3	16.3
4.2	5.2	4.9	2.8	6.1	13.7	18.0
0.5	0.6	0.4	0.7	2.7	6.1	8.0
16.8	15.6	11.4	7.8	21.8	54.1	40.7
1.2	1.5	1.5	1.4	1.8	3.0	5.5
28.5	29.7	25.8	20.7	42.6	89.2	88.5
1.7	2.2	2.8	3.1	3.9	4.2	4.8
0.6	0.8	1.4	2.0	2.5	2.2	2.2
1.1	0.8	1.4	1.7	0.8	1.1	0.8
10.9	14.0	7.8	7.3	7.6	8.1	9.0
0.3	0.3	–	0.3	–	-0.3	-0.3
14.6	18.1	13.4	14.4	14.8	15.3	16.5
51.3	56.1	60.9	63.3	65.9	67.8	70.0
11.9	10.3	8.6	9.3	11.9	10.5	11.6
0.6	0.5	0.6	1.0	1.4	2.2	5.2
106.8	71.5	50.0	62.6	76.5	66.1	65.7
1.8	2.4	3.0	4.5	5.2	7.0	8.4
172.4	140.8	123.1	140.7	160.9	153.6	160.9
68.9	76.0	82.2	123.6	136.5	144.4	151.9
22.3	19.9	18.3	18.0	28.7	35.9	52.8
4.7	3.9	4.6	9.2	12.5	18.1	26.2
163.1	125.2	80.1	103.7	182.1	223.2	202.8
10.6	11.2	11.8	25.3	27.6	35.7	57.0
269.6	236.2	197.0	279.8	387.4	457.3	490.7

[b] Iraq Petroleum Company Group.
[c] Kuwait Oil Company, Limited.
[d] Qatar Petroleum Company, Limited.
[e] Arabian American Oil Company.

APPENDIX TABLE 6

DIRECT PAYMENTS BY THE PETROLEUM COMPANIES TO THE GOVERNMENTS OF PRODUCING COUNTRIES, 1913-60
(Millions of Indicated Currency)

Period	Bahrein ($)	Iran[a] (£)	Iraq[b] (£)	Kuwait (£)	Neutral Zone: Share of Kuwait ($)	Neutral Zone: Share of Saudi Arabia ($)	Qatar (£)	Saudi Arabia ($)
1913-26	–	7.2	–	–	–	–	–	–
1927-36	(1.1)	15.3	5.7	–	–	–	0.1	0.2
1937	(1.4)	3.5	1.1	–	–	–	–	0.04
1938	(1.5)	3.3	2.2	–	–	–	–	0.1
1939	(1.1)	4.3	2.3	–	–	–	–	1.8
1940	1.0	4.0	1.8	–	–	–	–	1.2
1941	1.0	4.0	1.7	–	–	–	0.1	1.0
1942	0.9	4.0	1.7	–	–	–	0.1	1.1
1943	0.9	4.0	2.0	–	–	–	0.1	1.2
1944	1.0	4.5	2.4	–	–	–	0.1	1.8
1945	1.1	5.6	2.5	–	–	–	0.1	4.3
1946	1.2	7.1	2.5	0.2	–	–	0.1	12.0
1947	1.4	7.1	1.9	0.5	–	–	0.1	18.0
1948	1.6	18.7[c]	2.3	1.5	7.6	–	0.1	52.5[d]
1949	1.5	22.9[c]	3.3	3.0	0.7	10.5	0.1	39.2
1950	2.0	32.5[c]	6.9	4.2	0.7	1.0	0.4	111.7
1951	2.9	17.8[c]	15.1	6.0	0.7	1.0	1.3	164.2
1952	4.2	–	40.6	20.0	0.7	1.0	3.5	211.1
1953	5.1	–	58.3	60.0	0.7	1.0	6.4	225.1
1954	11.1	3.1	68.4	69.0	0.8	(1.8)	10.4	279.3
1955	8.5	32.3	73.7	100.0	1.6	(2.7)	12.2	272.6
1956	9.6	54.8	68.9	104.0	2.1	3.4	12.9	279.9
1957	10.0	76.0	51.4	109.0	2.6	9.7	15.9	292.8
1958	12.0	97.3[e]	84.4	125.0	4.1	11.1	21.5[f]	291.3
1959	13.0	93.7	86.6	146.0[g]	(5.0)	(12.0)	(19.0)	293.6
1960	13.0	101.9	95.1	146.0	(6.0)	(14.0)	19.3	332.0

Sources: Bahrein: 1934-39: Data have been estimated on the basis of royalty payment of 3½ rupees per ton and the annual production of crude petroleum. Adjustments have been made for changes in foreign exchange rates. 1940-49: United Nations, Department of Economic Affairs, *Middle East: Petroleum,* Research Memorandum No. 18 (New York, March, 1951), p. 35. 1950-56: "Middle East Oil, a Special Study," *The Banker* (London, November, 1956), p. 681. 1957-60: United Nations, *Economic Developments in the Middle East, 1959-61* (New York, 1962), p. 146.

Iran: 1913-51: International Court of Justice, *Anglo-Iranian Oil Company Case* (The Hague), pp. 188, 201, 210, 214; Anglo-Iranian Oil Company, Limited, *Annual Report and Accounts, 1950 and 1951* (London, 1951, 1952). 1954-60: Data have been obtained from the National Iranian Oil Company, Teheran, Iran.

Iraq: 1927-50: Ribhi Abu El-Haj, Oil Industry, *A Strategic Factor in the Economic Development of Iraq* (New York, 1957), unpublished Ph.D. dissertation submitted to Columbia University. 1951-60: Data have been obtained from the Department of Economic and Social Affairs of the United Nations. 1959: *Petroleum Press Service* (January, 1960).

Kuwait: 1946-59: United Nations, *Middle East: Petroleum,* Research Memorandum No. 18; *Economic Developments in the Middle East, 1959-1961.*

Neutral Zone: 1948-58: Data have been obtained from the United Nations, Department of Economic and Social Affairs. 1959-61: Estimates based on crude petroleum output, and terms of payments to the respective governments.

Qatar: 1950-59: Data have been obtained from the United Nations, Department of Economic and Social Affairs; see also United Nations, *Economic Developments in the Middle East, 1959-1961*, p. 146.

Saudi Arabia: 1936-49 and 1959: Data have been obtained from Arabian American Oil Company. 1950-58: Data have been obtained from the Department of Economic and Social Affairs, United Nations; see also *Economic Developments in the Middle East, 1959-1961*. Data for 1960 have been obtained from the Bureau of Economic Affairs of the United Nations.

[a]Figures for 1913-27 refer to fiscal years beginning first of April of the years stated; figures after 1927 are for calendar years.

[b]Figures until 1946 refer to fiscal years starting first of April of the years stated; the figures for 1947 cover the period April 1, 1947, through December 31, 1947; the data for the following years are for calendar years. Data for the period up to 1952 have been adjusted to include the payment of 10 per cent of the petroleum income of the Iraq Petroleum Company and the Mosul Petroleum Company to the Turkish government, under the 1926 agreement.

[c]Includes additional payments due to Iran under the supplemental agreement of July, 1949. These payments were never actually paid to Iran, but they were taken into account in the settlement of the claims and counterclaims of the Iranian government and the Anglo-Iranian Oil Company arising from the nationalization of the petroleum industry. They amounted to £9.5 million for 1948, £9.4 million for 1959, £16.5 million for 1950, and £9.5 million for 1951.

[d]Includes $20.3 million for payment in settlement of the gold pound controversy.

[e]Including $25 million bonus paid by the Pan American Oil Corporation in signing a petroleum agreement with the government of Iran.

[f]Including £1,173,400 in settlement of previous claims.

[g]Adjusted figure.

Note: Figures in parentheses have been estimated on the basis of production of crude petroleum and available information on terms of payments by oil companies to the respective governments.

Notes

Chapter I: GROWTH OF THE PETROLEUM INDUSTRY IN THE MIDDLE EAST.

1. Petroleum has been used since ancient times. In fact, ". . . the history of the oil business in the Middle East goes back many centuries before Christ. The Old Testament contains a number of references to the large oil and gas seepages and to uses of petroleum in that region. Noah smeared his ark with pitch, or bitumen within and without. Herodotus and other ancient historians, the cuneiform records of ancient kings and businessmen, and the excavations of modern archeologists have revealed that the products of seepages were used for many purposes and in relatively large quantities, considering the amounts available and the primitive methods of recovery. The oil men of Mesopotamia also did a fair export business. . . . The principal uses were as mortar, and for waterproofing, as medicine and in some cases as fuel for lamps."—Arabian American Oil Company, *Aramco Handbook* (The Netherlands: Arabian American Oil Company, 1960), p. 97. See also R. J. Forbes, *Studies in Early Petroleum History* (Leiden: E. J. Brill, 1958).

2. "They are easy to handle, easy to transport and easy to feed to furnaces without manual work. They burn cleanly, leave no ashes and have a high heat value per unit and a high thermal efficiency. They are ordinarily less expensive except where coal is available close at hand."—Arabian American Oil Company, *op. cit.*, 102.

3. United Nations, *Economic Application of Atomic Energy*, E/3005 (New York, 1957).

4. United Nations, *New Sources of Energy and Economic Development*, E/2997 (New York, 1957).

5. Most postwar estimates of the ultimate reserves of crude oil in the United States range from 140 billion barrels to 300 billion, but one estimate puts the total at 1,000 to 2,000 billion; in 1960, proved reserves were 31.6 billion barrels. For details and sources, see Sam H. Schurr and Bruce C. Netschert, *Energy in the American Economy, 1850–1975* (Baltimore: The Johns Hopkins Press, 1960), pp. 347–59. In other parts of the world, the ratio of ultimate reserves to proved reserves is probably much higher than in the United States, since the latter is one of the most intensively explored parts of the earth, and the one from which two-thirds the amount of oil so far proved has been extracted (see Table 3).

6. Figures for 1936 and 1944 are taken from the "Review of Middle East Oil," *Petroleum Times* (London, June, 1948), p. 4; data for 1952 and 1961 are obtained from *World Oil* (Houston, Texas, July 15, 1952, p. 71 and August 15, 1961).

7. For full details on the history of Middle East oil, see Stephen H. Longrigg, *Oil in the Middle East* (London: Oxford University Press, 1961); Benjamin Shwadran, *The Middle East, Oil and the Great Powers, 1959* (New York: Council for Middle Eastern Affairs Press, 1959); United States Federal Trade Commission, Staff Report, *International Petroleum Cartel* (Washington, 1952); and Arabian American Oil Company, *Middle East Oil Developments* (4th ed., March, 1956).

8. Heat value varies in different kinds of crude and natural gas. On the average, a barrel of crude petroleum has a heat value of 6 million Btu and one Mcf (thousand cubic feet), of natural gas has a heat value of about 1 million Btu. Consequently, 1 metric ton of crude oil in terms of heat value equals 45 Mcf of natural gas.

9. Mention may be made of two schemes for delivering natural gas from the Middle East to the European market. In 1951, a project was drawn for a 2,500-mile

pipeline from the Persian Gulf to Western Europe, with a daily capacity of 1 billion cubic feet; the investment was estimated at $775 million and the delivered price at 32¢ per Mcf. In 1954, it was estimated that liquefied methane could be delivered from Saudi Arabia to Europe at 43¢ per Mcf; the required investment, including tankers, was put at $235–350 million, depending on the capacity of the processing plants. See Abdullah Tariki, *Natural Gas in the Middle East* (Third Arab Petroleum Congress, Alexandria: The Secretariat General of the League of Arab States, October, 1961). For a case study of gas injection, see Mohammed Said Mishal, *Gas Injection in the Ain Dar Area of the Ghawar Field* (Third Arab Petroleum Congress, Alexandria: The Secretariat General of the League of Arab States, October, 1961).

10. In 1929, tanker cargoes in ocean shipping amounted to 65 million tons out of a total of 470 million; by 1959, the figures were 470 million and 990 million, respectively. See United Nations, *Monthly Bulletin of Statistics* (New York, January, 1961), p. ix.

11. In 1959, the Suez Canal Authority launched a five-year program of development for the widening and deepening of the Canal to allow for the transit of tankers drawing 37 feet with a gross tonnage of about 45,000 tons. This program, which will cost 62.8 million Egyptian pounds ($176 million), will make it possible to increase traffic by 20 per cent as compared with 1959. Work has also started with the ultimate aim of doubling the Canal over its entire length. See Suez Canal Authority, *Suez Canal Report, 1959* (Ismailia, United Arab Republic, 1960), p. 62.

12. In 1957–58, a 24-inch pipeline was laid in Israel from the Gulf of Aqaba to the Mediterranean. Its present capacity is about 80,000 barrels a day; this can be raised up to 200,000 barrels a day.

13. See John A. Loftus, "Middle East Oil, The Pattern of Control," *The Middle East Journal* (Washington, D.C., January, 1948), Vol. 2, No. 1, pp. 17–32.

14. United Nations, *Review of Economic Conditions in the Middle East,* E/1910 Add. 2/Rev. 1 (New York, 1951), p. 25.

15. See, for example, Longrigg, *Oil in the Middle East;* Shwadran, *The Middle East, Oil and the Great Powers, 1959;* Federal Trade Commission, *International Petroleum Cartel;* and Arabian American Oil Company, *Middle East Oil Development.*

16. See Chapter VI, Section C; for the text of this concession, see Abolfazl Lisani, *Talai Siah ya Balai Iran* (*Black Gold or Iran's Misfortune*) (Tehran: Tchape Mehr, 1950), pp. 8–13.

17. For text see J. C. Hurewitz, *Diplomacy in the Near and Middle East* (2 vols.; Princeton: D. Van Nostrand, 1956), I, pp. 249–51.

18. For text see International Court of Justice, *Anglo-Iranian Oil Case* (The Hague, n.d.), pp. 247–70.

19. International Court of Justice, *Anglo-Iranian Oil Case,* pp. 274–77. Mention may be made at this point of some other concessions granted, between 1910 and 1940, to American, Russian, and other interests, none of which led to actual operations in Iran, and of the unsuccessful Soviet attempt to obtain a concession in 1945–46 (see Chapter VI, Section C).

20. For text see International Court of Justice, *Anglo-Iranian Oil Case,* pp. 279–80.

21. For text of the agreement see United States House of Representatives, Eighty-Fourth Congress, *Current Antitrust Problems,* Hearings before Antitrust Sub-Committee of the Committee on the Judiciary (4 parts; Washington, D.C., 1955), Part II, pp. 1563–1651. For the list of consortium members see the Appendix.

22. Moody's Investors Service, *Moody's Industrial Manual, 1960* (New York: D. F. Shea, 1960), p. 2380.

23. For text see International Court of Justice, *Anglo-Iranian Oil Case,* p. 273.

24. Mona Palmer Publishing Corporation, *World Petroleum Legislation* (New York, 1956–61).

25. For an official view on this matter, see Mohammed Reza Shah Pahlavi, *Mission for My Country* (New York: McGraw-Hill Book Co., 1961), p. 282, where it is stated that ". . . the yardstick we have established in Iran will inevitably be applied in other countries, as indeed it already has been."

26. For text see Hurewitz, *Diplomacy in the Near and Middle East,* I, pp. 276–79.

27. For text of the "Red Line" Agreement see United States House of Representatives, *Current Antitrust Problems,* pp. 1004–1034.

28. This consisted of five American companies: Standard Oil Company of New Jersey; Standard Oil Company of New York; Gulf Refining Company; Atlantic Refining Company; and American Petroleum Corporation (the first two of these had been assigned 25 per cent of the shares each, and the others 16⅔ per cent each). In 1930, the latter two companies sold their shares in the Near East Development Corporation to the first two companies; and in 1934, the Gulf Oil Corporation also sold its interest to Standard Oil Company of New Jersey and Standard Oil Company of New York, thus giving each 50 per cent of the shares of Near East Development Corporation.

29. In return for giving up nearly half its shares in the Turkish Petroleum Company, the Anglo-Persian Oil Company obtained the right to a 10 per cent overriding royalty on all crude oil to be produced by that company; in 1934 this was reduced to 7.5 per cent and was limited only to the output of oil in the concession area of the Iraq Petroleum Company.

30. See text of Frontier Treaty of June 5, 1926, in Hurewitz, *Diplomacy in the Near and Middle East,* II, p. 146.

31. For text see Hurewitz, *Diplomacy in the Near and Middle East,* II, pp. 131–42. The Arabic texts of all oil agreements concluded by Iraq are to be found in Muhammad Labib Shuqair and Sahib Dhahab, *Ittifaqat wa uqud al betrol fil bilad al Arabiyya* (*Petroleum Agreements and Contracts in the Arab Countries*) (2 vols.; Cairo: Al Matbaa al alamia, 1959).

32. For text of this agreement see *Iraq Government Gazette,* No. 49, Annexure II (Baghdad, 1938).

33. For text of this agreement, which is called "Supplemental Heads of Agreement," see United States House of Representatives, *Current Antitrust Problems,* Part II, pp. 970–83.

34. The Arabic texts of oil agreements concluded by Bahrein are to be found in Shuqair and Dhahab, *Ittifaqat. . . .*

35. See United States Federal Trade Commission, *International Petroleum Cartel,* p. 114. Arabic texts of petroleum agreements concluded by Saudi Arabia, including those for the Neutral Zone, are to be found in Shuqair and Dhahab, *Ittifaqat. . . .*

36. For texts see United States House of Representatives, *Current Antitrust Problems,* Part II, pp. 1055–1228.

37. Article IV of "Articles of Incorporation of Arabian American Oil Company," United States House of Representatives, *Current Antitrust Problems,* Part II, pp. 1074–78.

38. The Arabic texts of concession agreements granted by Kuwait until 1960, including those for the Neutral Zone, are to be found in Shuqair and Dhahab, *Ittifaqat. . . .*

39. Longrigg, *op. cit.,* 111.

40. See text in *Petroleum Times,* Supplement (London, February 24, 1961), vol. LXV.

41. United States Federal Trade Commission, *International Petroleum Cartel,* p. 86.

42. Longrigg, *op. cit.,* 216.

43. *Ibid.,* 309.

44. For text see *Agreement between the Saudi Arab Government and the Japan*

Trading Company, Ltd. (Cairo: Imprimerie Misr, 1958). The Arabian Oil Company is the operating subsidiary of the Japan Trading Company, a group consisting of sixty Japanese firms, including Mitsui and Mitsubishi interests, formed for the purpose of securing this concession.

45. Longrigg, *op. cit.*, 231–34, 317–19; Arabian American Oil Company, *Middle East Oil Development*, p. 40.

46. Longrigg, *op. cit.*, 320.

47. The British Petroleum Company, Ltd., *Facts and Figures from the Annual Report, for the Year Ended 31st December 1960* (London, 1961).

Chapter II: INVESTMENT

1. This chapter is devoted mainly to a discussion of capital investment in fixed assets (including property, plant, and equipment), both gross and net, i.e., after depreciation. A very rough estimate has also been given of the total assets of the industry, including its liquid assets. No attempt has been made to estimate the net worth of the industry; this would have to take into account, in addition to the above, the estimated value of discovered petroleum reserves, profits, and other elements of a speculative nature.

2. The data on investments or on fixed assets presented in this chapter include the cost of drilling dry holes and lease-concession acquisitions but exclude geological and geophysical expenses and lease rentals.

3. To give only one example, the Nelson index of refinery construction cost in the United States rose from 100 in 1946 to 146.2 in 1950 and 228.2 in 1960; see "Nelson Refinery Cost Indexes," *The Oil and Gas Journal* (July 3, 1961), vol. 60, p. 115.

4. The data for the years 1926 and 1935 have been taken from Arabian American Oil Company, *Middle East Oil Developments* (New York, 1952), p. 19; the figures for the other years have been taken from Table 10.

5. Originally, exploration risks were as high in the Middle East as elsewhere, and in some areas the gestation period was longer. But in subsequent years, after numerous discoveries had been made in the various countries bordering on the Persian Gulf, the probability of discovering oil in the region became very great.

6. Anglo-Iranian Oil Company, *Annual Report and Accounts as of 31 December 1950* (London, 1951).

7. See "Agreement between Iran and the Consortium of Oil Companies," published in the United States House of Representatives, Eighty-Fourth Congress, *Current Antitrust Problems,* Hearings before Antitrust Sub-Committee of the Committee on the Judiciary (4 parts; Washington, D.C., 1955), Part II, Article 1, pp. 1563–1651.

8. United States House of Representatives, *Current Antitrust Problems,* Part II, p. 1564.

9. *Ibid.*, II, Art. 6, 1577–80.

10. *Ibid.*, II, 1004–34.

11. United States Senate, Eighty-Fifth Congress, *Emergency Oil Lift Program and Related Oil Problems* (4 parts; Washington, D.C., 1957), Part IV, Appendix B, pp. 2838–39. The gross fixed assets were distributed as follows: producing facilities and pipelines, $166.5 million; refinery and marine terminal, $76.9 million; motor, marine, aircraft, and construction, $58.4 million; drilling, $10.4 million; product distribution, $7.1 million; housing and community facilities, $113.3 million; utilities, $85.7 million; maintenance and general, $46.1 million; and construction in progress, $44.4 million.

12. United States Senate, Seventy-Ninth Congress, *Report of the Group of American Petroleum Interests in Foreign Countries, Submitted to the Special Senate Committee Investigating Petroleum Resources* (Washington, D.C., 1945), II, p. 8.

13. International Bank for Reconstruction and Development, *The Economic Development of Iraq* (Baltimore: The Johns Hopkins Press, 1952), p. 34.

14. *The Oil and Gas Journal* (December 14, 1950), vol. 49, p. 68. The equity share of Gulf Exploration Corporation (half-owner in Kuwait Oil Company) was $65 million at the end of 1950; see Argus Research Corporation, *Oil Companies in the Middle East* (New York, July 3, 1951).

15. The development of Qatar's oil resources started before the war, but the war interrupted further development activities and investment.

16. This does not include about $25 million paid by the oil companies as bonuses and rents to the governments of Kuwait and Saudi Arabia before production of crude oil started in the Neutral Zone.

17. This consisted of the following: capital stock, $100,000; earned surplus, $55.5 million; capital surplus, $28.2 million; and surplus reserves, $8.7 million. See United States Senate, Eightieth Congress, *Investigation of the National Defense Program* (Washington, D.C., 1949), p. 25031.

18. The capital-output ratio of the Middle East oil industry, as distinct from the ratio of capital to capacity, is discussed in Chapter V, Section D.

19. The value of total fixed assets in Table 15 are at current prices, and in view of the declining purchasing power of currencies, this point must also be taken into account in comparing the data.

20. In the earlier years of petroleum development in Saudi Arabia (in 1947), the ratio of capital expenditures for social overhead to total investment in the oil industry was stated to be 50 per cent, while at the end of 1956 the share of social overhead in total gross fixed assets of the industry in Saudi Arabia (excluding investments in the Trans-Arabian Pipeline Company) had declined to 20 per cent. See United States Senate, Eighty-Fifth Congress, *Investigation of the National Defense Program,* p. 24840; United States Senate, *Emergency Oil Lift* (Washington, D.C., 1957), pp. 2838–39. It must be added that the relative cost of social overhead in Saudi Arabia is the highest in the Middle East; the average for the region being under 10 per cent. (See Table 14.)

Chapter III: Prices and Receipts

1. The import duties were originally imposed at the rate of 10.5¢ per barrel of crude and were raised to 21¢ on January 1, 1951; imports of crude, within a fixed quota, most of which is allocated to Venezuela, pay only half the duty. See Percy W. Bidwell, *Raw Materials: a Study of American Policy* (New York: Harper & Bros., 1958). For information on the recently imposed quotas see *Petroleum Press Service* (March, 1959, and subsequent issues).

2. Federal Trade Commission, *International Petroleum Cartel,* p. 29.

3. *Ibid.,* 349.

4. See Leonard M. Fanning, *Foreign Oil and the Free World* (New York: McGraw-Hill, 1954), chap. 20.

5. *Petroleum Press Service* (London, March, 1956).

6. William Fellner, *Competition Among the Few* (New York: Alfred A. Knopf, 1960), p. 16.

7. George W. Stocking and Myron W. Watkins, *Monopoly and Free Enterprise* (New York: Twentieth Century Fund, 1951), Chap. 6.

8. *Ibid.,* Chap. 7, and the literature cited therein. See also Arthur R. Burns, *The Decline of Competition* (New York: McGraw-Hill, 1936). The extent and nature of competition in the United States oil industry is ably studied by Melvin G. De Chazeau and Alfred E. Kahn, *Integration and Competition in the Petroleum Industry* (New Haven: Yale University Press, 1959) and by Ralph Cassady, *Price Making and Price Behavior in the Petroleum Industry* (New Haven: Yale University Press, 1954), especially in Chap. 6.

9. This, of course, has not always been true. Starting from very humble origins at the beginning of this century, the Royal Dutch–Shell group won its present position by bitter competition with the Standard Oil group. This competition, and the ruinous price wars to which it gave rise, was ended by the celebrated "as is" or Achnacarry agreement of 1928, which is extensively summarized and discussed in Federal Trade Commission, *International Petroleum Cartel,* pp. 197–210. Multi-volume histories of Shell and Standard Oil are being published, namely Carel Gerretson, *History of the Royal Dutch* (4 vols.; Leiden: E. J. Brill, 1953–57) and Ralph W. Hidy, *History of Standard Oil Company* (*New Jersey*) (2 vols.; New York: Harper & Bros., 1955–56).

10. Paul H. Frankel and Walter L. Newton, "Product-Mix of Foreign Oil Refineries and Profitability of International Oil Companies," *The Analysts Journal* (New York, November, 1959).

11. Edith Penrose, "Middle East Oil: The International Distribution of Profits and Income Taxes," *Economica* (London, August, 1960).

12. A study made in the United States in 1951 showed that the cost of gasoline represented 25 per cent of the total cost of owning and operating a car. A study of the price elasticity of demand for gasoline made in 1925–32 in four states showed it as "ranging from below 0.2 for Kansas to about 0.5 for Pennsylvania." See Robert S. Nielsen, *Oil Tanker Economics* (Bremen: Weltschiffahrts-Archiv, 1959), pp. 35–37.

13. Cassady, *op. cit.,* p. 78; see also P. H. Frankel, *Essentials of Petroleum* (London: Chapman and Hall, 1946), pp. 51–56.

14. See Walter J. Levy, "The Past, Present and Likely Future Price Structure for the International Oil Trade," *Proceedings, Third World Petroleum Congress* (Leiden: E. J. Brill, 1951); Federal Trade Commission, *International Petroleum Cartel,* pp. 349–78; United Nations, Economic Commission for Europe, *The Price of Oil in Western Europe* (Geneva, March, 1955); De Chazeau and Kahn, *op. cit.,* pp. 211–13.

15. In the United States itself, oil prices have been determined by competition among firms, with a greater or lesser monopolistic element prevailing in the various stages of operations. Moreover, oil has had to meet intense competition from coal, natural gas, and electricity. Until prorationing was applied in 1935, prices of crude fluctuated violently. Thus, the Gulf price per barrel of 34 degree crude, which had stood at 80¢ in 1913 and 40¢ in 1914, rose from $1.00 in 1919 to $2.50 in 1920 and fell again to $1.25 in 1921, and, during the depression, fell as low as 10¢. Earlier, fluctuations had been even more violent; thus, in the early 1860's, prices fell to as little as 10¢ and rose to a high of $10 per barrel. Between 1933 and 1940 the price showed very little change, and during the war it was controlled at $1.36. Following the removal of price controls, the price rose to $1.81 in 1946 and $2.68 in 1947. Since 1933, petroleum prices have followed very closely the movement in the index of wholesale prices, the total rise between 1933 and 1958 being almost identical in both series. See American Petroleum Institute, *Petroleum Facts and Figures* (New York, 1960).

16. Alexander Melamid, "The Geography of World Petroleum Prices," address delivered before the Congress of International Geographical Union, Stockholm, August 6–13, 1960—to be published in *Proceedings of the Congress.*

17. Levy, *op. cit.*

18. Federal Trade Commission, *International Petroleum Cartel,* pp. 355–56.

19. The price of crude oil changes according to its gravity, as well as to its other properties; during the postwar years prices in the Middle East have been 2¢ a barrel higher per degree API gravity; sweet crude has commanded a premium of about 15¢ a barrel over sour crude, i.e., one with a high sulphur content.

20. Levy, *op. cit.*

21. Melamid, *op. cit.*

22. Whereas in the immediate postwar years crude oil posted prices in the Persian Gulf and the Gulf of Mexico were identical, by 1959 the former had declined to approximately 60 per cent of the latter.

23. Frankel and Newton, *op. cit.*

24. *Petroleum Week* (New York, July 22, 1960) and *Oil and Gas Journal* (Tulsa, August 15, 1950), quoted by Helmut J. Frank, *The Pricing of Middle East Crude Oil* (unpublished doctoral dissertation presented to Columbia University in 1961), p. 183; several other examples of discounts are given in Chaps. IV and V of that dissertation.

25. The Chase Manhattan Bank, *Petroleum Industry, 1959* (New York, July, 1960), p. 20.

26. The main exception was Anglo-Iranian Oil Company which directly produced and marketed Iranian oil through its own extensive outlets. But, since 1951, Anglo-Iranian Oil Company is no longer a direct producer of crude oil in the region. Another exception is constituted by the independent companies operating in the Neutral Zone.

27. The "Red Line" agreement stipulated that this fee would not exceed 5s per ton (Article 13). In 1934, it was fixed at 1s per ton and the change received the consent of the British Board of Inland Revenue; this was necessary since it involved selling oil below market price and reducing profits and, consequently, taxes to be paid to the British Government.

28. No attempt has been made to estimate the income of the oil companies from operations outside the Middle East; however, the value added by the transport of oil in pipelines crossing national borders within the Middle East has, of course, been included.

29. For a discussion of the general question of transfer prices in the oil industry in the United States, see John G. McLean and Robert W. Haigh, *The Growth of Integrated Oil Companies* (Boston: Harvard University, Graduate School of Business Administration, 1954), pp. 502–6.

30. The text of several of these contracts may be found in United States House of Representatives, *Current Antitrust Problems,* pp. 839–1521.

31. Actual receipts are in fact available for local sales of petroleum, which constitute only a small fraction of petroleum marketed; these are shown in Table 23.

32. Sheikh Abdullah Tariki, *The Pricing of Crude Oil and Refined Products* (Second Arab Petroleum Congress, The Secretariat General of Arab States, Beirut, October 17–22, 1960). In the First Arab Oil Congress, held in Cairo in April, 1959, further claims had been made, viz., that the oil companies realized profits of 20¢ a barrel on tanker and pipeline transport of Middle Eastern crude, $1 on its refining and $2 on its marketing, a total of $3.20 a barrel in the post production stage, but these high claims seem to have been abandoned. See *The Economist* (London, April 18, 1959).

33. William S. Evans, *Petroleum in the Eastern Hemisphere* (New York, Petroleum Department, First National City Bank of New York, 1959) pp. 11–12. In the United States, the bulk of profit is generally attributed to crude production.

34. United Nations, *The Price of Oil.*

35. A depletion allowance is a deduction from taxable income derived from a wasting asset, and may be calculated either on the basis of a percentage of the gross income from the property in question or on the basis of volume of production. It is usually applied in mining. Depletion differs from depreciation in that the asset subject to depletion cannot be replaced. The depletion allowance is therefore granted to compensate for the diminution in capital value of wasting assets as they are produced and consumed.

36. Penrose, *op. cit.*

37. The National Iranian Oil Company took over the distribution of products in Iran, but these operations lie outside the scope of this study.

38. United States Federal Trade Commission, *International Petroleum Cartel,* p. 95.

39. Longrigg, *Oil in the Middle East,* pp. 66–67.

40. See Arabic text of letters in Shuqair and Dhahab, *Ittifaqat,* vol. II, pp. 41 and 64.

41. United States Department of the Interior, Bureau of Mines, *World Retail Prices and Taxes on Gasoline, Kerosene and Motor Lubricating Oils* (Washington, D.C., 1950). The high figure for Iran is partly due to the fact that the official rate of exchange was used in converting the rial price into United States currency.

42. National Iranian Oil Company, *Iran Petroleum Statistics: 1957, 1958, 1959* (Tehran, July, 1960).

43. United States Department of the Interior, *World Retail Prices* (March, 1958). The decline in prices in Iran reflects the devaluation of the rial; in terms of local currency, prices of petroleum products changed very little. It should be noted that in the oil-producing countries of the Middle East retail prices (excluding taxes) of kerosene, an article of mass consumption, are generally low compared to those of gasoline.

44. It should be remembered that all major refinery products are joint products. For although catalytic cracking and other technical improvements have made it possible to vary considerably the proportion in which the products are made, it still remains true that *all* of them must be produced in significant quantity if *any* of them is to be produced at all. This raises very interesting questions regarding costing and pricing policy, which will not be explored here.

45. United Nations, *World Energy Supplies, 1929–50* (New York, 1952); and *World Energy Supplies, 1957–60* (New York, 1962); Organization for European Economic Cooperation, *Towards a New Energy Pattern in Europe* (Paris, 1960), p. 17.

46. In 1955, a comparison of unit values of imported coal and oil of equivalent energy contents showed that coal was dearer by 34 per cent in France, 1 per cent in West Germany, 30 per cent in Sweden, 27 per cent in the United Kingdom, and 52 per cent in Japan. Nathaniel B. Guyol, "The Role of Petroleum in World Energy Supplies," *Fifth World Petroleum Congress, Proceedings* (New York, 1959), Section IX, p. 28. Moreover, in many uses the efficiency of oil products, relative to coal, is much greater than the ratio of the calorific value of oil to coal, viz., 1.5; particularly striking is the ratio of 12 in diesel shunting locomotives, 5 in main line diesel locomotives and 3 in marine motor vessels, while for central heating it is 2. Organization for European Economic Cooperation, *Oil—the Outlook for Europe* (Paris, 1956), p. 85. Finally, costs of transport of oil, per unit of energy content, are much lower than, and over long distances are less than one half of, those of coal. See table in Bruce C. Netschert and George O. Löf, *New Sources of Energy in the World Energy Economy,* United Nations Conference on New Sources of Energy (New York, May 17, 1961), p. 27.

47. For a discussion of this factor, see Horst Mendershausen, *Dollar Shortage and Oil Surplus in 1949–50,* Essays in International Finance No. 11 (Princeton: Princeton University, Department of Economics and Social Institutions, 1950); and *Petroleum Press Service* (London, November, 1957).

48. Iran's main refinery, at Abadan, has been working well below capacity since the nationalization crisis; the 1960 output represented some two-thirds of capacity.

49. Iraq's concentration on exports of crude petroleum has been due partly to its geographical position and partly to the restrictive provisions of Article 16(i) of the 1928 "Red Line" agreement.

50. United States Department of the Interior, Bureau of Mines, *World Petroleum Statistics, 1960* (Washington, D.C., 1961).

51. See the papers presented by S. Morris Livingston, "Economics of Refinery Location in the United States," and P. H. Frankel and W. L. Newton, "Current Trends in Location and Size of Refineries in Europe," and the ensuing discussion in *Fifth World Petroleum Congress, Proceedings* (New York, 1959), Section IX, pp. 75–105.

52. The gap has resulted from two factors. First, posted prices of crude in internal markets have, over the last decade, fallen relatively to those of refined products. Secondly, owing to technical improvements, it has become possible to extract a larger proportion of the more valuable products out of a given barrel of crude, and thus raise the total value of the refined products; of course, this has involved higher investment in the increasingly elaborate refineries, but this fact does not affect the question at issue, viz., that the foreign exchange gain from refining at home has increased. Thus, in 1950 prices, the value of the products produced in the United States from a barrel of crude by a 1927 refinery was $3.52 and from a 1946 refinery $4.25; quality was also greatly superior in the latter. See McLean and Haigh, *The Growth of Integrated Oil Companies*, p. 547.

53. See Hameed Al-Qaysi, "An Economic Appraisal of Iraq Petroleum Concessions," unpublished doctoral dissertation (New York: Columbia University, 1960), p. 304.

54. Frankel and Newton, *op. cit.*, 90, 103.

55. See *Petroleum Press Service* (July, 1959).

56. Alexander Melamid, "Center of Gravity of Domestic Refineries," *Oil Forum* (June, 1955); see also *idem*, "Geographical Distribution of Petroleum Refining Capacities," *Economic Geography* (April, 1955).

57. Livingston, *op. cit.*, 82.

58. The number of products usually produced by a refinery ranges from 50 to over 80. See Frankel and Newton, *op. cit.*, 103.

59. *Ibid.*, 92; and *Petroleum Press Service* (July, 1959).

60. *Petroleum Press Service* (January, 1960 and February, 1960).

61. *Petroleum Press Service* (March, 1961); a third category, "intermediate," accounted for 8.6 per cent in 1960 and for an estimated 7.8 per cent in 1963. These figures agree with those of Frankel and Newton, *op. cit.*, 86.

Chapter IV: COSTS AND OUTLAYS

1. Raymond F. Mikesell and Hollis B. Chenery, *Arabian Oil* (Chapel Hill, N.C., 1949), p. 148.

2. McLean and Haigh, *op. cit.*, 560–63. The general formula is: $y = Ax^n$, with n equal to 0.6, and therefore substituting h.c. for Log A: $\text{Log } Y = .6 \text{ Log } X + C$ where Y is capital cost in millions of dollars, X capacity in barrels daily, and C a constant which in this case is negative. (Information supplied by Continental Oil Company.)

3. Livingston, *op. cit.*, 76.

4. *Ibid.* However, "The unit savings in variable costs achieved by the larger size refineries did not contribute significantly to the economic superiority of the larger plants."—McLean and Haigh, *op. cit.*

5. *Petroleum Press Service*, November, 1960. Figures only slightly different are given in P. H. Frankel and W. L. Newton, *op. cit.* For further details see *Oil Forum* (New York, January, 1957); *The Economist* (London, February 2, 1957); and P. P. Nibley and D. W. Dreier, *Pipeline Economics and Technology in the Middle East* (Second Arab Petroleum Congress, The Secretariat General of Arab States, Beirut, October, 1960), p. 6. Capital costs fall particularly sharply with the increase in scale, but labor expenses also decline; thus, whereas a 45,000 ton tanker needs a crew of 60

men, two 22,000 ton tankers would need 80 men or more. Moreover, fuel, maintenance, and repair costs are proportionately lower for larger tankers.

6. Nielsen, *op. cit.*, 90.
7. *The Statist,* Special Supplement on the Oil Industry (London, April 22, 1950).
8. McLean and Haigh, *op. cit.*, 185–86.
9. See the charts in *Petroleum Press Service* (July, 1960).
10. Fanning, *Foreign Oil,* pp. 13–23; *Petroleum Press Service* (November, 1960); Petroleum Commission, *Petroleum Development in Libya 1954 through mid-1960* (Tripoli, Libya, n.d.), plate 5.
11. *Petroleum Press Service* (April, 1961).
12. United States Senate, Eighty-Fifth Congress, *Emergency Oil Lift Program and Related Oil Problems, Joint Hearings before the Special Subcommittee on Minerals, Materials and Fuel Economics of the Committee on Interior and Insular Affairs* (Washington, D.C., 1957), p. 997.
13. De Chazeau and Kahn, *op. cit.*, 67–68.
14. Frankel, *op. cit.*, 29.
15. McLean and Haigh, *op. cit.*, 563. It should, however, be noted that the authors included the cost of "operating and supervisory labor," estimated at 10 per cent of the total, among fixed costs, on the assumption that, in the short run, the refinery would keep all its workmen even if it cut down on production, since most of them are skilled and not easily replaceable. Total labor costs including "operating labor, supervision, maintenance, overhead, and payroll burdens amounted to approximately 30 per cent of the total costs."
16. A. Martin, R. G. de Lilliac, and A. Giraud, "La Marge de Raffinage en France," *Proceedings of the Third World Petroleum Congress* (The Hague-Leiden; E. J. Brill, 1951), Section X, p. 157.
17. *Petroleum Press Service* (January, 1958). Another source puts the proportion at 75–80 per cent for crude pipelines. De Chazeau and Kahn, *op. cit.*, 69.
18. The data have been calculated from Table 12 and Appendix Tables 1 and 5; adjustments have been made to exclude investment expenditures and refining cost from total expenditures, and to add estimated depreciation.
19. Costs of moving equipment from the United States to other regions and within these regions over poor means of transport, as well as higher expenditure on camps, workshops, etc., may raise drilling costs abroad to a level of 50 per cent or more above that prevailing in the United States. I. S. Solnikov, "New Developments in Drilling Equipment and Techniques," *Proceedings of the United Nations Scientific Conference on the Conservation and Utilization of Resources* (New York: United Nations, 1952), vol. 3, p. 13. "Drilling costs per foot in Venezuela appear to be over twice as high as in the United States and those in the Middle East cannot be much smaller"—United Nations, *The Price of Oil,* p. 14.
20. United States Senate, Eighty-Third Congress, *Hearings Before the Special Subcommittee on Minerals, Materials and Fuel Economics of the Committee on Interior and Insular Affairs* (Washington, D.C., 1953–54), p. 811.
21. Elwell-Sutton, *op. cit.*, 14–20.
22. United States Senate, *Emergency Oil Lift Program,* p. 1412.
23. In recent years, exploration costs have been raised by the higher bonuses paid to Middle Eastern governments (see Chapter VI) and sometimes by the obligation to spend a specified minimum amount on exploration. Thus, in Iran, in 1958, Pan-American Company undertook, in addition to a $25 million bonus, to spend a minimum of $82 million on exploration over a twelve-year period; if the total were not spent by the time oil was discovered, half of what remained was to be given to the National Iranian Oil Company. The agreement of 1961 between Kuwait and Shell also provides for large bonuses (see Chapter I, Section I, and Chapter VIII, Section B).

24. United States Senate, *Investigation of the National Defense*, pp. 25008 and 25022. The parallelisms between the petroleum companies operating in the Middle East and the East India Company have often been noted. In this context, the following remarks by Edmund Burke, in a letter to "a Prussian gentleman" in 1772, are interesting: "However, one advantage has arisen from the magnitude of this object [i.e., the East India Company] and the discussions which have grown from its importance, that almost everything relative to it is become very public. The proceedings in Parliament and in the India House, have given as many lights to the foreign stockholders as to the inhabitants of this kingdom."—*Letters of Edmund Burke: a Selection* (London: Oxford University Press, 1922), p. 163. In the same way, much of the information regarding the oil companies has come by way of United States Congressional investigations.

25. United States Federal Trade Commission, *International Petroleum Cartel*, p. 150.

26. Shuqair and Dhahab, *Ittifaqat*, vol. 2, p. 83.

27. *Petroleum Week* (May 13, 1955).

28. In 1956, a field was discovered by the National Iranian Oil Company near Qum, in central Iran. It was proposed to connect the field to the Mediterranean at Iskenderun, Turkey, by a pipeline nearly 1,000 miles long. The high cost of the pipeline, estimated at some $600 million, the lack of sufficient proved reserves and the general slackness in oil markets, however, have caused postponement of the exploitation of this field.

29. *World Oil* (August 15, 1960).

30. Wallace E. Pratt and Dorothy Good, *World Geography of Petroleum* (Princeton, N. J.: Princeton University Press, 1950), p. 142.

31. *Oil and Gas Journal* (December 26, 1960).

32. See also statement by Vice President of Aramco, United States Senate, Eighty-Third Congress, *Hearings*, p. 811.

33. American Petroleum Institute, *Petroleum Facts and Figures, 1959*, p. 27.

34. *Oil and Gas Journal* (December 26, 1960).

35. Of course the situation is far better in Venezuela than in the United States. "Of the 116 active oil fields in Venezuela at the end of 1953, 78% had single operators, and it has been relatively simple to allocate production between pools and concessions in an efficient and orderly manner."—J. M. Battisti, S. Vasquez, and L. Herrera, "Oil and Gas Conservation in Venezuela," *Proceedings, Fourth World Petroleum Congress* (Rome, 1955), Section IX, p. 29.

36. See the diagram in Arabian American Oil Company, *Middle East Oil Developments* (New York, 1952), p. 9.

37. For data see *World Oil* (August 15, 1961); and G. A. Vvedensky, "The Soviet Oil Industry," *Bulletin, Institute for the Study of the U.S.S.R.* (Munich, March, 1961).

38. *World Oil* (February 15, 1961); and *Oil and Gas Journal* (December 28, 1959).

39. Theodore Shabad, *Russia's Potential in Future Oil Markets* (Second Arab Petroleum Congress, The Secretariat General of Arab States, Beirut, October, 1960). More recently, the proportion of free flow seems to have risen to nearly 74 per cent. See Vvedensky, *op. cit.* In recent years, a policy has been adopted of introducing gas and water injection as soon as a field starts producing, so that pumping wells will not be necessary.

40. *Qaysi, op. cit.*, 284.

41. For a fuller discussion of this point, see Albert Y. Badre and Simon G. Siksek, *Manpower and Oil in Arab Countries* (Beirut: Economic Research Institute, American University, n.d.), pp. 78–103; David H. Finnie, *Desert Enterprise* (Cambridge, Mass: Harvard University Press, 1958), Chap. 6; George Lenczowski, *Oil and State*

in the Middle East (Ithaca: Cornell University Press, 1960), Chap. 15; and the annual reports of the various companies. For conditions prevailing at the beginning of the period under study, see International Labour Office, *Labour Conditions in the Oil Industry in Iran* (Geneva, 1950).

42. Qaysi, *op. cit.*, 281; Lenczowski, *op. cit.*, 295.

43. The 1948 figure in Iraq was abnormally high; comparison with 1947 would show an 11 per cent fall over the period, and comparison with 1949, one of 3 per cent; the index refers to the cost of living of unskilled laborers in Baghdad.

44. Qaysi, *op. cit.*, 282.

45. Calculated from table in Albert Y. Badre and Simon G. Siksek, *op. cit.*, 145.

46. Arabian American Oil Company, *Report of Operations.*

47. International Labour Office, *op. cit.;* Iranian Operating Oil Companies, Report for 1957.

48. Qaysi, *op. cit.*, 281.

49. Badre and Siksek, *op. cit.*, 59–60.

50. David Finnie, "Recruitment and Training of Labor: The Middle Eastern Oil Industry," *The Middle East Journal* (Washington, D.C., Spring, 1958), Vol. 12.

51. Iraq Petroleum Company, *Iraq Oil in 1954.*

52. Kuwait Oil Company, *Annual Review of Operations* (1959).

53. Arabian American Oil Company, *Report of Operations, 1959.*

54. American Petroleum Institute, *Petroleum Facts and Figures,* p. 420.

55. Qaysi, *op. cit.*

56. United States Senate, Eighty-Third Congress, *Hearings,* p. 608; and letter by President of Standard Oil Company (New Jersey) to *New York Times,* July 6, 1961.

57. Finnie, *op. cit.*, 118.

58. United States Senate, *Investigation of the National Defense,* p. 25372.

59. The estimate for Saudi Arabia is based on the data published on the accounts of Aramco in United States Senate, Eighty-Fifth Congress, *Hearings,* p. 2839. The total value of refined products given in this source represents the total cost of that oil plus the refining fee of Aramco. In order to arrive at the refining cost, the value of refined products has been reduced by $2 million, as refining fee, plus the value of crude oil input into the refinery. The balance thus arrived at has been divided by the volume of the output of refined products. The estimate for Iran has been based on the total cost incurred by the industry less the cost of crude exported or refined locally; the balance has been divided by the volume of refined output to arrive at tł unit cost of refining. Data for total cost is based on Appendix Table 5, adjustment being made for investment and depreciation; unit cost of crude production has been derived from the Annual Reports of the National Iranian Oil Company, which show volume and production costs of crude exports.

60. W. T. Cravens, "Refining Costs," *IBM Advanced School. Petroleum* (mimeographed). The refining cost at current prices has continued to increase in the United States. The Nelson Index of Refining Operating Cost rose from 58.5 in 1958 to 108.8 in 1960 (1960=100); see *The Oil and Gas Journal* (July 3, 1961).

61. Hubbard, M. E., *The Economics of Oil Transport and Refining Operations,* United Nations Inter-Regional Seminar on Techniques of Petroleum Development (New York: United Nations, January–February, 1962).

62. These standard rates were established by the United States Government during World War II for requisitioned tankers.

63. J. E. Pogue, *Oil in Venezuela* (New York, Chase National Bank, June, 1949).

64. Claude E. Boillot, "The Effect on Oil Prices of Suez Canal Transit Tolls," *Oil Forum* (New York, November, 1954); canal dues on laden ships were raised by 40 per cent in 1941 and reduced by 6 per cent in 1951 and 7 per cent in 1954.

65. P. P. Nibley and D. W. Dreier, *Pipeline Economics and Technology in the Middle East* (Second Arab Petroleum Congress, Beirut, October, 1960), p. 9.

66. United States Senate, *Emergency Oil Lift Program,* p. 1495; and Zuhayr Mikdashi, *Some Economic Aspects of Pipeline Transport in the Arab World* (Third Arab Petroleum Congress, Alexandria, October, 1961). The cost of transporting Saudi Arabian crude to Bahrein through the 34-mile 12-inch submarine pipelines is about 2¢ per barrel, or 59¢ per 1,000 barrel-miles. The figure for the 32-inch crude Tapline was 23.4¢ and for the Trans-Iranian 10-inch products pipeline, which runs from Abadan to Tehran and is being prolonged to the Caspian Sea, $1.20. These figures are not comparable since the pipelines have different diameters and lengths, run over widely different terrains, and carry different kinds of oil.

An interesting comparison of the relative costs of moving oil products within the region by various means of transport is provided by the National Iranian Oil Company. Costs per ton-mile in 1960 were: by road tanker 4.421¢, by railway 2.648, by barge 2.709, by the Trans-Iranian pipeline 1.041, and by Nafti Shah-Kermanshah pipeline 0.087. National Iranian Oil Company, *Iran Petroleum Statistics.* For purposes of comparison, it may be stated that in Europe the cost of moving oil is estimated at between 3.3¢ and 5.7¢ per ton-mile by road tankers, between 2.6¢ and 4.1¢ by railway, and 3.3¢ by barges of 200-ton capacity. The corresponding cost in Europe for pipelines of 1,000-mile length is calculated to amount to 0.15¢, 0.33¢, and 1.12¢ per ton-mile in the lines with a yearly capacity of 20 million, 5 million and 1 million tons, respectively; similar costs in sea transport for a distance of 2,000 miles is estimated at 0.10¢ per ton-mile in super tankers, 0.15¢ in medium-size tankers, and 0.26¢ in small tankers. See Hubbard, M. E., *The Economics of Oil Transport and Refining Operations,* United Nations Inter-Regional Seminar on Techniques of Petroleum Development (New York: United Nations, January–February, 1962).

67. British Petroleum Company, Ltd., *Statistical Review of the World Oil Industry, 1959* (London, n.d.).

68. The largest tanker to pass the Canal partly laden drew 35 feet and carried 44,000 tons of oil; the largest to pass in ballast displaced 85,600 tons. *Petroleum Press Service* (June, 1959), p. 232.

69. Frank, "The Pricing of Middle East Crude Oil," p. 144.

70. *Ibid.,* 203–4. For a detailed table, showing landed costs of different crudes at various destinations at different freight rates, see United States Senate, *Emergency Oil Lift Program,* p. 2223.

Chapter V: Returns on Investment

1. For a given enterprise, value added consists of the difference between the value of the goods and services produced and sold by it, at market prices, and the cost of the materials and services purchased by it from others. Value added may be gross or net. Gross value added includes wages, salaries and other employee benefits, interest, rent, profits, reserves for depreciation, and taxes. By deducting depreciation, net value added at market prices is obtained. The sum of the gross value added by all the productive units in a country constitutes its gross domestic product. If, from this total, factor income paid to the rest of the world is deducted and factor income received from the rest of the world is added, the gross national product of the country is obtained. Therefore, for the economies of the oil-producing countries of the Middle East, it is the total value added by the oil industry minus its factor payments abroad that is of greatest significance (see Chapter VII, Section A).

2. Following Alfred Marshall, *Principles of Economics* (8th ed., New York: Macmillan, 1953), pp. 167, 427, and 438. Royalty may be regarded as payment for the quantity withdrawn from an exhaustible resource, and therefore distinguished from rent. However, royalty is earned because of the existence of economic rent and is in general determined by institutional factors. Throughout this study royalty payments are treated as part of economic rent and not as part of costs of production.

3. In special cases, interest rates have been even lower; for instance, in 1948, Trans-Arabian pipeline contracted a loan for $125 million from insurance companies in the United States, bearing 2.55 per cent interest and repayable by 1962 (see *Moody's Industrials, 1960*, p. 2272).

4. In Chapter III, Section E, the difficulty of estimating the actual receipts of the Middle Eastern oil industry from sales of crude oil—in the absence of published data—was discussed and the necessary qualifications to the "pro-forma" receipts used in this study were made. Since this has a close bearing on the question of "value added," the reader is referred to the previous section.

5. There is a minor discrepancy in the coverage of investment and income figures. The data on investment include capital expenditures in the oil industry by the major international oil companies, as well as by independent oil companies and local governments, while the data on gross receipts and incomes refer to the operations of the major international oil companies in the Persian Gulf States and Aden Colony, plus the operations of oil companies in the Neutral Zone. Hence, the actual transfer of income abroad by the latter group may have been somewhat higher than the above figure.

6. Under most contracts concluded since 1950, profit sharing applies only to income derived from production of crude oil and does not cover income arising from refining and transport, whereas in the above calculations such income is included. Moreover, until 1955, discounts allowed to parent companies were deducted from receipts for calculation of profit sharing, while this factor has not been taken into account here. These considerations explain why the share of governments shown in the text is below 50 per cent.

7. The value of net assets, in turn, depends partly on the depreciation policy followed by the enterprise—the higher the rate of depreciation the lower are the net assets and hence the higher the ratio of income to net assets. In this study, the depreciation rates specified in agreements have been used; where no depreciation rate was available, a rate of 8 per cent of net assets has been used.

8. The 1959 ratio declined to 123 per cent as a result of the decrease in petroleum prices. There was, however, a considerable excess capacity in the oil industry in 1959, which if utilized, would have substantially raised the ratio. No attempt has been made to adjust the data for this excess capacity nor for the gestation period of investment.

9. The return on capital is measured by the net income of oil companies (including net income plus interest charges and income applicable to minority interests), divided by their net assets.

10. This relative profitability of production of crude oil is brought out most strikingly by calculating returns on investment. In 1958, net income of oil companies from production of crude oil, divided by their net assets engaged in crude production, ranged from 45 per cent in the Neutral Zone to between 75 and 105 in Qatar, Saudi Arabia, and Iraq and between 250 and 270 per cent in Kuwait and Iran. The corresponding ratios ranged from 20 to 40 per cent in major refineries and pipelines.

11. This figure represents the cost of the whole pipeline, from the oil fields in Saudi Arabia to the Mediterranean; of its 1,067 miles, 842 miles are operated by Tapline.

12. An Iranian Government official has estimated the gross income of the Anglo-Iranian Oil Company, for the period 1914–51, at $3,640 million of which $450 million was paid to the Iranian Government. (See "Iran Presents Its Case for Nationalization," by an Iranian Government official, in *The Oil Forum* [New York, March, 1952], pp. 79–94.) The difference between the two estimates of gross income arises from the fact that in the article the earning of the company has been evaluated on the basis of volume of output and prices of petroleum at the Gulf of

Mexico, while the estimate presented in the text is based, for the period 1913–47, on the value of petroleum exports (presented by the company to the government and published by the latter) plus the estimated value of domestic sales based on the volume of sales of various products and their prices. With respect to the difference in payments to the Iranian Government, the figure given in the text includes the additional payments, due to the government under the supplemental agreement of 1949, which was taken into account in settlement of claims and counter-claims between the government and the company in 1954 (see Article 1-A of Part II of the agreement between Iran and the Anglo-Iranian Oil Company, dated September 19, 1954).

13. While this observation applies to the petroleum operations of the oil consortium as a whole, the agreement between the British Petroleum Company and other consortium members provides for payment of 10¢ per barrel to the former until the withdrawal of the ten billion barrels of petroleum from Iran—i.e., until the British Petroleum Company shall have received one billion dollars for turning its rights in Iran over to the consortium members, including itself. Hence, the members of the oil consortium, excluding the British Petroleum, will earn 10¢ per barrel less for the period of the agreement. (See United States House of Representatives, *Current Antitrust Problems,* pp. 711–15.)

14. See *Moody's Industrials,* 1948, p. 1894; 1949, p. 1758; 1951, p. 2241.

15. Out of this sum, an amount of $1,373 million accrued in the period 1950–56 (see United States Senate, *Emergency Oil Lift Program,* p. 2315); the balance has been estimated to be equal to the government's share in net income of the company in the period 1957–60, $1,220 million.

16. *Ibid.,* 2839.

17. United States Senate, Eightieth Congress, *Investigation of the National Defense,* p. 25031. This figure does not include the $25.4 million surplus earned by the Caltex Oil Company.

18. *Moody's Industrials,* 1948 and 1951.

19. The International Monetary Fund has estimated in its *Balance of Payments Yearbook* (Washington, D.C.) the investment income of the group that has been transferred abroad since 1946. According to this estimate, the group's net income transferred abroad in 1948–60 amounted to $1,850 million. However, this does not include a part of net income that has been invested for the expansion of the oil industry in Iraq; in addition, the income of the industry is based on the value of oil at the Iraqi border, which is substantially lower than the posted prices at the eastern Mediterranean and thus does not take into account the income derived from the transit of petroleum by pipelines.

Chapter VI: Government Receipts

1. Lester C. Uren, *Petroleum Production Engineering* (New York: McGraw-Hill, 1950), p. 170.

2. See Edwin Lieuwen, *Petroleum in Venezuela: A History* (Berkeley: University of California Press, 1954).

3. See Aliro A. Parra and Gustavo Escobar, *Fiscal Obligations of the Venezuelan Petroleum Industry* (Second Arab Petroleum Congress, Beirut, October 17–27, 1960).

4. In the period under review, Venezuela had a system of multiple exchange rates varying from 3.05 to 3.35 bolivares to the dollar; for oil transactions a rate of 3.09 was used.

5. Other Middle Eastern countries not covered in this study, namely Israel, Turkey, and the United Arab Republic, also have a general petroleum law.

6. For example, in an amendment to the Iraq Petroleum Company's concession in 1931, the company undertook to pay £60,000 gold per annum for the first 4 million tons of oil produced and £20,000 for each additional million tons in lieu of taxes; in Iran, under Article 11 of the 1933 concession, the company undertook to pay 9d for each of the first 6 million tons and 6d for each additional ton for the first fifteen years, and 1s and 9d, respectively, thereafter for another fifteen years; similar provisions existed in the original concessions of British Oil Development Company and Basrah Petroleum Company. The Kuwait Oil Company secured exemption by paying 4 annas per ton of oil produced, in lieu of taxes (Article 7 of 1934 Concession Agreement) and the American Independent Oil Company by paying 7.5¢ per ton (Article 7 of 1948 Agreement with Kuwait).

7. No bonuses were provided for in the 1933 agreement; however, the company agreed to advance £50,000 gold to the government, to be repaid from royalties if production started.

8. For more details, see Longrigg, *Oil in the Middle East;* Shwadran, *The Middle East, Oil;* and Lenczowski, *Oil and State.*

9. An earlier concession with an enormously wide scope, including minerals, had been granted to de Reuter on July 25, 1872. It was thus described by Lord Curzon: "The most complete and extraordinary surrender of the entire industrial resources of a kingdom into foreign hands that has probably ever been dreamt of, much less accomplished, in history." George Curzon, *Persia and the Persian Question* (London: Longmans, Green & Co., 1892), vol. 1, p. 480. However, owing to Russian and local opposition and to lack of British support, this concession never came into force.

10. For the reasons see Elwell-Sutton, *op. cit.*, chap. 6.

11. See text of letter in Hurewitz, *Diplomacy*, vol. 1, p. 286.

12. H. St. J. B. Philby, *Arabian Jubilee* (New York, 1953), p. 69.

13. Four gold shillings represented, approximately, one-eighth of the value of a ton of crude oil at the time. Thus the royalty rate paid to the Iraqi Government was equal to the one generally paid to owners of oil-bearing lands in the United States.

14. For a good discussion of this point see Elwell-Sutton, *op. cit.*, 80–85.

15. All three sheikdoms were, in fact, British protectorates, although the exact status of Bahrein in international law is confused, owing to the Iranian claim upon it. All three were bound not to grant petroleum concessions without British approval: Bahrein by the agreement of May 14, 1914, Kuwait by that of October 27, 1913, and Qatar by the treaty of November 3, 1916. However, Kuwait achieved independence in late 1961.

16. See text of Memorandum in Elwell-Sutton, *op. cit.*, 168.

17. For the history of this period see George Kirk, *The Middle East, 1945–50* (London: Oxford University Press, 1954), p. 71; Nasrollah S. Fatemi, *Oil Diplomacy: Powderkeg in Iran* (New York: Whittier Books, 1954), chaps. xvi–xix; Elwell-Sutton, *op. cit.*, 115–16; and George Lenczowski, *Russia and the West in Iran, 1918–1948* (Ithaca, N. Y., 1949), chap. xi.

18. Abolfazl Lisani, *Talai siah ya balai Iran*, p. 448.

19. United Nations, *Review of Economic Conditions in the Middle East, 1951–52* (New York, 1953), pp. 60–62.

20. This agreement, in turn, had been inspired by the 1948 Venezuelan legislation mentioned above.

21. This modification, while appreciably increasing the Saudi share, caused little if any loss to Aramco, which could credit income taxes paid abroad against its liability for income tax in the United States. See United States Senate, *Emergency Oil Lift Program*, pp. 1236–41 and 1407–77.

22. See text of Iran-Consortium Agreement in Hurewitz, *op. cit.*, II, 348.

23. It may be pointed out that the fact the discounts are allowed on the company's share of the oil, but not on that of the government, gives the latter an induce-

ment to offer its share of oil to producing companies rather than to other customers who could obtain oil from the companies at a discount.

24. See Longrigg, *op. cit.*, 76, 88 and English text of convention published in *Bulletin Officiel des Actes Administratifs du Haut Commissariat* (Beirut, December 31, 1931); see also Zuhayr Mikdashi, *Some Economic Aspects of Pipeline Transport in the Arab World* (Third Arab Petroleum Congress, Alexandria, October, 1961).

25. Shwadran, *op. cit.*, 333.

26. Longrigg, *op. cit.*, 242; and *Le Commerce du Levant* (Beirut, May 24, 1952).

27. See English text of convention in *Al jarida al rasmia* (Official Journal, No. 26, Damascus, May 26, 1949).

28. Shwadran, *op. cit.*, 413–23.

29. *The Financial Times* (London, November 29, 1955), and Lenczowski, *op cit.*, 43.

30. The official Lebanese point of view is given in a pamphlet, *Bayanat wa wathaiq rasmia an qadiat aidat naql al betrol fi Lubnan* (Beirut: Ministry of Information, July 28, 1956).

31. See English and Arabic texts of Convention in *Al jarida al rasmia* (Official Journal, No. 39, Beirut, July 15, 1959).

32. See table on transit payments in: United Nations, *Economic Developments in the Middle East, 1959–61* (New York, 1962), p. 147.

Chapter VII: Contribution to Local Economy

1. For Iran see Plan Organization of Iran, *Outline of the Third Plan (1341–46)* (Tehran, 1961), p. 138; for Iraq see sources quoted in United Nations, *Economic Developments in the Middle East, 1956–57* (New York, 1958), p. 32; for Kuwait see United States Department of Commerce, *World Trade Information Series: Kuwait* (Washington, D.C., January, 1954), which gives a figure of $240 million for 1952, when Kuwait's oil income was $57 million as compared with $415 million in 1960. For Saudi Arabia see *Al Ummal* (Jidda, October, 1959), quoted by Qaysi, "An Economic Appraisal," p. 323.

2. See United Nations, *Economic Developments in the Middle East.*

3. Arabian American Oil Company, *Aramco Handbook,* p. 244. The lower figure may be nearer the mark in view of the following statement: "One may doubt whether the total [population of the Arabian peninsula] approaches 10,000,000, and it may well fall several millions short of this figure," *Encyclopaedia of Islam* (2nd. ed., Leiden: E. J. Brill), vol. 1, p. 534.

4. See Finnie, *Desert Enterprise,* chap. 7; *Aramco Handbook,* part 3; and the annual reports and pamphlets issued by the various oil companies.

5. Part of the required local currency is, of course, obtained by the companies from the sale of crude petroleum or products within the producing or transit country.

6. United Nations, *Economic Developments in the Middle East, 1954–55,* p. 151, and Closed Accounts of the Government Budget. These figures do not include returns on investment or on foreign-exchange holdings of oil-producing countries abroad.

7. *The Statesman's Yearbook* (New York: St. Martin's Press, 1960), p. 1304.

8. *The Statesman's Yearbook;* United Nations Relief and Works Agency, *Quarterly Bulletin of Economic Development,* No. 13 (Beirut, 1956); Riyadh Bank, *Government Statement of the Budget for the Financial Year 1378/1379* (mimeographed, n.d.).

9. United Nations, *Statistical Yearbook, 1961* (New York, 1962).

10. Government of Iraq, *Statistical Abstract* (Baghdad); and *Quarterly Bulletin of the Central Bank of Iraq* (Baghdad).

11. International Bank for Reconstruction and Development, *The Economic Development of Jordan* (Baltimore: The Johns Hopkins Press, 1957), p. 387.

12. For a brief account of the development plans of Iran and Iraq, see United Nations, *Economic Developments in the Middle East, 1945–54* and *1958–59* (New York).

13. United Nations, *Economic Developments in the Middle East, 1958–59,* pp. 38 and 111.

14. *Ibid.,* p. 113.

15. *Ibid.,* 116.

16. Shwadran, *op. cit.,* 381.

17. United Nations, *Economic Developments in the Middle East, 1958–59,* p. 119.

18. United Nations, *The Development of Manufacturing Industry in Egypt, Israel and Turkey* (New York, 1958), pp. 104, 115, and 117; figures on employment and value added refer to 1954 and that on capital to 1950; all figures refer to establishments employing ten persons or over. In 1960, the net capital per worker in the region's oil industry was $22,000 and the value added per worker, $25,000.

19. Badre and Siksek, *Manpower and Oil,* p. 35.

20. Badre and Siksek, *Manpower and Oil;* Finnie, *Desert Enterprise;* Shwadran, *The Middle East, Oil;* Lenczowski, *Oil in the Middle East;* Arabian American Oil Company, *Aramco Handbook;* Kuwait Oil Company, *The Story of Kuwait;* Annual Reports of various companies; International Labour Office, *Labour Conditions in Iran.*

21. For breakdown see Arabian American Oil Company, *Aramco Handbook,* p. 206.

22. See Willard A. Beling, *Pan-Arabism and Labor* (Cambridge: Harvard University Press, Middle Eastern Monographs, 1960).

23. *Ibid.*

24. *Ibid.,* 66–68.

25. International Court of Justice, *Anglo-Iranian Oil Case,* p. 208; *Iranian Oil Operating Companies, 1959; The Anglo-Iranian Oil Company and Iran* (London, July, 1951).

26. Qaysi, *op. cit.,* 262.

27. Arabian American Oil Company, *1959 Report of Operations.*

28. *Petroleum Press Service* (September, 1960).

29. United Nations, *Economic Developments in the Middle East, 1958–59,* p. 81; and *1959–61,* pp. 139–42.

30. United Nations, *World Energy Supplies, 1955–58 and 1957–60.*

31. Kuwait Oil Company, *The Story of Kuwait,* pp. 26 and 41.

32. *Chemical Week* (New York: McGraw-Hill, June 10, 1961). Latest reports indicate that the implementation of these projects has been held up.

33. Arthur D. Little, *A Plan for Industrial Development in Iraq,* 4 vols. (mimeographed, Cambridge, Mass., 1956).

34. Deutsche Projekt-Union GMBH, *Report on the Utilization of Natural Gas in Saudi Arabia* (Frankfurt, 1959).

35. For a discussion of this subject see M. D. Attiyah, *Petrochemicals: World Trends and Arab Prospects* (Third Arab Petroleum Congress, Alexandria, October, 1961).

Chapter VIII: Recent Changes and Trends

1. The only exception was Iran which, under the 1933 agreement, was entitled to 20 per cent of the amount distributed in dividends or paid into reserves but, owing to the British Government's policy of dividend limitation, payments to Iran under this heading were small during the war and postwar years (see chapter VI).

2. Walter J. Levy and Milton Lipton, "Some Major Determinants of Future Oil Requirements and Supplies," Nathaniel B. Guyol, "The Role of Petroleum in World

Energy, Supplies," and Paul R. de Ryckère "Les Prévisions des Besoins Energétiques du Monde et l'Importance du Pétrole" and subsequent discussion in *Fifth World Petroleum Congress,* pp. 11–51.

3. Kenneth E. Hill, Harold H. Hammar, and John G. Winger, *Future Growth of the World Petroleum Industry* (New York: Chase Manhattan Bank, 1957); and Frederick G. Coqueron, Harold H. Hammar, and John G. Winger, *Future Growth of the World Petroleum Industry* (New York: Chase Manhattan Bank, 1958).

4. Edward Symonds, Petroleum Economist, the First National City Bank, *Life with a World Surplus,* Address at Fort Worth Petroleum Club (Fort Worth, April 28, 1960).

5. Sam H. Schurr and Bruce C. Netschert, *Energy in the American Economy,* pp. 88, 163, 195, 234, and 238.

6. Organization for European Economic Cooperation, *Towards a New Energy Pattern in Europe* (Paris, 1960), pp. 17 and 30; and M. E. Hubbard, *Long Term Demand for Energy and Oil* (Second Arab Petroleum Congress, Beirut, October 17–22, 1960).

7. Hubbard, *op. cit.*

8. In 1959, oil consumption by the U.S., Canada, and Western Europe amounted to 68 per cent of world consumption and that of the Soviet bloc to 13 per cent. Between 1954 and 1959, world consumption including the Soviet bloc increased by an average of 7 per cent per annum; the average rise for the U.S. was 4 per cent, for Western Europe 11, and for the Soviet bloc 14; certain underdeveloped regions showed a very rapid rate of growth, for example, the Middle East, "Other Eastern Hemisphere," and South America (excluding the Caribbean) and most were above the world average. British Petroleum, *Statistical Review of the World Oil Industry, 1959* (London, n.d.).

9. Hubbard, *op. cit.*

10. A still more recent estimate also shows a small anticipated deceleration in demand for oil in 1959–65, excluding the Soviet bloc, to about 5½ per cent a year. The main constituents of the increase are a 3 per cent annual growth in the U.S., 10 per cent in Western Europe, 6 in Latin America and Canada, 15 in Japan, and 8 in the rest of the world. *Petroleum Press Service* (February, 1961). Finally, in October, 1961, the anticipated annual rate of increase of demand for petroleum in 1960–70 was put at 4.5 per cent, compared with 6.6 per cent in 1950–60. Shell International Petroleum Company, *Marketing* (Third Arab Petroleum Congress, Alexandria, October, 1961).

11. This estimate has been criticized by Harold Lubell, *Survey of Energy and Oil Demand Projections for Western Europe* (Santa Monica, Cal.: Project Rand, Research Memorandum, May 21, 1959) who puts the income elasticity of demand for energy at one.

12. For an interesting discussion of this question in its American context, see Schurr and Netschert, *op. cit.,* 164–90.

13. *Ibid.,* 325–42.

14. United Nations, Economic Commission for Europe, *Monthly Bulletin of Coal Statistics for Europe;* and *Quarterly Bulletin of Coal Statistics for Europe* (Geneva).

15. United Nations, *Monthly Bulletin of Statistics* (New York).

16. Schurr and Netschert, *op. cit.,* 19.

17. Guyol, "The Role of Petroleum in World Energy Supplies," pp. 26 and 33.

18. Schurr and Netschert, *op. cit.,* 130, 255.

19. *Petroleum Press Service,* April, 1961.

20. Schurr and Netschert, *op. cit.,* 387–89.

21. *Ibid.,* 22–28.

22. In 1959, the oil industry outside the Soviet bloc had an excess capacity of 5.5 million barrels a day of which 2.5 million was in the United States, 1.4 million in the

Middle East and 700,000 in Venezuela. Since most of the capacity outside the United States is owned by the major oil companies, while production within the United States is subject to government prorationing, this excess capacity has not weighed greatly on prices. The 1959 and 1960 price reductions in the Middle East and Venezuela were caused mainly by competition from independent companies and the Soviet Oil Trust.

23. *Petroleum Press Service* (March, 1960), pp. 92–93.

24. *Petroleum Press Service* (November, 1960); see also May, 1960, June, 1960, and October, 1960; and *World Oil* (January, 1961), special issue on North Africa.

25. Eastman, Dillon Union Securities and Company, by Kenneth E. Hill, *Outlook for Oil Stocks* (New York).

26. *Petroleum Press Service* (April, 1961); *New York Times* (January 21, 1962).

27. *Petroleum Press Service* (December, 1960).

28. United States Senate, Eighty-Seventh Congress, *Soviet Oil in the Cold War, a Study Prepared by the Library of Congress at the Request of the Subcommittee to Investigate the Administration of the Internal Security Act and other Internal Security Laws of the Committee on the Judiciary* (Washington, D.C., 1961), pp. 4 and 8.

29. Figures are published in *The New York Times,* July 27, 1962. It may be added that transport is not likely to prove a bottleneck. As long as the present tanker surplus persists, the Soviets will probably find no difficulty in hiring idle tankers. As for internal transport, it is being improved by the laying of huge pipelines, including a 2,876-mile pipeline, with annual crude-oil capacity of 40 to 50 million tons, from Kuibyshev to Unecha, in Bielo Russia, from where one branch will extend through Polotsk to the two Baltic ports of Klaipeda in Lithuania and Ventpils in Latvia; another branch will go to Bratislava in Czechoslovakia; a third branch through Poland to Schwedt in East Germany. Another pipeline, with a yearly capacity of 20 million tons, is under construction from Tikhoretsk to two Black Sea ports. Finally, a third pipeline, with an annual capacity of 16 million tons, is being extended from the Urals to Leningrad. Soviet plans in 1958 envisaged the "expenditure of the equivalent of $45 billion in the ensuing 15-year period in oil exploration, production, refining, and transportation." United States Senate, Eighty-Seventh Congress, *Soviet Oil,* p. 4.

30. *Ibid.,* 20.

31. *Petroleum Press Service* (September, 1960), 322.

32. *Petroleum Press Service* (October, 1960), 380.

33. *Petroleum Press Service* (October, 1960), 374.

34. Organization for European Economic Cooperation, *Towards a New Energy Pattern in Europe,* p. 45.

35. Sir Donald MacDougall, *The Dollar Problem: a Reappraisal,* Essays in International Finance (Princeton, November, 1960), p. 39.

36. *World Oil* (February 15, 1961), 61; and *Petroleum Press Service* (February, 1961), 66.

37. Chase Manhattan Bank, *Future Growth of the World Petroleum Industry* (November, 1958), p. 37.

38. The Soviet oil industry has well been described as "the largest integrated 'company' of its kind in the world," "Soviet Oil," *Atlantic Monthly* (Boston, February, 1961).

39. United States Senate, Eighty-Seventh Congress, *Soviet Oil,* p. 5.

40. *Ibid.* In 1960 Soviet crude oil was sold to non-Communist countries at an average price of $1.57 a barrel as compared with $3.03 to the countries within the Soviet bloc. Crude oil was delivered to Japan at $1.95 a barrel—i.e., 35 cents lower than Middle Eastern oil. The corresponding price for West Germany was $1.38 a barrel as compared to $2.69 for East Germany. There was also a difference in the export prices of refined products; for instance, India received a discount of 25 per

cent on imports of Soviet gas oil from the Abadan posted prices, while Ceylon obtained a 10 per cent discount. Similarly, Sweden was given a discount of 25 per cent from the United States Gulf prices for the same product, as compared to 15 per cent for Greece and 10 per cent for the United Arab Republic.

41. *Petroleum Press Service* (September, 1960). See also *Petroleum Press Service* (April, 1960): "The finding of the [Venezuelan] Commission was that three of the United States independents with producing interests in Venezuela—Superior, Signal, and San Jacinto—had for some months past been selling Maracaibo crude at $1.50–2.00 a barrel, when the posted price was around $2.50."

42. See *Petroleum Press Service* (October, 1960 to March, 1961); and *Petroleum Week* (New York, December 9 and 16, 1960).

43. It may be argued that, even if demand for oil were elastic (which it does not seem to be—see chapter III) and if therefore total revenues were to fall as the volume of sales was reduced, the producing countries would benefit from maintaining prices, since that would prolong the life of their oil reserves. However, given the huge size of present reserves in the Persian Gulf area, and the high probability of further large discoveries, this does not seem to be an important consideration, or one to which the governments concerned have given much weight.

44. In addition to all the usual obstacles which have wrecked various schemes for international commodity restriction, notably the entry of newcomers and the determination of the quotas of the various members, there is the knotty problem of relations between the international companies and the governments, and the corollary question of transport, since oil unlike other commodities can be carried only in tankers. Unless the international companies cooperate in the scheme, they can probably frustrate the efforts of the governments, but the companies may well judge it in their interest to participate in price maintenance, Attention should also be drawn to the divergence of interests between Venezuela, with its dependence on the United States market, its relatively small reserves, and its large number of producing firms and the Middle Eastern countries with their huge reserves, their single producing firms, and their great vulnerability to Soviet competition in the European market. See Economic Studies Department, Ente Nazionale Idrocarburi, *Cooperation between Producing and Consuming Countries* (Third Arab Petroleum Congress, Alexandria, October, 1961). For a discussion of the issues involved in price stabilization and the various possible approaches see Alirio A. Parra, *Oil and Stability* (Third Arab Petroleum Congress, Alexandria, October, 1961).

45. United Nations, *Economic Developments in the Middle East,* 1958–59, p. 79.

46. *Petroleum Press Service* (March, 1960), pp. 102–3.

47. *Petroleum Press Service* (October, 1960), 381.

48. *Petroleum Press Service* (February, 1960), 63.

49. See the papers presented at the Arab League's First Oil Congress held in Cairo, 1959, published by Arab League, Office of Petroleum Affairs, *Majmuat al buhuth al muqaddama ila al mutamar* (Cairo, Jaridat al Sabah Press, 1959); and discussion in *The Economist* (London, April 18, 1959). Of all the concessions granted before 1957, only that of Anglo-Iranian Oil Company provided for participation by the host government in profits made at later stages.

50. The agreement between National Iranian Oil Company and Canadian Sapphire was cancelled in 1960.

51. It may be added that under the 1952 agreement with Shell Company, Qatar received a down payment of £260,000.

52. For an interesting discussion, see Edith T. Penrose, "Profit Sharing Between Producing Countries and Oil Companies in the Middle East," *The Economic Journal* (London, June, 1959).

Bibliographical Notes

The volume of literature on Middle East petroleum, especially on its political and social aspects, is enormous and any attempt to give even a selective bibliography would add appreciably to the size of this book. Fortunately, this task has been admirably accomplished by Benjamin Shwadran in his *The Middle East, Oil and the Great Powers, 1959,* New York: Council for Middle Eastern Affairs Press, 1959, whose bibliography covers forty-two pages and deals thoroughly with the literature published up to 1958. The following remarks are mainly designed to indicate some of the more important sources on the economic aspects of the Middle Eastern oil industry and its chief competitors.

A. *General Studies on the Petroleum Industry*

A clear description of the technical aspects of the petroleum industry is to be found in BRITISH PETROLEUM. *Our Industry.* London: British Petroleum, 1958.

The interrelationships of petroleum and other forms of energy—in their United States context—are very thoroughly studied in SCHURR, SAM H., and BRUCE C. NETSCHERT. *Energy in the American Economy, 1850–1975.* Baltimore, Md.: Published for Resources for the Future, Inc., by The Johns Hopkins Press, 1960.

A more general discussion of the same subject is "The Outlook for Energy Sources," *Resources for Freedom, A Report to the President by the President's Materials Policy Commission,* Vol. III. Washington, D.C., June, 1952.

Data on various forms of fuels and energy sources are to be found in UNITED NATIONS. *Statistical Papers Series J: World Energy Supplies, No. 1: 1929–1950; No. 2: 1951–1954; No. 3: 1955–1958; No. 4: 1956–1959; No. 5: 1957–1960.* New York, 1952, 1957, 1960, 1961, 1962.

A very lucid introduction to oil economics is FRANKEL, P. H. *Essentials of Petroleum.* London: Chapman and Hall, 1946. Other books that may be recommended in this field are DEGOLYER, E. (ed.). *Elements of the Petroleum Industry.* New York: The American Institute of Mining and Metallurgical Engineers, 1940; and HAGER, DORSEY. *Fundamentals of the Petroleum Industry.* New York: McGraw-Hill Book Co., 1939.

A recent book of a more specialized nature may also be noted: NIELSEN, ROBERT S. *Oil Tanker Economics.* Bremen: Weltschiffahrts-Archiv, 1959.

A vast amount of information is contained in *World Petroleum Congress, Proceedings.* London, 1934, Paris, 1937, The Hague, 1951, Rome, 1955, and New York, 1959.

A summary of the annual reports of the principal oil companies is published yearly in *Moody's Industrials* (New York); and price quotations are given in Platt's Oilgram Price Service, *Platt's Oilgram* (Cleveland, Ohio).

B. *The Petroleum Industry in the United States*

The United States oil industry has been covered in numerous volumes that shed much light on the nature of oil operations and the basic problems faced by the industry in all parts of the world. Only a few of the more recent titles are noted here:

Watkins, Myron W. *Oil: Stabilization or Conservation.* New York: Harper & Brothers, 1937.

Kemnitzer, William J. *Rebirth of Monopoly.* New York: Harper & Brothers, 1938.

Cook, Roy C. *Control of the Petroleum Industry by Major Oil Companies.* ("Temporary National Economic Committee, Monograph No. 39.") Washington, D.C., 1941.

Bain, Joe S. *The Economics of the Pacific Coast Petroleum Industry.* 3 vols. Berkeley, Calif.: University of California Press, 1944–1947.

Rostow, Eugene V. *A National Policy for the Oil Industry.* New Haven, Conn.: Yale University Press, 1948.

Uren, Lester C. *Petroleum Production Engineering.* New York: McGraw-Hill Book Co., 1950.

Fleming, Harold. *Oil Prices and Competition.* New York: American Petroleum Institute, 1953.

McLean, John H., and Robert W. Haigh. *The Growth of Integrated Oil Companies.* Boston: Graduate School of Business Administration, Harvard University, 1954.

Cookenboo, Leslie. *Crude Pipe Lines and Competition in the Oil Industry.* Cambridge, Mass.: Harvard University Press, 1955.

Special mention should be made of the Petroleum Monograph Series being published by Yale University Press. So far the three following books have appeared.

Cassady, Ralph. *Price Making and Price Behavior in the Petroleum Industry.* New Haven, 1954.

Zimmerman, Erich W. *Conservation in the Production of Petroleum.* New Haven, 1957.

De Chazeau, Melvin G., and Alfred E. Kahn. *Integration and Competition in the Petroleum Industry.* New Haven, 1959.

Lastly, there are the numerous periodical publications of the American Petroleum Institute, of which the Centennial Edition of *Petroleum Facts and Figures,* 1959, is the most comprehensive and contains much information on oil operations outside the United States.

C. *The Petroleum Industry in Venezuela*

Among the more accessible publications in English on Venezuela are:

Pogue, Joseph E. *Oil in Venezuela.* New York: Chase National Bank, 1949.

Estados Unidos de Venezuela, Ministerio de Minas e Hidrocarburos. *National Petroleum Convention.* Caracas, 1951.

Walter J. Levy Associates. *Venezuelan Oil in the Framework of Western Hemisphere Supplies.* Caracas: Government of Venezuela, March 26, 1951.

LIEUWEN, EDWIN. *Petroleum in Venezuela: A History.* Berkeley, Calif.: University of California Press, 1955.
NATIONAL PLANNING ASSOCIATION. *United States Business Performance Abroad—The Case Study of the Creole Petroleum Corporation.* Washington, D.C.: The National Planning Association, 1955.
MARKS, LAURENCE M. *Oil in Venezuela.* New York: Laurence Marks and Company, 1957.
SHOUP, CARL S. *The Financial System of Venezuela.* Baltimore, Md.: The Johns Hopkins Press, 1959.
The following publications, in Spanish, may also be noted:
BETANCOURT, ROMULO. *Venezuela: Politica y Petroleo.* Mexico-Buenos Aires: Fondo de Cultura Economica, 1956.
MINISTERIO DE MINAS E HIDROCARBUROS. *Anuario Petrolero de Venezuela.* Mexico-Buenos Aires: Fondo de Cultura Economica, 1956.
———. *Memoria de Ministerio de Minas e Hidrocarburos.*

D. *The Petroleum Industry in the Soviet Bloc Countries*

The most useful studies in English are:
SHIMKIN, DEMITRI B. *Minerals, a Key to Soviet Power.* Cambridge, Mass.: Harvard University Press, 1953.
HASSMANN, HEINRICH. *Oil in the Soviet Union.* Princeton, N.J.: Princeton University Press, 1953.
JORDAN, CONSTANTIN N. *The Romanian Oil Industry.* New York: New York University Press, 1955.
SHABAD, THEODORE. *Russia's Potential in Future Oil Markets.* Beirut: Second Arab Petroleum Congress, October, 1960.
VVEDENSKY, G. A. "The Soviet Oil Industry," *Bulletin, Institute for the Study of the USSR* (Munich), March, 1961.
UNITED STATES SENATE, EIGHTY-SEVENTH CONGRESS. *Soviet Oil in the Cold War, A Study Prepared by the Library of Congress at the Request of the Subcommittee to Investigate the Administration of the Internal Security Act and other Internal Security Laws of the Committee on the Judiciary.* Washington, D.C., 1961.
In Russian, recent books include:
DUNAYEV, F. F. *Ekonomika i planirovaniye neftyanoy promyshlennosti SSSR (Economics and Planning of the Oil Industry of the USSR).* Moscow, 1957.
KELLER, A. A. *Neftyanaya i gazovaya promyshlennost SSSR v poslevoyennye gody (Oil and Gas Industries of the USSR in Post War Years).* Moscow, 1958.
LISICHKIN, S. M. *Ocherki razvitiya neftedobyvayushchey promyshlennosti SSSR (Sketch of the Development of the Oil Extractive Industry of the USSR).* Moscow ,1958.

E. *The Petroleum Industry in the Middle East*

I. Among the numerous books on the international oil industry that cover the Middle East, two works, with sharply opposing points of view, may be mentioned: FANNING, LEONARD M. *Foreign Oil and the Free World.* New York: McGraw-Hill Book Co., 1954; and O'CONNOR, HARVEY. *The Empire of Oil.* New York: Monthly Review Press, 1955.

An indispensable work is the Staff Report of the Select Committee on Small Business to the Federal Trade Commission submitted to the Sub-Committee on Monopoly. UNITED STATES SENATE, 82ND SESSION. *The International Petroleum Cartel.* Washington, D.C., 1952.

By far the clearest analyses of the international pricing of oil are to be found in LEVY, WALTER J. "The Past, Present and Likely Future Price Structure for the International Oil Trade," *Proceedings, Third World Petroleum Congress.* The Hague, 1951; UNITED NATIONS, ECONOMIC COMMISSION FOR EUROPE. *The Price of Oil in Western Europe.* Geneva, March, 1955; and LEEMAN, WAYNE. *The Price of Middle East Oil.* Ithaca, N.Y.: Cornell University, 1962.

Many of the publications of the Organisation for European Economic Cooperation are very useful for students of Middle Eastern oil problems, notably *Europe's Growing Needs for Energy.* Paris, 1956; *Europe's Need for Oil: Implications and Lessons of the Suez Crisis.* Paris, 1958; and *Towards a New Energy Pattern in Europe.* Paris, 1960.

Similarly several of the publications of the Petroleum Department of the Chase Manhattan Bank are invaluable, notably their annual survey *Petroleum Industry,* (New York); their *Investment Patterns in the World Petroleum Industry* (1956); their *Future Growth of the World Petroleum Industry* (1957); and their *Capital Investments by the World Petroleum Industry* (November, 1959, and October, 1960).

The annual survey issued by the British Petroleum Company, *Statistical Review of the World Oil Industry,* provides a handy compendium of useful statistical data.

II. Several valuable books have been written on Middle Eastern oil. Of these:

LONGRIGG, STEPHEN H. *Oil in the Middle East: Its Discovery and Development.* London: Oxford University Press, 1961, provides the best historical account of the growth of the industry.

SHWADRAN, BENJAMIN. *The Middle East, Oil and the Great Powers 1959.* New York: Council for Middle Eastern Affairs Press, 1959, is the most comprehensive single work on the subject and is to be specially recommended for its discussion of the diplomatic background of the oil concessions.

LENCZOWSKI, GEORGE. *Oil and the State in the Middle East.* Ithaca, N.Y.: Cornell University Press, 1960, is devoted mainly to a study of the relations between the oil companies and the various Middle Eastern governments.

FINNIE, DAVID H. *Desert Enterprise: The Middle East Oil Industry in its Local Environment.* Cambridge, Mass.: Harvard University Press, 1958, discusses the economic and social relations between the oil companies and the communities in which they operate.

BADRE, ALBERT Y. and SIMON G. SIKSEK. *Manpower and Oil in Arab Countries.* Beirut: Economic Research Institute, American University, deals with the managerial and labor problems of the industry.

AL-ABUSY, MUHAMMAD JAWAD. *Al betrol fil bilad al Arabiyya (Petroleum in the Arab Countries).* Cairo: League of Arab States, Institute for Higher Arab Studies, 1956, represents an Arab point of view on this highly controversial subject.

A great amount of additional information is to be found in various other publications. Among these, the most important are: *Review of Economic*

Conditions in the Middle East, issued annually since 1951 by the United Nations, Department of Economic and Social Affairs in New York; TRANS ARABIAN PIPELINE COMPANY. *Tapline and the Transportation of Oil* (1954); and the following pamphlets published by the Arabian American Oil Company: *Summary—Middle East Oil Developments* (Second edition, 1948); *Middle East Oil Developments* (1952, 1956).

The three Arab Petroleum Congresses, held in Cairo in 1959, in Beirut in 1960, and in Alexandria in 1961, produced many interesting papers. The proceedings of the first Congress have been issued in Arabic by the Arab League's Office of Petroleum Affairs under the title *Majmuat al buhuth al muqaddama ila al mutamar.* Cairo: Jaridat al sabah press, 1959; and several of the papers presented to the Second Congress have been summarized in *Petroleum Press Service.* London, November, 1960. An unpublished doctoral dissertation presented to Columbia University in 1961, FRANK, HELMUT J. "The Pricing of Middle East Crude Oil" presents a good account and analysis.

III. No student of Middle East oil can afford to overlook the vast records of United States Congressional inquiries on various petroleum questions. In recent years, the following have been the most important hearings:

UNITED STATES SENATE, SEVENTY-NINTH CONGRESS. *Hearings Before Special Committee Investigating Petroleum Resources: American Petroleum Interests in Foreign Countries.* Washington, D.C., 1945.

UNITED STATES SENATE, EIGHTIETH CONGRESS. *Hearings Before a Special Committee Investigating the National Defense Program.* Washington, D.C., 1948.

UNITED STATES SENATE, EIGHTY-THIRD CONGRESS. *Hearings Before the Special Subcommittee on Minerals, Materials and Fuels Economics of the Committee on Interior and Insular Affairs.* Washington, D.C., 1953–1954.

UNITED STATES HOUSE OF REPRESENTATIVES, EIGHTY-FOURTH CONGRESS. *Current Antitrust Problems, Hearings Before Antitrust Subcommittee (Subcommittee No. 5) of the Committee on the Judiciary.* Washington, D.C., 1955.

UNITED STATES SENATE, EIGHTY-FIFTH CONGRESS. *Emergency Oil Lift Program and Related Oil Problems, Joint Hearings Before Subcommittees of the Committee on the Judiciary and Committee on Interior and Insular Affairs.* Washington, D.C., 1957.

A certain amount of information can also be gleaned from the British *Parliamentary Debates, House of Commons* and *Parliamentary Debates, House of Lords* (London).

IV. Of the numerous petroleum and other journals, the following contain most information on the Middle East: *Middle East Economic Survey* (Beirut weekly); *The Oil and Gas Journal* (Tulsa, Oklahoma); *The Oil Forum* (New York); *Platt Oilgram News Service* (New York and Chicago); *Petroleum Press Service* (London, monthly); *Petroleum Times* (London, biweekly); *Petroleum Week* (New York, weekly); *World Oil* (Houston, Texas, monthly and especially annual International Issue published in July or August); *World Petroleum* (New York, monthly).

V. Summaries of the text of several concession agreements may be found in *World Petroleum Legislation* (New York), a periodical publication; others are published in full in HUREWITZ, J. C. *Diplomacy in the Near and Middle East: A Documentary Record.* 2 Vols. Princeton, N.J.: D. Van Nostrand Co., 1956; and in UNITED STATES HOUSE OF REPRESENTATIVES, EIGHTY-FOURTH CONGRESS. *Current Antitrust Problems.* Washington, D.C., 1955. The latter also contains texts of certain important agreements between the various oil companies operating in the Middle East.

A comparison of the main provisions of petroleum agreements in various parts of the world is given in UNITED NATIONS, GENERAL ASSEMBLY—UNITED NATIONS COMMISSION ON PERMANENT SOVEREIGNTY OVER NATURAL RESOURCES, THIRD SESSION. *The Status of Permanent Sovereignty over Natural Wealth and Resources.* Vol. 1. New York, December, 1960.

The Arabic texts of concession agreements in the Arab countries are being published by the Arab League, Institute for Higher Arab Studies. MUHAMMAD LABIB SHUQAIR and SAHIB DHAHAB (eds.). *Ittifaqat wa Uqud al betrol fil bilad al Arabiyya (Petroleum Agreements and Contracts in the Arab Countries).* Cairo: Al matbaa al alamia, 1959–1960. Two volumes have appeared. They cover Egypt, Iraq, Saudi Arabia, Bahrein, Qatar, and Kuwait.

VI. Company reports are, of course, an indispensable source. These include:

ANGLO-IRANIAN OIL COMPANY (or ANGLO-PERSIAN OIL COMPANY). *Report of the Directors and Balance Sheet.* London, 1910–1948.

——— *Annual Report and Accounts.* London, 1949–1953.

ARABIAN AMERICAN OIL COMPANY. *Report of Operations to the Saudi Arab Government,* 1948–

BAHRAIN PETROLEUM COMPANY. *Annual Report to the Ruler of Bahrain,* 1953–

BRITISH PETROLEUM COMPANY. *Annual Report of Accounts,* 1955–

IRANIAN OPERATING OIL COMPANIES. *Review,* 1956–

IRAQ PETROLEUM COMPANY. *Iraq Oil.* 1951–

KUWAIT OIL COMPANY. *Report to the Ruler of Kuwait,* 1954–

NATIONAL IRANIAN OIL COMPANY. *Annual Report,* 1956–

VII. In conclusion, mention may be made of some books and pamphlets dealing with oil problems in the individual countries.

The Iranian point of view is given in LISANI, ABOLFAZL. *Talai siah ya balai Iran (Black Gold or Iran's Misfortune).* Tehran, 1950; and FATEMI, NASROLLAH S. *Oil Diplomacy: Powderkeg in Iran.* New York: Whittier Books, 1954. Another book that is very sympathetic to the Iranian viewpoint is ELWELL-SUTTON, L. P. *Persian Oil: A Study in Power Politics.* London: Lawrence and Wishart, 1955. The opposing cases for the British and Iranian governments may be found in INTERNATIONAL COURT OF JUSTICE. *Anglo-Iranian Oil Company Case (United Kingdom v. Iran) Judgment of July 22, 1952,* The Hague; and a study of the legal aspects of the nationalization crisis in FORD, ALAN W. *The Anglo-Iranian Oil Dispute of 1951–1952.* Berkeley and Los Angeles: University of California Press, 1954. The International Labor Office's report, *Labour Conditions in the Oil Industry in Iran,* Geneva, 1950, is an indispensable source on labor conditions prevailing at that time.

Of the general books on Iraq, the two that deal most extensively with petroleum are: QUBAIN, FAHIM I. *The Reconstruction of Iraq, 1950–1957.*

New York: Frederick A. Praeger, 1958; and LANGLEY, KATHLEEN M. *The Industrialization of Iraq*. Cambridge, Mass.: Harvard University Press, 1961. Much information is also to be found in AL-PACHACHI, NADIM. *Haqaiq wa arqam ala al siasa al naftia* (*Facts and Figures on Oil Policy*). Baghdad, 1957; and in an unpublished doctoral dissertation presented to Columbia University by AL-QAYSI, HAMEED. "An Economic Appraisal of Iraq Petroleum Concessions—A Comparative Study," New York, 1961.

On Saudi Arabia, the following books may be consulted: MIKESELL, RAYMOND F., and HOLLIS B. CHENERY. *Arabian Oil: America's Stake in the Middle East*. Chapel Hill, N.C.: University of North Carolina Press, 1949; and LEBKICHER, ROY. *Aramco and World Oil*. New York: Moore, 1952; as well as the above-mentioned reports published by the Arabian American Oil Company and its *Aramco Handbook* (1960).

On Bahrein there is BELGRAVE, JAMES H. *Welcome to Bahrain*. 2nd edition. London: Stourbridge Mark and Moody, 1954; and his *Personal Column*. London: Hutchinson, 1960.

On Kuwait: DICKSON, H. R. P. *Kuwait and her Neighbours*. London: Allen and Unwin, 1956; KUWAIT OIL COMPANY. *The Story of Kuwait*. London: Kuwait Oil Company, 1957; and SHAMMA, SAMIR. *Betrol al Kuwait* (*The Oil of Kuwait*). Damascus, 1959.

For the transit countries, there are the two reports by the INTERNATIONAL BANK FOR RECONSTRUCTION AND DEVELOPMENT, *The Economic Development of Syria*. Baltimore, Md.: Johns Hopkins Press, 1955; and *The Economic Development of Jordan*. Baltimore, Md.: Johns Hopkins Press, 1957.

Index